HRM

NELSON SERIES IN HUMAN RESOURCE MANAGEMENT

Management of Occupational Health and Safety

THIRD EDITION

E. KEVIN KELLOWAY
SAINT MARY'S UNIVERSITY

LORI FRANCIS
SAINT MARY'S UNIVERSITY

JAMES MONTGOMERY

SERIES EDITOR:
MONICA BELCOURT
YORK UNIVERSITY

THOMSON
NELSON

Australia   Canada   Mexico   Singapore   Spain   United Kingdom   United States

THOMSON

★

NELSON

Management of Occupational Health and Safety

Third Edition

by E. Kevin Kelloway, Lori Francis, and James Montgomery

**Associate Vice-President,
Editorial Director:**
Evelyn Veitch

Senior Acquisitions Editor:
Anthony Rezek

**Senior Executive Marketing
Manager:**
Don Thompson

Senior Developmental Editor:
Karina Hope

Permissions Coordinator:
Nicola Winstanley

Production Editor:
Lara Caplan

Copy Editor:
Dawn Hunter

Proofreader:
Margaret Crammond

Indexer:
Elizabeth Bell

**Senior Production
Coordinator:**
Kathrine Pummell

Creative Director:
Angela Cluer

Interior Design:
Sarah Battersby

Cover Design:
Sarah Battersby

Compositor:
Integra

Printer:
Transcontinental

**Library and Archives Canada
Cataloguing in Publication**

Kelloway, E. Kevin (Edward Kevin), 1959–

Management of occupational health and safety/E. Kevin Kelloway, Lori Francis, James Montgomery. —3rd ed.

Second ed. written by James Montgomery and Kevin Kelloway.

Includes bibliographical references and index.
ISBN 13: 978-0-17-641610-2
ISBN 10: 0-17-641610-2

1. Industrial hygiene—Management—Textbooks.
2. Industrial safety—Management—Textbooks.
I. Francis, Lori D. (Lori Denise), 1974– II. Montgomery, James, 1932– Management of occupational health and safety.
III. Title.

HD7261.M65 2005   363.11
C2004-907441-5

For Debra, Laura, and John R., each of whom has contributed to my health and safety. (EKK)

I extend sincere thanks to Brian, who was so encouraging and patient during the long hours I spent working on this project. (LF)

Brief Contents

Detailed Contents

Part Three: Interventions   199

About the Series

More than ever, human resources management (HRM) professionals need the knowledge and skills to design HRM policies and practices that not only meet legal requirements but also are effective in supporting organizational strategy. Increasingly, these professionals turn to published research and books on best practices for assistance in the development of effective HR strategies. The books in the *Nelson Series in Human Resources Management* are the best source in Canada for reliable, valid, and current knowledge about practices in HRM.

The texts in this series include

- *Managing Performance through Training and Development*
- *Management of Occupational Health and Safety*
- *Recruitment and Selection in Canada*
- *Strategic Compensation in Canada*
- *Strategic Human Resources Planning*
- *An Introduction to the Canadian Labour Market*
- *Research, Measurement, and Evaluation of Human Resources*

The *Nelson Series in Human Resources Management* represents a significant development in the field of HRM for many reasons. Each book in the series (except for *Strategic Compensation in Canada*) is the first Canadian text in its area of specialization. HR professionals in Canada must work with Canadian laws, statistics, policies, and values. This series serves their needs. It is the only opportunity that students and practitioners have to access a complete set of HRM books, standardized in presentation, that enables them to access information quickly across many HRM disciplines. The books are essential sources of information that meet the requirements for the CCHRA (Canadian Council of Human Resource Associations) National Knowledge exam for the academic portion of the HR certification process. This one-stop resource will prove useful to anyone looking for solutions for the effective management of people.

The publication of this series signals that the field of human resources management has advanced to the stage where theory and applied research guide practice. The books in the series present the best and most current research in the functional areas of HRM. Research is supplemented with examples of the best practices used by Canadian companies that are leaders in HRM. Each text begins with a general model of the discipline, and then describes the implementation of effective strategies. Thus, the books serve as an introduction to the functional area for the new student of HR and as a validation source for the more experienced HRM practitioner. Cases, exercises, and endnotes provide opportunities for further discussion and analysis.

As you read and consult the books in this series, I hope you share my excitement in being involved in the development of a profession that has such a significant impact on the workplace.

Monica Belcourt, Ph.D., CHRP
SERIES EDITOR
September 2004

About the Authors

E. Kevin Kelloway

Dr. Kelloway is a professor of management and psychology at Saint Mary's University, Halifax, Nova Scotia. He is the founding executive director of the CN Centre for Occupational Health and Safety and a founding principal of the Centre for Leadership Excellence. He continues to hold adjunct appointments at the University of Guelph (Psychology), University of Waterloo (Psychology), and Queen's University (School of Business).

Dr. Kelloway is a prolific researcher, having published more than 90 articles, book chapters, and technical reports. His research interests include occupational health psychology, leadership, the development and measurement of work attitudes and values, unionization, and the management of knowledge workers. He is coauthor of *The Union and Its Members*: *A Psychological Approach* (Oxford University Press), *Using Flexible Work Arrangements to Combat Job Stress* (John Wiley & Sons), and *Management of Occupational Health and Safety* (Nelson), and the author of *Using LISREL for Structural Equation Modeling*: *A Researcher's Guide* (SAGE Publications). With Dr. Julian Barling (Queen's University), he edited the book series *Advanced Topics in Organizational Psychology* (SAGE Publications) and has coedited the volume *Young Workers*: *Varieties of Experience* (APA Books). Current projects include coediting the *Handbook of Work Stress* and the *Handbook of Workplace Violence* (both with SAGE Publications).

Dr. Kelloway frequently reviews for academic journals or conferences and serves on the editorial boards of both the *Canadian Journal of Behavioural Science* and the *Journal of Occupational Health Psychology*. As a consultant, Dr. Kelloway maintains an active practice consulting with private- and public-sector organizations on issues related to leadership, safety and safety leadership, occupational stress, performance management, and measurement of employee attitudes and performance.

Lori Francis

Lori Francis earned a Ph.D. in industrial/organizational psychology from the University of Guelph. She has held the position of assistant professor in the department of psychology at Saint Mary's University in Halifax, Nova Scotia, since 2002. Dr. Francis has broad research interests in occupational health psychology, including work stress, health-related interventions in the workplace, and organizational justice. Her Ph.D. dissertation on organizational injustice as a workplace stressor was awarded the International Alliance of Human Resources Researchers best doctoral dissertation award. She is a member of the CN Centre for Occupational Health and Safety and the Centre for Leadership Excellence. Dr. Francis also has an extensive consulting record, having worked with government, military, and private industry.

James A. Montgomery

Mr. Montgomery, CRSP(R), P.Eng(R), is a professor emeritus from Humber (College) Institute of Technology and Advanced Learning (ITAL), having retired in 1996 after being with ITAL for 25 years. He earned his bachelor's degree in mechanical engineering from the University of Toronto and his master's degree in automotive engineering from the Chrysler Institute of Engineering (University of Michigan). He later received a diploma in Occupational Health and Safety from McMaster University. He was the coordinator for Mechanical and Industrial Engineering Technologies and specialized in the Safety Engineering Technology program, which he developed. Before joining Humber ITAL, he was the plant manager for a transportation equipment manufacturer in Mississauga.

Mr. Montgomery has taught Occupational Health and Safety at Atkinson College, York University. He is an examiner and course author for the Human Resources Professional Association of Ontario.

Preface

Occupational health and safety (OH&S) has long been the preserve of safety engineers and technical experts. However, in most organizations health and safety is housed within the human resource management function for a number of reasons (see Chapter 1 of this text). The immediate implication is that human resource managers must have a solid understanding of health and safety issues, legislation, and programs. Like the previous two editions of this text, the third edition is intended to give the HR manager and the HR professional a basic understanding of the elements that combine to create an occupational health and safety program.

We think of the third edition as comprising three relatively distinct areas relevant to health and safety. In the first set of chapters, we set the stage by providing an overview of health and safety with specific reference to the human resource function (Chapter 1), the legislative context of health and safety in Canada (Chapter 2), and issues relating to Workers' Compensation and disability management (Chapter 3).

The next set of chapters focuses on the types of hazards in the workplace with special reference to techniques for controlling those hazards. Chapter 4 considers physical agents such as noise, vibration, temperature, and radiation. Chapter 5 focuses on chemical and biological agents in the workplace. Chapter 6 extends the focus on hazards to include psychosocial hazards in the workplace. Chapter 7 takes a more general approach to hazard recognition and assessment. While these are arguably the most technical chapters in the book, we have tried to maintain a nontechnical focus and to present the information in a way that is most useful to human resource managers.

The last set of chapters in the book speak more directly to human resource managers and outline some of the major ways in which human resource managers become actively involved in health and safety. Chapter 8 considers techniques of hazard control including fundamental processes (e.g., evacuation plans) that should be in place in all organizations. Chapter 9 focuses on training—one of the most popular, and arguably the most effective, health and safety interventions. Chapter 10 focuses on motivating safe working behaviour and considers the role of both safety culture and safety leadership in organizations. Chapter 11 presents an overview of emergency response planning, while Chapter 12 summarizes accident investigation techniques. Finally, Chapter 13 summarizes attempts to promote employee health and wellness in the workplace.

Throughout the text we have attempted to provide the reader with current examples, clear definitions of technical terms, and links to the vast amount of information found on the web. The nature of occupational health and safety legislation in Canada, and the existence of jurisdictional differences, means that the information presented in this text will need to be supplemented with (for example) provincial or territorial standards and legislative requirements. It is our hope that the student will find this book to be useful in and of itself and will also use it as a guide to other resources.

In addition to the new material and updating incorporated into this third edition, several new features have been added:

Opening vignettes: Each chapter starts with a short discussion of a topic relevant to that chapter. Many vignettes cover current issues in OH&S.

Using the Internet: Each chapter contains at least one exercise using the Internet. These exercises should be particularly beneficial for those students taking a course in using computers.

Weblinks: Internet websites are provided for some topics discussed in the text.

We have included new features throughout the text to enhance learning opportunities and to make the text more interactive, including using websites and having expanded exercises. One of these deserves special mention. Provincial and territorial human resources associations throughout Canada have agreed on a common framework for granting the designation of certified human resources professional (CHRP). Applicants for the CHRP designation must now pass two national exams based on 203 required professional capabilities. We have linked sections of the text to relevant RPCs through icons appearing in the text. These RPCs are listed by functional area on the Professional Assessment Resource Centre (PARC) website at http://www.cchra-ccarh.ca/parc//en/section_3/ss33e.asp.

This text, and others in this series, covers material that may cut across functional lines, as presented on PARC. The RPCs on PARC are not numbered, making it difficult for us to reference them. We have adopted the following system. When we reference an RPC, we designate it with a margin icon. Each RPC is numbered and is preceded by the chapter number. For example, RPC 8.2 is the second RPC presented in Chapter 8. At the end of the chapter, we list the specific RPCs that we have identified as being relevant to the text. We have also included additional information on the RPCs that is not included on PARC. This material suggests knowledge, skills, abilities, and other tasks that we think are essential to a broader understanding of the duties specified by the RPC. We hope that this linkage of our content to the RPCs will help students and practitioners in preparing for the CHRP assessments.

For instructors, new to this edition are an Instructor's Manual, with test questions and PowerPoint slides that can be downloaded directly from http://www.hrm.nelson.com.

We hope that students and instructors find these changes as exciting as we do and that they help to facilitate and maximize learning.

Acknowledgments

For taking the time to read the draft manuscript and share with us their extensive and detailed comments, we thank the following instructors: Alan Chapelle, Malaspina University College; Julie Aitken Harris, University of Western Ontario; Linda Lauzon, Fanshawe College; Linda Piper, Canadore College; Martha Reavley, University of Windsor; and D. J. (Nick) Sunday, Cambrian College of Applied Arts & Technology.

We would especially like to thank Catherine Fitzgerald of Okanagan University College for her comments and suggestions for exercises to include in the book.

We would like to thank our colleagues at the CN Centre for Occupational Health and Safety (Vic Catano, Arla Day, Mark Fleming, Debra Gilin, Camilla Holmvall, Steve Smith, Veronica Stinson, and Anthony Yue) here at Saint Mary's for their support and acknowledge our network of colleagues across the country who are making significant contributions to the human resource side of occupational health and safety. These include Julian Barling (Queen's University), Kate Dupre (Memorial University), Gail Hepburn (University of Lethbridge), Rick Iverson (Simon Fraser University), Catherine Loughlin (University of Toronto), Aaron Schat (McMaster University), and Nick Turner (Queen's University). We are also grateful for the support and guidance of Monica Belcourt (York University) and both Anthony Rezek and Karina Hope at Thomson Nelson.

E. Kevin Kelloway, Ph.D.
Professor of Management and Psychology
Director, CN Centre for Occupational Health and Safety
Saint Mary's University

Lori Francis, Ph.D.
Assistant Professor of Psychology
Saint Mary's University

James Montgomery, CRSP(R), P.Eng(R)

PART ONE

Introduction and Overview

Chapter 1

Introduction

THE IMPORTANCE OF TRAINING

It was his first day on the job at Redden Manufacturing. He was assigned to the shearing machine, which is used to cut pieces of rebar. His new supervisor was in a meeting, so coworkers showed him basically how to work the machine, and he set to work. Before the day ended, he had suffered a broken finger because of an improper hand position.

Investigation by the Nova Scotia Department of Labour resulted in five orders to the company:

1. The employee could not return to this task until he had received orientation and training.
2. The firm had to develop a safe work practice for working on the shearing machine.
3. An accident investigation had to be conducted and a copy of the report filed with the Department of Labour.
4. The shearing machine had to be inspected and brought to standard.
5. The shearing machine had to be taken out of use until the "banana" arms were repaired to manufacturer's specifications.

As this incident illustrates, occupational health and safety is an integral part of human resources management. The injury to the worker was attributed to a lack of proper orientation and training, traditional responsibilities of the human resources department. As a result of the incident, the worker was off work until his injury healed. During this time, the company incurred costs attributable to absenteeism, as well as a potential increase in Workers' Compensation premiums. Minimizing these costs while ensuring that workers return to work as soon as possible is also the responsibility of the human resources department. Finally, the provincial Department of Labour made several orders that the company had to comply with. Several of these orders dealt with repairing equipment; others dealt with providing adequate training and ensuring that safe working procedures were developed. Again, the human resource department plays these roles.

Source: Worker in NS did not receive OH&S training before first shift. (2003, September 22). *Canadian Occupational Health and Safety News*.

Most of us go to work each day expecting to return home in more or less the same condition as when we left. However, for a distressingly high number of workers, this is not the case. Workplace accidents continue to occur, with consequences ranging from minor property damage to death. As the organizational unit most clearly responsible for the well-being of employees, it is clear that human resource management has to focus on occupational health and safety. The costs of failing in this responsibility are immense.

As shown in Figure 1.1 the number of workplace fatalities in Canada continues to increase. Approximately 900 workers each year die as a result of workplace accidents and more than 350,000 suffer an injury serious enough to warrant missing time from work (frequently called a **lost-time injury**; see Table 1.1). It is estimated that a workplace accident occurs every nine seconds. A worker is 28 times more likely to be injured or die on the job than an ordinary citizen is to be injured or die at the hands of a criminal.

Occupational health and safety (OH&S) is the identification, evaluation, and control of hazards associated with the work environment. These hazards range from chemical, biological, and physical agents to psychosocial disorders such as stress. The goal of an organization's health and safety program is to reduce occupational injuries and illnesses. An **occupational injury** is any cut, fracture, sprain, or amputation resulting from a workplace accident. An **occupational illness** is any abnormal condition or disorder caused by exposure to environmental factors associated with employment.

OH&S issues affect a wide range of players, from employers, employees, and their families to all those who contribute to the insurance and compensation systems that are designed to assist and rehabilitate workers. Moreover, health and safety concerns are no longer limited to industrial-sector workers who face such hazards as mine explosions and transportation accidents; employees in white-collar environments are increasingly anxious about repetitive-strain injury and sick-building syndrome. The rising costs associated with work-related

lost-time injury
a workplace injury that results in the employee missing time from work

occupational health and safety (OH&S)
the identification, evaluation, and control of hazards associated with the work environment

occupational injury
any cut, fracture, sprain, or amputation resulting from a workplace accident

occupational illness
any abnormal condition or disorder caused by exposure to environmental factors associated with employment

FIGURE 1.1

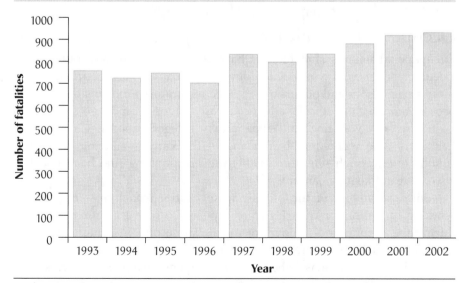

Workplace Fatalities in Canada: A Ten-Year History

Source: Association of Workers' Compensation Boards of Canada, "National Work Injuries Statistics Program." Retrieved from http://www.awcbc.org/english/NWISP_Stats.htm, September 27, 2004.

TABLE 1.1

Lost-Time Injuries by Province and Territory, 2002

	NUMBER OF LOST-TIME INJURIES
Alberta	38,426
British Columbia	59,530
Manitoba	17,919
New Brunswick	4,685
Newfoundland and Labrador	5,517
Northwest Territories and Nunavut	968
Nova Scotia	8,724
Ontario	95,568
Prince Edward Island	1,475
Quebec	110,244
Saskatchewan	15,623
Yukon	495
CANADA	359,174

Source: Based on data available from Association of Workers' Compensation Boards of Canada, "National Work Injuries Statistics Program." Retrieved from http://www.awcbc.org/english/NWISP_Stats.htm, September 27, 2004.

injuries and illnesses and, more important, the public's decreasing tolerance for work-related hazards, underlie the need to understand and implement effective occupational health and safety policies and programs.

Historical Development of Modern Occupational Health and Safety

Occupational injuries and illnesses have been with us throughout history. Documented cases of work-related illnesses go back as far as ancient Egypt, when stonemasons and potters experienced respiratory problems. As societies became more technologically advanced, cases of copper-induced dermatoses (skin diseases), vomiting, and hepatic (liver) degeneration began to occur. Labourers who worked with iron and in the various alloying operations risked not only such symptoms as high fever, coughing, and headache, but also diseases like lung cancer.[1]

With the advent of the Industrial Revolution, machinists and others working in the new industries were exposed to oils used for lubrication during the cutting and removal of metal. These oils, in conjunction with poor personal hygiene practices, resulted in serious dermatoses, such as acne and skin melanomas. When the spinning and weaving industries were mechanized, the resultant dust from hemp and flax caused byssinosis (**brown lung**).

brown lung

a disease of the lungs caused by excessive inhalation of dust; the disease is in the pneumoconiosis family and frequently afflicts textile workers

In Canada, concern for occupational health and safety was first evident in the late nineteenth century, when Ontario passed legislation that established safety standards such as mandating guards on machines. Quebec soon followed suit, and by the early twentieth century, every jurisdiction in Canada had passed factory laws that regulated heating, lighting, ventilation, hygiene, fire safety, and accident reporting. Factory inspectors were appointed in each province and territory to enforce these standards and to conduct regular inspections of workplaces.

The Royal Commission on the Relations of Capital and Labour in Canada (1889) had an important influence on the development of health and safety regulations. First, the commissioners made several recommendations about improving health and safety by establishing standards and mandating regular inspections. Second, the commissioners were the first to recommend a system for compensating victims of industrial accidents, regardless of who was at fault in the accident. Finally, the commissioners recommended that a labour bureau be created to oversee these activities.

The 1960s and 1970s were an important time for health and safety in Canada, witnessing the implementation of the Canada Labour (Standards) Code and the Canada Labour (Safety) Code. In 1974, the Ontario government formed the Royal Commission on the Health and Safety of Workers in Mines. Chaired by Dr. James Ham, this commission was the first to articulate the three principal rights of workers: the right to refuse dangerous work without penalty, the right to participate in identifying and correcting health and safety problems, and the right to know about hazards in the workplace. These three rights continue to be enshrined in current legislation and provide the basis for much of the health and safety programming in Canada. For example, in 1988, legislation was passed that established the Workplace Hazardous Materials Information System (WHMIS). Through federal and

Occupational Health and Safety Notebook 1.1

Preventing Computer Vision Syndrome

Work related health concerns are not just of historical interest. The advent of new technologies has resulted in new health and safety concerns. One of these is computer vision syndrome, which results from the glare caused by the combination of bright office lights and computer monitors. To reduce the health concerns associated with glare, organizations can do several things:

- Reduce ambient lighting levels (most offices are more than twice as bright as they need to be).
- Place monitors so that they are 90 degrees from any light source.

- Use task lighting (i.e., adjustable desk lamps).
- Ensure that monitors are functioning properly with minimal flicker and are adjusted for the comfort of the user.

Sources: Home Vision Therapy System, "Frequently Asked Questions." Retrieved from http://www.homevisiontherapy.com/faqs.html, September 27, 2004; and Canadian Centre for Occupational Health and Safety, "Eye Discomfort in the Office." Retrieved from http://www.ccohs.ca/oshanswers/ergonomics/office/eye_discomfort.html, September 27, 2004.

The Costs of Unhealthy Behaviour

Although there is no doubt that substantial human and economic costs are associated with unsafe workplaces, employers also incur substantial costs attributable to individual lifestyle choices. In their effort to promote "wellness" (see Chapter 13), many employers have implemented smoking-cessation programs (often in conjunction with provincial or territorial legislation that prohibits smoking in the workplace). Substantial economic gains may be associated with such initiatives. Based on a review of research from around the world, Kelloway and Barling concluded that smokers were absent from work 43%

more often than nonsmokers. Although such estimates do not show up in the lost-time injury figures, absenteeism associated with smoking is a real and substantial cost for employers.

Sources: Kelloway, E. K., & Barling, J. (2003). Smoking and absence from work. In M. Krausz & M. Koslowsky (Eds.), *Voluntary employee withdrawal and inattendance* (pp. 167–178). New York: Plenum; and Henningfield, J. E., Ramstrom, L. M., Husten, C., Giovino, G., Barling, J., Weber, C., Kelloway, E. K., Strecher, V. J., & Jarvis, M. J. (1994). Smoking and the workplace: Realities and solutions. *Journal of Smoking-Related Diseases, 5*, 261–270.

to cope with when the media learned that one of its chemicals caused sterility in the workers handling the compound. However, managers who are committed to safety can turn adverse publicity into a marketing and recruitment advantage by advertising their concerns for employee safety. Employers who are *not* concerned about the health and safety of their employees affect other employers and tax-paying citizens. Workers' Compensation rates are determined by industry sector. A negligent employer forces others in the sector to pay higher rates, and these costs are significant. The 12 Workers' Compensation Boards across Canada pay out $3 billion annually. The Alberta board estimates that a totally disabled young worker with children will have received $7 million in payments by age 72. Unsafe working conditions cause insurance premiums to escalate and health expenditures to increase.

In contrast, industry estimates indicate that up to 90% of safety-related changes made can result in positive paybacks through the associated reduction in Workers' Compensation premiums. Programs such as the New Experimental Experience Rating (NEER) reward employers for implementing safe work practices by reducing Workers' Compensation costs based on the company's actual experience. Therefore, organizations have an economic interest in lowering the number of accidents and providing a safe working environment.

Legal Considerations

due diligence

an expected standard of conduct that requires employers to take every reasonable precaution to ensure safety

Every worker has the legal right to safe working conditions under occupational health and safety acts. The Occupational Health and Safety Act of Ontario, section 25(2)(h), requires an employer to "take every precaution reasonable in the circumstances for the protection of a worker." The legal term for this requirement is **due diligence**.

From a legal perspective, due diligence is considered a measure of prudence to be expected from, and ordinarily exercised by, a reasonable and prudent person under the particular circumstances depending on the relative facts of the special case. In other words, due diligence is a standard of conduct measured by what could be expected of a reasonable person in the same circumstances. Due diligence requires a business to foresee all unsafe conditions or acts and requires them to take precautions to prevent accidents that can reasonably be anticipated.[6] Similarly, a worker is required to work in compliance with health and safety legislation. This legislation is discussed at length in Chapter 2.

RPC 1.1

Moral Considerations

Aside from legal and economic considerations, employers have a moral obligation to employees and their families to provide the safest working environment possible. Two decades of research have provided consistent evidence that management commitment to health and safety will result in higher levels of employee motivation to work safely and better organizational safety records. Similarly, workers have a moral responsibility to learn about safety and health, to follow recommended workplace practices, and to be alert and responsible. In at least one study, the perception that managers, supervisors, and coworkers were committed to health and safety was the single biggest predictor of an employee's willingness to participate in health and safety programs.[7] Clearly, the economic, human, and social costs associated with workplace injury and illness are intolerable, and both employers and employees must work together to enhance occupational health and safety.

The Stakeholders

Government

In Canada, Ontario was the first province to enact compensation legislation with the passage of the Workmen's Compensation Act in 1914. This legislation provided lost-time wages to almost every injured worker, thereby removing the right of workers to sue their employers. Following World War I, the federal and other provincial and territorial governments began to enact legislation designed to protect the worker. The two main goals of this legislation were (1) to ensure that injured workers received compensation and that employers accepted liability, and (2) to prevent accidents and illness through the establishment of safe work environments.

RPC 1.2

As a result of continued improvement to health and safety legislation, the number of workplace accidents declined. For example, despite the addition of two million workers to the Canadian workforce between 1985 and 1993, the number of accidents dropped from 554,793 to 423,184.[8]

In addition to their legislative function, governments solicit or conduct research on health and safety issues and disseminate information. Ontario, Nova Scotia, and British Columbia are world leaders in the development of chemical-exposure standards that are as strict as reasonably attainable based on hard scientific evidence. The federal government created the Canadian Centre for Occupational Health and Safety (CCOH&S) as a vital health and safety research and resource organization. CCOH&S accesses a number of databases from around the world in addition to creating and maintaining its own comprehensive database. The goal of this organization is to provide health and safety information to any worker who requests it.

One important contribution of CCOH&S has been the creation of an online information service called CCINFOWEB. This program's vast database contains information on chemicals, material safety data sheets (MSDS), toxicological effects of chemicals and biological agents, and health and safety legislation for all jurisdictions in Canada. CCOH&S also produces a wide variety of safety infograms and other publications.

Employers

Although every player has a role in occupational health and safety, that of a company's management team is the most pivotal. Managers have the means and the authority to monitor the workplace and to ensure compliance with safe practices. Moreover, organizations have the resources to hire health and safety professionals.

The employer is responsible for preparing a written occupational health and safety policy and ensuring that it is prominently displayed in the workplace. Employers are also required to

- provide and maintain equipment, materials, and protective devices
- ensure that the manner in which the work is performed is safe and that the environment is free from hazards and serious risks
- monitor their workplace and report minor, critical, disabling, and fatal injuries, as well as occupational illnesses and toxic substances (and to maintain the records of these occurrences for many years)
- establish health and safety committees with strong employee representation
- alert employees to any known or perceived risks and hazards in the workplace
- provide employees with health and safety training

Managers have to be trained in the recognition and control of unsafe work environments; they cannot monitor and control what they do not recognize as unsafe. Supervisors who participated in a study of 70 construction sites failed to recognize 44% of the workplace hazards and felt that another 64% did not fall within their jurisdiction. Further, these supervisors stated that 20% of the hazards were inevitable.[9] Clearly, in order to fulfill their responsibilities, managers must receive health and safety training.

Employees

Employees of an organization have a role to play in occupational health and safety both as individuals and as members of organized labour groups. As individuals, employees are required to perform their duties and tasks in a safe and responsible manner and to wear protective equipment in compliance

Occupational Health and Safety Today 1.3

A Predictable Path to Disaster at Westray

On May 9, 1992, at 5:20 a.m., the Westray coal mine in Plymouth, Nova Scotia, exploded. Despite extensive rescue efforts involving more than 170 mine rescue workers, 26 miners died in the mine. Charged with investigating the cause of the disaster, Justice Peter Richard entitled his final report *The Westray Story: A Predictable Path to Disaster*, emphasizing that the disaster that had rocked the community had been entirely preventable.

Although Justice Richard documents many causes of the disaster, he particularly focuses on a management style that emphasized production over safety and showed disdain for safety concerns: Workers were not provided training in safe mining procedures; supervisors did not have the authority to correct unsafe conditions; and dangerous shortcuts were taken in the performance of mine tasks. Work procedures (e.g., the use of 12-hour shifts for

miners) were also in violation of safety regulations. Despite excessive levels of gas and coal dust in the mine, unsafe procedures (e.g., the use of torches) were condoned if not encouraged. No meaningful dialogue existed on safety matters at the Westray mine—the joint health and safety committee did not function effectively. As Justice Richard notes, the operation of the mine defied every principle of safe mining.

The explosion at Westray also provides a cautionary tale for human resource managers—it illustrates what happens when management does not make safety a priority and does not promote a culture of safety.

Source: Government of Nova Scotia, "The Westray Story: A Predictable Path to Disaster." Retrieved from http://www.gov.ns.ca/enla/pubs/westray/execsumm.htm, September 27, 2004.

with company and legislative regulations. They are also required to report defective equipment and other workplace hazards to the safety professional, the joint health and safety committee, or the manager. Any employees who feel that a particular activity will endanger them or others have the right to refuse to carry out the activity.

Organized Labour

Organized labour also has a role to play in ensuring the proper management of safety at work.[10] One role of organized labour is to bring emerging problems and issues in health and safety to the attention of government and employers and to pressure other stakeholders to take corrective action. Organized labour and professional associations have also used the collective bargaining process to incorporate health and safety provisions in many contracts. These labour contracts attempt to formalize voluntary measures and extend legislative programs. For example, some contracts state that a union must have a full-time safety representative in all plants. Others bargain for more training on safety measures or more information on exposure to known toxic chemicals.

Partnerships

Although all stakeholders support the concept of safe working conditions, not everyone is committed to the implementation of OH&S programs. There may be several reasons for stakeholders' lack of action in this area. Employers may be more concerned with production quotas than with safety health experts may be hired or consulted. Health and safety experts can be located through their associations, the Yellow Pages, or safety associations and provincial departments. There are no legal requirements for the practice of occupational health and safety.

The Role of Human Resources

Traditional views of safety have emphasized **the three Es**. The goal was to develop *engineering* solutions to ensure safe work environments, equipment, and personal protective devices. Then, health and safety professionals were tasked with *educating* supervisors and employers in the use of the equipment. Finally, health and safety programs focused on *enforcing* existing regulations and practices. To a great extent, these approaches have been successful in creating safer workplaces. However, we now recognize that the three Es do not provide a total solution and that focusing on the people side of the workplace is likely to result in a safer workplace.

Not surprisingly, you will find that occupational health and safety is almost exclusively "managed" under the human resources function. There are several reasons for this organizational structure.

Safety Is a People Issue

Although great advances have been made through engineering solutions, it is increasingly apparent that effective safety programming depends on developing individual skills and abilities and on motivating individuals. These are the traditional concerns of human resources. Through the use of orientation and other training programs, human resource professionals develop employee knowledge and skills. Through a variety of strategies including compensation and awareness programs, human resource professionals motivate safe working.

Perhaps most important, research has increasingly identified variables such as safety leadership[14] and safety climate[15,16] as predictors of safety outcomes (e.g., incidents, accidents, injuries). These issues are discussed in Chapter 10. Traditional areas of human resource practice such as job design have also been linked to safety outcomes.[17] Finally, safety concerns have direct implications for outcomes such as stress and turnover,[18] traditional areas of HR concern.

Safety Requires Legislative Compliance

As we have already seen, and will discuss in detail in Chapter 2, occupational health and safety is a very well developed area of labour law. Numerous standards and requirements are imposed on employers to maintain workplace safety. Administering compliance is a natural outgrowth of the human resource function. Human resource professionals already ensure compliance with other areas of labour law (e.g., employment equity, human rights legislation) and thus are well versed in dealing with such concerns.

Safety Decreases Costs

Workers' Compensation premiums, long-term disability coverage, sick time provisions, and health plans all add to the costs of doing business. It is the responsibility of human resources to see that such costs are minimized. This duty has assumed increasing importance in an era in which double-digit increases in benefit premiums are not uncommon. Aside from minimizing costs, human resources has a role in ensuring that the benefits that an organization pays for are used most effectively to help injured workers and ensure a prompt return to health (and to work).

Safety Relates to Other Human Resource Functions

Safety is also linked to other human resource functions and needs to be considered in all areas of human resource management. Indeed, occupational health and safety is one of the outcomes of adopting a particular strategic orientation to health and safety.[19]

Safety programming in organizations frequently hinges on training initiatives, a traditional human resource function. Training is one of the most popular, and arguably one of the most effective, health and safety initiatives available[20] and is discussed in detail in Chapter 9. Research has established links between job insecurity and safety,[21] such that individuals who experience job insecurity are more likely to commit safety violations. The use of performance-based pay systems has been associated with increased injury rates, while the implementation of teams in organizations may be associated with reduced injuries.[22] Clearly, the way we manage human resources has direct implications for occupational health and safety.

Summary

This chapter has established the importance of occupational health and safety. First, the economic, legal, and moral considerations for enhancing OH&S were presented. Second, government, employers, and employees were presented as the major stakeholders involved in OH&S, and the value of partnerships among those stakeholders was emphasized. Finally, the role of health and safety professionals was described and the role of human resources in managing health and safety was briefly outlined.

Key Terms

accident proneness, p. 8
assumption of risk, p. 8
brown lung, p. 6
due diligence, p. 10
lost-time injury, p. 5

occupational health and safety
(OH&S), p. 5
occupational illness, p. 5
occupational injury, p. 5
the three Es, p. 16

Weblinks

Business News Network, "Health and Safety News,"
http://www.esourcecanada.com/bnn/healthandsafety.asp (p. 5)

Civilization.ca, "Beginnings: Craft Unions,"
http://www.civilization.ca/hist/labour/labv08e.html (p. 7)

Canadian Centre for Occupational Health and Safety,
http://www.ccohs.ca (p. 8)

WorkSafe B.C., "Safety Calculator,"
http://www.healthandsafetycentre.org/sc/calculator/default.htm (p. 8)

Workplace Safety and Insurance Board of Ontario, "New Experimental
Experience Rating Program (NEER) Program Overview,"
http://www.wsib.on.ca/wsib/wsibsite.nsf/public/NEER (p. 10)

Workers' Health and Safety Centre, Ontario,
http://www.whsc.on.ca/home.html (p. 13)

Young Worker Awareness Program,
http://www.youngworker.ca/english/index.htm (p. 13)

RPC Icons

**RPC 1.1 Ensures due diligence and strict liability requirements are met,
e.g., records are kept and formal procedures established.**

- relevant legislation and common law
- company policies and procedures
- industry best practices
- program and policy development
- training and development techniques
- risk analysis
- common and statutory law (e.g., employment standard: labour
  relations)
- worker protection (including health and safety and Workers'
  Compensation)
- theories and practices for protection of individuals and groups

TASK & KNOWLEDGE REQUIREMENTS
- occupational health and safety legislation (e.g., Occupational Health
  and Safety Act of Ontario, Workplace Safety and Insurance Act—Bill 99,
  Workplace Hazardous Materials Information System, transportation
  of dangerous goods legislation, environmental legislation, smoking in
  the workplace legislation, civil rights legislation)
- management techniques for OH&S programs

RPC 1.2 Ensures that security programs and policies minimize risks while considering the obligation of the employer and the rights of employees, union, and third parties.

- nature of the business and physical work environment
- relevant legislation
- industry best practices
- program and policy development
- safety and security equipment in the workplace
- risk assessment/techniques
- cost/benefit analysis

TASK & KNOWLEDGE REQUIREMENTS
- available community resources
- worker protection (including health and safety and Worker's Compensation)
- unions' role in health and safety and in employee involvement
- occupational health and safety legislation (e.g., Occupational Health and Safety Act of Ontario, Workplace Safety and Insurance Act—Bill 99, Workplace Hazardous Materials Information System, transportation of dangerous goods legislation, environmental legislation, smoking in the workplace legislation, civil rights legislation)
- emergency preparedness procedures
- management techniques for OH&S programs
- types of employee assistance and wellness programs

RPC 1.3 Establishes a joint responsibility system as required by law e.g., worker-management health & safety committees, investigations, audits, testing and training, to ensure employee safety.

- relevant occupational health and safety legislation
- inspection techniques and procedures
- hazard recognition
- principles of training and development

TASK & KNOWLEDGE REQUIREMENTS
- program and policy development
- audit processes
- joint health and safety committee functions
- worker protection (including health and safety and Workers' Compensation)
- occupational health and safety legislation (e.g., Occupational Health and Safety Act of Ontario, Workplace Safety and Insurance Act—Bill 99, Workplace Hazardous Materials Information System, transportation of dangerous goods legislation, environmental legislation, smoking in the workplace legislation, civil rights legislation)
- management techniques for OH&S programs

Discussion Questions

1. Why have people historically been more concerned with work-related injuries than work-related illnesses?
2. How has our understanding of personal liability for accidents changed over the years?
3. On what grounds, beside humanitarian ones, should workplace hazards be controlled?
4. Who are the stakeholders in health and safety? What roles do they play?

Using the Internet

1. How do organizations treat occupational health and safety? Find the websites for major corporations in your area. Search the website for information on health and safety. Who in the organization administers health and safety programs? What kinds of programs are in place?

Exercises

1. Are the media stakeholders in health and safety? For one week, read the local newspapers and listen to the news. Make a note of the main topic of every article or item pertaining to occupational health and safety. What role are the media playing? What OH&S issues are most likely to gain attention? Give reasons for your answers.
2. Interview a human resource manager regarding occupational health and safety. What is HR's role in the effective management of health and safety at work? What HR functions are involved in meeting the health and safety requirements?

Case 1: Production or Safety?

Atlantic Radiators Inc. manufactures automotive radiators. Demand for their products has resulted in an empty warehouse and there is an urgent need to increase production to satisfy current customers. John Roberts is an employee of Atlantic Radiators Inc. His job is to spray each radiator core with a dilute solution of hydrochloric acid and to bake the radiators in an oven. The acid acts as a flux on the solder-coated tubes and the baking process solders the radiator together.

John's supervisor has spoken to him several times about the need to speed up and not be the bottleneck in the production process. As a result, John has been taking some shortcuts, including neglecting to wear the proper eye protection. Today, he splashed some of the acid mixture in his eye and will now be off work for several days. As plant manager, you are responsible for reviewing this incident. Who is at fault here? What can be done to ensure that similar incidents will not occur in the future?

Case 2: Do We Need Health and Safety?

As the newly appointed manager of Global Insurance Company, Anuradha Das was trying to learn as much as possible about her new workplace. She was surprised to note the absence of the traditional health and safety bulletin board and asked her manager how health and safety information was communicated to employees. "Are you kidding?" he replied. "This is an office. Our employees are mostly data-entry clerks. We don't have machines or equipment—what do we need with health and safety programs?" If you were Anuradha, how would you reply?

Endnotes

1. Janson, H. W. (1985). *History of art* (2nd ed.). Englewood Cliffs, N.J.: Prentice Hall.
2. Moro, T. (2004, July 9). Ontario hiring 200 workplace inspectors. *London Free Press.*
3. Barling, J., Kelloway, E. K., & Zacharatos, A. (2002). Occupational health and safety. In P. B. Warr (Ed.), *Psychology and work* (6th ed.). London: Penguin.
4. Moro, T. (2004, July 9). Ontario hiring 200 workplace inspectors. *London Free Press.*
5. Barling, J., Kelloway, E. K., & Zacharatos, A. (2002). Occupational health and safety. In P. B. Warr (Ed.), *Psychology and work* (6th ed.). London: Penguin.
6. Strahlendorf, P. (2000). *Occupational health and safety law study guide.* Toronto: Ryerson Polytechnic University Press.
7. Cree, T., & Kelloway, E. K. (1997). Responses to occupational hazards: Exit and participation. *Journal of Occupational Health Psychology, 2,* 304–311.
8. Statistics Canada. (1994). *Work injuries, 1991–1993.* Ottawa: Ministry of Supply and Services.
9. Abeytunga, P. K., & Hale, H. R. (1982, July). Supervisor's perception of hazards on construction sites. Paper presented at the 20th Congress of the International Association of Applied Psychology, Edinburgh, U.K.
10. Kelloway, E. K. (2003). Labor unions and safety. In J. Barling & M. Frone (Eds.), *Psychology of occupational safety.* Washington, DC: APA Books.
11. Barling, J., Kelloway, E. K., & Zacharatos, A. (2002). Occupational health and safety. In P. B. Warr (Ed.), *Psychology and work* (6th ed.). London: Penguin.
12. Kelloway, E. K. (2003). Labor unions and safety. In J. Barling & M. Frone (Eds.), *Psychology of occupational safety.* Washington, DC: APA Books.
13. Boyes, S. (1993, July/August). Doubles strategy: When human resources and occupational health and safety work in synchrony, everybody wins. *Human Resources Professional, 10*(7), 17–19.
14. Barling, J., Loughlin, C., & Kelloway, E. K. (2002). Development and test of a model linking safety-specific transformational leadership and occupational safety. *Journal of Applied Psychology, 87,* 488–496.
15. Zohar, D. (2000). A group-level model of safety climate: Testing the effect of group climate on microaccidents in manufacturing jobs. *Journal of Applied Psychology, 85,* 587–596.
16. Zohar, D. (2002). The effects of leadership dimensions, safety climate, and assigned priorities on minor injuries in work groups. *Journal of Organizational Behavior, 23,* 75–92.

17. Barling, J., Kelloway, E. K., & Iverson, R. (2003). High-quality work, job satisfaction and occupational injuries. *Journal of Applied Psychology, 88,* 276–283.

18. Barling, J., Kelloway, E. K., & Iverson, R. (2003). Accidental outcomes: Attitudinal consequences of workplace injuries. *Journal of Occupational Health Psychology, 8,* 74–85.

19. Shaw, J. D., & Delery, J. E. (2003). Strategic HRM and organizational health interventions. In D. A. Hoffman & L. E. Tetrick (Eds.), *Health and safety in organizations: A multilevel perspective.* San Francisco: Jossey-Bass.

20. Burke, M. J., & Sarpy, S. A. (2003). Improving worker safety and health through interventions. In D. A. Hoffman & L. E. Tetrick (Eds.), *Health and safety in organizations: A multilevel perspective.* San Francisco: Jossey-Bass.

21. Probst, T. (2002). Layoffs and tradeoffs: Production, quality, and safety demands under the threat of job loss. *Journal of Occupational Health Psychology, 7*(3), 211–220.

22. Kaminksi, M. (2001). Unintended consequences: Organizational practices and their impact on workplace safety and productivity. *Journal of Occupational Health Psychology, 6*(2), 127–138.

Chapter 2

Legislative Framework

Chapter Learning Objectives

After reading this chapter, you should be able to

- describe the regulatory framework surrounding occupational health and safety
- outline the duties of the major players under occupational health and safety legislation
- describe the structure and role of joint health and safety committees
- list and describe the three central elements of a WHMIS program
- describe the purpose and basic provisions of the transportation of dangerous goods acts

THE RIGHT TO REFUSE UNSAFE WORK

Sheriff's officers enforce court orders involving evictions, seizures of cash or goods from homes and businesses, and other civil matters. In August 2003, the Toronto Police Services Board decided that police should not be involved in civil matters and, as a result, suspended the practice of having police accompany sheriff's officers in high-risk situations.

As a result, the 10 sheriff's officers employed by the Ontario Ministry of the Attorney General refused to work, citing their right to refuse unsafe work under the Occupational Health and Safety Act. After investigation, the Ministry of Labour determined that the employees were within their rights and that work-related conditions were likely to endanger their safety. The Ministry imposed three orders requiring the Ministry of the Attorney General to revise its practices to ensure worker safety. Until such procedures were implemented, the sheriff's officers were not required to undertake potentially dangerous work.

This case illustrates one central feature of Canadian occupational health and safety legislation—the right of the worker to refuse unsafe work. Other rights of workers and employers are discussed in this chapter.

Source: Orders follow work refusal by Toronto sheriff's officers. (2003, August 4). *Canadian Occupational Health and Safety News*.

R P C 2.1

act
a federal, provincial, or territorial law that constitutes the basic regulatory mechanism for occupational health and safety

regulations
explain how the general intent of the act will be applied in specific circumstances

guidelines and policies
more specific rules that are not legally enforceable unless referred to in a regulation or act

Occupational health and safety is regulated under a variety of mechanisms, including acts, regulations, guidelines, standards, and codes. Moreover, each province and territory publishes its own regulations in addition to the federal regulations (see Occupational Health and Safety Notebook 2.1 for a complete list of regulations). Although this may seem confusing, the vast majority of workers and workplaces are regulated by provincial or territorial legislation. Thus, employers and employees who operate in one area typically only have to be familiar with, and comply with, one set of safety standards. The purpose of this section is to provide an overview of the regulatory framework for occupational health and safety.

An **act** is a federal, provincial, or territorial law that constitutes the basic regulatory mechanism for occupational health and safety. Each jurisdiction publishes an act that sets out the basic intent and the general rights and duties of individuals affected by the law. **Regulations** explain how the general intent of the act will be applied in specific circumstances. Typically developed by Ministry of Labour officials, regulations have the same force of law as the act. **Guidelines and policies** are more specific rules but are not legally

Occupational Health and Safety Notebook 2.1

Occupational Health and Safety Legislation in Canada

Jurisdiction	Legislation Enforcement
Canada	Canada Labour Code, Regulations, Labour Canada
Alberta	Occupational Health and Safety Act, Department of Labour
British Columbia	Regulations under Workers' Compensation Board Compensation Act
Manitoba	Workplace Safety and Health Act, Department of Environment & Workplace Health and Safety
New Brunswick	Occupational Health and Safety Act, Occupational Health and Safety Commission
Newfoundland and Labrador	Occupational Health and Safety Act, Department of Labour
Nova Scotia	Occupational Health and Safety Act, Department of Labour
Ontario	Occupational Health and Safety Act, Ministry of Labour
Prince Edward Island	Occupational Health and Safety Act, Department of Fisheries and Labour
Quebec	Act Respecting Occupational Health and Safety, Commission de la santé et de la sécurité du travail
Saskatchewan	Occupational Health and Safety Act, Department of Labour
Northwest Territories and Nunavut	Northwest Safety Act, Commissioner of the Northwest Territories/Nunavut
Yukon	Occupational Health and Safety Act, Commissioner of the Yukon Territory, administered by the Workers' Compensation Board

enforceable unless referred to in a regulation or act. Finally, **standards and codes** are design-related guides. Standards are established by the Canadian Standards Association (CSA), the American National Standards Institute (ANSI), the International Labour Organization (ILO), the International Standards Organization (ISO), the National Institute for Occupational Safety and Health (NIOSH), or the American Conference of Governmental Industrial Hygienists (ACGIH). Occupational health and safety regulations frequently refer to standards set by these last two agencies.

standards and codes
design-related guides established by agencies such as the CSA or ANSI

 2.1

The Scope of OH&S Legislation

The scope of the OH&S legislation differs from jurisdiction to jurisdiction. The statutes and regulations that have been enacted to protect the rights of workers have also established duties that require compliance. The statutes provide the legal foundation, while the regulations enacted under the statute establish the framework within which the employer will conduct business in order to comply with the law.

Under common law, an employer is obliged to take reasonable precautions in ensuring the safety of an employee. This common-law duty is dormant in some jurisdictions, because it has been superseded by other legislation relating to Workers' Compensation. The compensation legislation either bars or limits the employer's duty by proscribing civil actions between employees and their employers in exchange for awards or pensions that may be allowed following an occupational accident or illness. All Canadian occupational health and safety legislation includes the following elements:

- an act
- powers of enforcement
- the right of workers to refuse to do unsafe work
- protection of workers from reprisals
- duties and responsibilities assigned to employers and others

Other elements, which differ among jurisdictions, include mandatory establishment of joint labour/management health and safety committees, health and safety policies, accident-prevention programs, and advisory councils on occupational health and safety.

Those responsible for the management of health and safety and Workers' Compensation should be familiar with the administrative structure as it relates to enforcement, education, and compensation in their particular jurisdiction. Multinational and transportation companies may fall under two or more jurisdictions, which increases the administrative complexities.

Occupational Health and Safety Notebook 2.2

Canadian Government Departments Responsible for OH&S

Below are the websites for agencies across Canada that are responsible for occupational health and safety in federal, provincial, and territorial jurisdictions.

Federal

Human Resources Development Canada, "Occupational Health and Safety Contacts: Provincial and Territorial Governments,"
http://www.hrsdc.gc.ca/asp/gateway.asp?hr=/en/lp/lo/offices.shtml&hs=oxs
Human Resources Development Canada, "Labour Program,"
http://www.hrsdc.gc.ca/en/gateways/nav/top_nav/program/labour.shtml

Alberta	http://www.gov.ab.ca/hre/whs
British Columbia	http://www.worksafebc.com
Manitoba	http://www.gov.mb.ca/labour/safety/
New Brunswick	http://www.whscc.nb.ca/
Newfoundland and Labrador	http://www.gov.nl.ca/gs/ohs/
Nova Scotia	http://www.gov.ns.ca/enla/ohs/contacts.htm
Ontario	http://www.gov.on.ca/LAB/english/hs/index.html
Prince Edward Island	http://www.wcb.pe.ca
Quebec	http://www.csst.qc.ca
Saskatchewan	http://www.labour.gov.sk.ca
Yukon	http://www.wcb.yk.ca
Northwest Territories and Nunavut	http://www.gov.nt.ca

The general duty provision requiring employers to take every reasonable precaution to ensure employee safety is Canada-wide. In the federal jurisdiction, the duty is sufficiently broad in scope that an employer could be held liable for having failed to ensure the health and safety of an employee even if there was an absence of a specific violation to a regulatory provision. The term "ensure" is applied across Canada and is accepted to mean the strongest responsibility possible short of a guarantee.

Duties and Responsibilities of the Major Players

The statutes in most provinces and territories outline the duties and responsibilities of the major players in occupational health and safety. These include employers, owners, contractors, supervisors, and workers. Some provinces and territories also impose duties on joint health and safety committees or representatives, but the majority are silent on this subject. The human resource practitioner should be well versed in labour laws and OH&S laws in order to make informed decisions about the corporation's health and safety program. The OH&S components attached to the various jurisdictions are listed in Occupational Health and Safety Notebook 2.3.

R P C 2.2

Duties of Employers, Owners, and Contractors

Employers have a primary duty to provide a safe work environment. Other duties include providing supervision, education, training, and written instructions where applicable, as well as assisting the joint health and safety committee or representative and complying with statutes and regulations. In Ontario, the employer's responsibilities are extensive and include the following:

- ensuring that equipment is provided and properly maintained
- appointing a competent supervisor
- providing information (including confidential information) in a medical emergency
- informing supervisors and workers of possible hazards
- posting the OH&S Act in the workplace
- preparing and maintaining a health and safety policy annually and reviewing it (see Occupational Health and Safety Today 2.1)

All federal and provincial or territorial occupational health and safety acts include **prescribed** duties that may come into effect by regulation at some time. These prescribed duties may include an employer's responsibility to establish occupational health services, or a description of the written procedures that may be required.

Constructors/primary contractors have responsibilities similar to those outlined for employers. In some jurisdictions, when a construction project is scheduled to commence, a constructor/primary contractor has a duty to notify the authority within a specified time. Some jurisdictions require a written "Notice of Project" to be filed outlining the approximate cost, scope, commencement date, and duration of the project.

prescribed

under Ontario OH&S legislation, something to be undertaken because of legal or employer requirement, such as a rule or direction

constructor

in health and safety legislation, a constructor is a person or company who oversees the construction of a project and who is ultimately responsible for the health and safety of all workers

Occupational Health and Safety Notebook 2.3

Jurisdictions and OH&S Components

Jurisdictions	Committees	Duties	Advisory Councils	Safety Policies	Accident-Prevention Programs
Canada	✔	✔		✔	
Alberta	Minister may order	✔	Report to Minister, may hear appeals, other duties as assigned	✔	
British Columbia	✔	✔		✔	✔
Manitoba	✔	✔	✔	✔	
New Brunswick	✔	✔		✔	
Newfoundland and Labrador	✔	✔		✔	
Northwest Territories/Nunavut	✔	✔		✔	✔
Nova Scotia	✔	✔	✔	Director may order a code of practice	
Ontario	Minister may order	✔	Sector-based advisory councils/ associations	✔	
Prince Edward Island	Minister may order	✔	✔	✔	
Quebec	Established by request of certified association, or Commission may order	✔	Sector-based advisory councils/ associations	Supply personal protective equipment free of charge	
Saskatchewan	✔	✔	✔	✔	
Yukon	✔			✔	

In Ontario, an owner or contractor is responsible for notification by way of tender when any designated substance (e.g., asbestos or UFI insulation) is likely to be encountered during a construction project. Designated substances are those substances, identified by regulation and requiring strict control, that could inflict either acute or chronic damage on a worker when ingested, inhaled, or absorbed in the body.

Duties of Supervisors

The duties assigned to supervisors are similar across Canada. "Supervisor" is broadly interpreted to refer to a person (with or without a title) who has charge of a workplace and authority over a worker. Supervisors can be union members,

Thomson Nelson's Safety Philosophy

Thomson Nelson's Health & Safety committee is vitally interested in the health and safety of its employees. Protection from injury or occupational disease is a major continuing objective of Thomson Nelson and we will make every effort to provide a safe, healthy working environment.

Thomson Nelson will meet and, where possible, exceed the letter and intent of all applicable legislation. Health & Safety will be managed as a priority area in Thomson Nelson with adequate resources and employee involvement in the development of programs. Objectives and standards will be established for health and safety programs, and performance will be measured. Hazards in the workplace will be identified and eliminated or controlled. Where hazards cannot be eliminated, programs will be put into place to safeguard the health and safety of the employees. Information necessary for the protection of our employees will be maintained and communicated to those affected.

Every employee must recognize and accept their own responsibility to work safely, maintain a safe workplace, and to report any and all unsafe conditions and practices immediately.

association members covered under a collective agreement, plant managers, general managers, lead hands, forepersons, school principals, or self-employed individuals. The criteria used in Ontario to determine whether a person would be held to be a supervisor include having the authority to promote or recommend promotion, to discipline workers, or to schedule or assign work. In addition to these criteria, in Ontario a competent supervisor is familiar with the OH&S Act and regulations and has knowledge of potential hazards, and so on, in the workplace (OH&S Act, s.1(1), 25(2)(c)). A supervisor's duties include the following:

- ensuring that workers comply with the OH&S Act and regulations
- ensuring that workers use or wear safety equipment, devices, or clothing
- advising workers of possible hazards
- providing written instructions if applicable
- taking every reasonable precaution to ensure the protection of workers

Duties of Workers

Duties of workers are included in the majority of statutes. In some jurisdictions, the responsibilities are laid out by regulation. The inclusion of workers' responsibilities and duties is relatively new in health and safety legislation. Before the late 1970s, all responsibility for workplace health and safety rested with the employer. Now, though the employer is totally responsible for paying for health and safety activities, everyone is responsible for making them work.

A worker's duties include the following:

- complying with the OH&S Act and regulations
- properly using the safety equipment and clothes provided
- reporting hazards, such as defective equipment, to the supervisor
- reporting any contraventions of the act or regulations

Workers are prohibited from making any safety device ineffective, using any hazardous equipment or machine in unsafe conditions, or engaging in rough or boisterous conduct.

Joint Health and Safety Committees

A recent addition to OH&S legislation is the creation of joint health and safety committees in the workplace. These committees are required by law in nine jurisdictions; the minister responsible has the discretionary power to require the formation of committees in the remaining four jurisdictions.

The primary function of the joint health and safety committee is to provide a nonadversarial atmosphere in which labour and management can work together to create a safer and healthier workplace. Joint committees are structured such that equal or better representation is required from workers who do not exercise managerial responsibilities. Each workplace requiring a committee must train and certify at least one management member and one worker member. Subjects taught during the training (which may run from one to three weeks) include law, general safety, hygiene, routes of entry (into the body), indoor air quality, chemical safety, certified workers' rights and duties, and joint committees. Certified members may be involved in inspections, work refusals, and bilateral work stoppage when there is an imminent hazard to a worker. They may also investigate critical accidents, attend at the beginning of hygiene testing, and respond to worker concerns.

Occupational Health and Safety Notebook 2.4

Legislative Requirements for Joint Health and Safety Committees

Committees are mandatory in

Federal	Workplaces with 20 or more employees
Alberta	Workplaces that are required to establish a committee by the ministry
British Columbia	Workplaces with 20 or more employees
Manitoba	Workplaces with 20 or more employees
New Brunswick	Workplaces with 20 or more employees
Newfoundland and Labrador	Workplaces with 10 or more employees
Northwest Territories	As determined by the chief safety officer
Nova Scotia	Workplaces with 20 or more employees
Nunavut	As determined by the chief safety officer
Ontario	Workplaces with 20 or more employees
Prince Edward Island	Workplaces with 20 or more employees
Quebec	Workplaces where the union (or 10% of the workforce) requests the employer to establish a committee
Saskatchewan	Workplaces with 10 or more employees
Yukon	Workplaces with 20 or more employees

Occupational Health and Safety Notebook 2.5

Joint Health and Safety Committees at a Glance

Joint health and safety committees are made up of representatives from both management and unions or workers. They are charged with the responsibility of enhancing health and safety in the workplace.

Most health and safety legislation mandates the establishment of joint committees. For example, in Ontario the legislation requires a committee in workplaces with more than 20 employees, unless designated substances (such as asbestos) are present. The size of the committee varies with the number of employees, but the intent is to represent all areas of the workplace.

The committee has four principal functions:

1. identify potential hazards
2. evaluate these potential hazards
3. recommend corrective action
4. follow up implemented recommendations

To do so, the committee is required to meet regularly (at least every three months) and to regularly inspect the workplace. At least two members of the committee (one management and one labour) receive specialized training that meets standards established by the Workplace Safety and Insurance Board (in Ontario) and play more specialized roles as certified health and safety committee members.

Source: Ontario Ministry of Labour, "A Guide for Joint Health and Safety Committees (JHSCs) and Representatives in the Workplace." Retrieved from http://www.gov.on.ca/LAB/english/hs/jhsc/, October 7, 2004.

A review of the literature generally supports the effectiveness of joint committees in managing health and safety.[1] In particular, the existence of joint health and safety committees leads to a reduction in the number of workplace injuries.[2] As Weil points out, the existence of a joint health and safety committee does not mean that the committee is effective.[3] Indeed, like any other workplace group, committees may take some time before they become effective. Joint committees can improve health and safety through prevention, education, and training and by providing an ongoing forum for problem resolution.[4]

Work Refusals

The right to refuse unsafe work without fear of reprisals is now available to workers in every jurisdiction in Canada. Exceptions or limitations to the right to refuse unsafe work vary across the country. In essence, a worker does not have the right to refuse unsafe work if the work is a normal condition of employment, or if the worker, by his or her refusal, places another life in jeopardy.

In Ontario, police, fire fighters, teachers, and health care workers are among those professionals who have been granted what is known as a limited right of refusal. For example, a fire fighter has the right to refuse to use unsafe equipment during an exercise. A nurse has the right to refuse to use equipment suspected to be defective until his or her concern has been investigated and resolved; however, a nurse does not have the right to refuse unsafe work if the lives of patients are placed in jeopardy as a result of the refusal. The Ontario Provincial Police had their old revolvers replaced by modern pistols after a refusal based on the defectiveness of the old units; other police services followed.

The procedure for reporting a refusal to perform unsafe work is, for the most part, consistent across jurisdictions. Once the worker has apprised the supervisor of the suspected work hazard, an investigation is conducted by the supervisor and a worker representative (union, joint health and safety committee member, or coworker).

The investigation results in either a return to work or a continued refusal. In the latter situation, a ministry inspector/officer conducts an investigation and then provides a written decision. In the meantime, a replacement worker may not be assigned the work that has been refused unless he or she has been informed about the circumstances surrounding the refusal. The refusing worker who continues to receive the regular remuneration for the job may be assigned alternative work but not sent home.

In New Brunswick and Prince Edward Island, the supervisor and joint health and safety committee can make a judgment that the refusal is not based on reasonable grounds. The employee may then refer the matter to an occupational health and safety officer, who will make the final determination. As "reasonable grounds" is not defined, it appears to leave the door open for a subjective rather than an objective decision being reached.

Stop-Work Provisions (Ontario)

In 1990, an Act to Amend the Ontario Occupational Health and Safety Act was given royal assent. The amendments are far reaching and promise profound changes in how employers will do business in Ontario. Among the most significant provisions are expanded powers for certified members of the joint health and safety committee.

The provisions for stopping work take two forms, one bilateral and the other unilateral. A certified member of a joint health and safety committee may, in the course of an inspection or investigation, have reason to believe that a dangerous circumstance exists. The certified member will ask a supervisor (and possibly a second certified member of the joint health and safety committee) to investigate. Following the investigation and possible remedial actions taken by the supervisor, if the certified members, representing both management and labour, find that the dangerous circumstance still exists, they may direct the employer to stop work. The legislation defines "dangerous circumstance" as follows:

- a provision of the act or the regulation is being contravened
- the contravention presents a danger or a hazard to a worker
- the danger or hazard is such that any delay in controlling it may seriously endanger a worker

The unilateral provision will apply in the case of an employer who has, in the opinion of a government-appointed adjudicator, taken insufficient steps to protect workers from serious risk to their health and safety. The action will be taken by a certified worker member. A second circumstance may allow the unilateral provision to apply. An employer may advise the joint health and safety committee in writing of a willingness to adopt the unilateral power of the certified worker member to stop work in dangerous circumstance; this advisory is required in Ontario.

Workplace Hazardous Materials Information System

The Workplace Hazardous Materials Information System (WHMIS) began in the United States in the early 1980s in the form of the Hazard Communication Standard. WHMIS reflects the belief that workers have the right to know about hazards that may be associated with certain chemicals used in the workplace, and, by extension, the community. In Ontario this right to know extends to citizens.

RPC 2.5

WHMIS is the brainchild of industry, labour, and government representatives committed to developing regulations that meet the right-to-know standard. In Canada, all jurisdictions were involved in creating the first Canada-wide health and safety legislation. The federal government created a model OH&S regulation that was used by the provincial and territorial governments to ensure the desired consistency in regulations. The Hazardous Products Act defines a hazardous product and controls its use by requiring disclosure of the substance and its concentration in a manufactured product. Other federal statutes and regulations governing controlled products include the Controlled Products Regulations, the Ingredient Disclosure List, and the Hazardous Materials Review Act and related regulation.

The federal legislation, which was limited in application to federally regulated workplaces, required the provinces and territories to create enabling legislation to empower the jurisdictions. The WHMIS legislation came into force across Canada between 1988 and 1990. Workers now have a right to know about the potential hazards of any chemical they handle, including handling, storage, use, and emergency instructions.

The WHMIS legislation is based on three elements:

1. labels designed to alert the worker that the container contains a potentially hazardous product
2. material safety data sheets outlining a product's potentially hazardous ingredient(s) and procedures for safe handling of the product
3. employee training

Ontario added three further elements:

1. hazardous materials inventory requirement
2. physical agents (such as noise)
3. the public's right to know

Labels

That controlled substances need labelling is the most widely understood element of the WHMIS program. There are two types of WHMIS labels: workplace labels and supplier labels. Workplace labels identify the WHMIS class of the material. There are six WHMIS classes (some of which have subclasses) as follows:

Class A—Compressed Gas

Class B—Flammable and Combustible Material

>   Division 1: Flammable Gas
>   Division 2: Flammable Liquid
>   Division 3: Combustible Liquid
>   Division 4: Flammable Solid
>   Division 5: Flammable Aerosol
>   Division 6: Reactive Flammable Material

Class C—Oxidizing Material

Class D—Poisonous and Infectious Material

>   Division 1: Materials causing immediate and serious toxic effects
>   Subdivision A: Very toxic material
>   Subdivision B: Toxic material
>   Division 2: Materials causing other toxic effects
>   Subdivision A: Very toxic material
>   Subdivision B: Toxic material
>   Division 3: Biohazardous Infection Material

Class E—Corrosive Material

Class F—Dangerously Reactive Material

(See Figure 2.1 for WHMIS class symbols and subclass designations.)

FIGURE 2.1

WHMIS Class Symbols and Subclass Designations

What the symbol represents

 Class A—
Compressed gas

 Class D, Division 2—
Poisonous and
infectional material:
Other toxic effects

 Class B—
Combustible and
flammable material

 Class D, Division 3—
Poisonous and
infectional material:
Biohazardous
infectious material

 Class C—Oxidizing
material

 Class E—
Corrosive material

 Class D, Division 1—
Poisonous and
infectious material:
Immediate and
serious toxic effects

 Class F—
Dangerously
reactive material

The supplier label, the more comprehensive of the two, must be attached to the container when it is delivered to the workplace. (See Figure 2.2 for an example of a supplier label.) The supplier label must have a black-and-white border and must contain the following information (in both English and French):

1. The product identifier (Controlled Products Regulations, s.2(1)), including the brand name or code number. Information may include the chemical name, generic name, or trade name.
2. The supplier identifier (Controlled Products Regulations, s.2(1)), i.e., the name of the manufacturer or supplier.
3. A statement that the material safety data sheet is to be referred to for more information.
4. Hazard symbol(s) (Controlled Products Regulations, s.11) that correspond to the class and division that allocates the product as a controlled substance.
5. Risk phrases (Controlled Products Regulations, s.2(1)) that correspond to the class and division to which the product is allocated.
6. Precautionary measures to be followed when handling or using the controlled product.
7. First-aid measures to be taken in the event of an exposure to a controlled product.

The requirement for workplace labels takes effect when the product is removed from its original container to be used or distributed. Workplace labels are also required for storage tanks or large in-house containers. The workplace label must contain a product identifier, safe-handling instructions, and the location of a material safety data sheet. (See Figure 2.3 for an example of a workplace label.)

Material Safety Data Sheets

The objective of safety data information is to identify potentially harmful ingredients in products that the worker may be handling, to present factual information about the nature of the harmful ingredients, and to provide guidance in the use and disposal of the product.

The material safety data sheet (MSDS) must contain information as set out by the Hazardous Products Act, s.11(1) and the Controlled Products Regulations, ss.12 and 13. (See Figure 2.4 for an example.) The information must be comprehensive, up to date (revisions are required every three years), and made available in the two official languages. The following nine sections form the minimum standard:

1. Product information including the name, address, and phone number of the supplier or manufacturer and the product identifier and use.
2. A hazardous ingredients list, including all controlled substances in the product and their concentrations. The list generally includes

FIGURE 2.2

Example of a Supplier Label

ISOPROPYL ALCOHOL

FLAMMABLE
HARMFUL IF INHALED
HARMFUL IF SWALLOWED
MAY CAUSE SKIN IRRITATION
MAY CAUSE EYE IRRITATION

First Aid: Obtain medical attention. Induce vomiting by sticking finger down throat. If breathing stopped, begin artificial respiration. If inhaled, remove victim to fresh air. For skin contact, wash with soap and water while removing contaminated clothing. For eye contact, flush with running water for at least 15 minutes, call physician.

Precautions: Wear chemical goggles. Wear resistant gloves. Do not take internally. Do not inhale vapour or mist. Use with enough ventilation to keep below TLV. Avoid skin or eye contact. Wash hands thoroughly after use. Keep container closed. Never use pressure to empty container. Do not reuse container for any purpose until commercially cleaned. Container must be grounded when emptied. Use explosion-proof equipment. Keep away from heat, sparks, and flame. No smoking. Do not keep near foodstuffs.

ALCOOL D'ISOPROPYLE

INFLAMMABLE
NOCIF SI INHALÉ
NOCIF SI AVALÉ
RISQUE D'IRRITATION CUTANEE
RISQUE D'IRRITER LES YEUX

Premiers soins: Obtenir des soins médicaux. Faire vomir en enfonçant le doigt dans la gorge. En cas d'arrêt respiratoire, pratiquer la respiration artificielle. En cas d'inhalation, transporter la victime à l'air frais. En cas de contact avec la peau, laver au savon et à l'eau tout en retirant les vêtements souillés. En cas de contact avec les yeux, laver à l'eau courante pendant au moins 15 minutes. Appeler un médecin.

Mise en garde: Porter des lunettes antiproduits chimiques. Porter des gants résistants. Pour usage externe. Ne pas inhaler les vapeurs et les bruines. Utiliser avec assez de ventilation pour ne pas dépasser la QLP. Éviter tout contact avec la peau ou les yeux. Bien se laver les mains après utilisation. Garder le contenant ferme. Ne jamais utiliser de la pression pour vider le contenant. Ne pas réutiliser le contenant pour n'importe quel usage avant de l'avoir nettoyé professionnellement. Effectuer la prise de terre du contenant avant de le vider. Utiliser un equipment à l'épreuve des explosions. Tenir à l'écart des étincelles, des flammes et de la chaleur. Interdit de fumer. Ne pas garder à proximité d'aliments.

SEE MATERIAL SAFETY DATA SHEET FOR PRODUCT/ VOIR FICHE SIGNALÉTIQUE

Company X
Brampton, Ontario

FIGURE 2.3

Example of a Workplace Label

the chemical abstract number (when available); the allowable concentration limits, known as threshold limit values (TLV), set by the American Conference of Governmental Industrial Hygienists (ACGIH); the lethal-dose range tested for a specific animal population; and routes of entry.

3. Physical data including information on appearance: odour, density, boiling point, corrosiveness, and so on.

4. Fire and explosion information, including data on the flammability of the hazardous ingredients.

5. Reactivity information outlining the conditions under which the material may react with other chemicals or materials. The section will also identify the hazardous products produced by decomposition in a fire situation.

6. Toxicological data including all available information on the possible health effects from chronic or acute exposure.

7. Preventative measures to be used while dealing with the product, including information on personal protective equipment, ventilation requirements, storage, handling, and waste disposal.

8. First-aid measures, providing specific recommendations for treatment for exposure to the material.

9. Preparation information, including the name of the person(s) who prepared the MSDS, a phone number for contact, and the date of issue of the MSDS.

FIGURE 2.4

Material Safety Data Sheet

Form #CH3 **MATERIAL SAFETY DATA SHEET** name of product:

SECTION I—HAZARDOUS INGREDIENTS

Chemical Identity	Concentration	CAS Number	PIN Number	LD$_{50}$ Species and Route	LC$_{50}$ Species and Route

SECTION II—PREPARATION INFORMATION

Prepared by (Group, Department, Etc.)	Phone Number	Date of Preparation

SECTION III—PRODUCT INFORMATION

Product Identifier

Manufacturer's Name		Supplier's Name	
Street Address		Street Address	
City	Province	City	Province
Postal Code	Emergency Tel. No.	Postal Code	Emergency Tel. No.

Product Use

SECTION IV—PHYSICAL DATA

Physical State	Odour and Appearance		Odour Threshold
Specific Gravity (water=1)	Co-efficient of Water/Oil Distribution		Vapour Pressure
Boiling Point (°C)	Freezing Point (°C)	pH	Vapour Density (Air=1)
Evaporation Rate (BuAc=1)		Percent Volatile (by volume)	

The manufacturer or supplier must develop or cause to be developed an MSDS for each product supplied for use in the workplace. The MSDS must be transmitted to the purchaser on or before the date of sale or delivery of the product. The information on the MSDS must be current at the time of sale or delivery, and the MSDS must be dated no more than three years before the date of sale or delivery.

The requirement for supplying MSDS is twofold. Suppliers are regulated by the federal legislation under the Controlled Products Act and provincial or territorial regulations, while employers are regulated only under provincial or territorial regulations. Should an employer also be a manufacturer or produce research products not intended for sale, the responsibility for creating an MSDS becomes the employer's.

Training

Education in WHMIS is commonly defined as the process of acquiring knowledge through systematic instruction. By contrast, training is defined as bringing a person to a desired state or standard of efficiency by instruction and practice. One area that often escapes scrutiny when the inspector/officer applies a performance-based regulation is the application of the education received. A worker may know to check for labels, know where to find the MSDS, and know the employer's procedures for handling a spill; however, the same worker may not know how to read the MSDS or understand it in sufficient depth to apply it in the workplace. Training and education should include a practical process to ensure that the worker understands how to apply the knowledge acquired.

After completing a training program, the worker should understand the purpose and origin of WHMIS and be able to

- identify WHMIS hazard symbols
- read WHMIS supplier and workplace labels
- read and apply the applicable information on an MSDS

The WHMIS program must be reviewed annually or as changes occur in products or processes in the workplace.

Environmental Legislation

Environmental and occupational health and safety legislation are solidly entwined. In recognition of this fact, many companies and institutions have occupational environmental health and safety departments. The health and safety professional will be conscious of the overlap in environmental and OH&S statutes and regulations. Chemicals that can cause damage to a worker may also cause damage to the ecosystem if released into the environment. Federal and provincial or territorial statutes relating to some aspect of environmental or health and safety management are listed in Occupational Health and Safety Notebook 2.6 and Occupational Health and Safety Notebook 2.7.

Regulatory legislation related to environmental assessment, public health, waste disposal, buried fuel tanks, and storage or use of pesticides affects the environment, the occupational health and safety of employees, and the public. As the following scenario indicates, the practitioner is required to understand environmental and OH&S jurisdictions and the potential for overlap:

> If a release of a potentially hazardous substance occurs within a building (other than residential) it falls under the jurisdiction of the authority enforcing the health and safety legislation. If the release is outside the building, or if the potentially hazardous substance is released into the sewer, storm system, water, or air, it falls under the jurisdiction of the authority enforcing the environmental legislation. Any single occurrence might involve both authorities.

The parallels between environmental and OH&S legislation have extended to the courts. In *R. v. Bata Industries Ltd., Bata, Marchant and Weston*, Bata Industries Ltd. and three of its directors were charged with allowing a large chemical waste storage site containing many deteriorating and leaking containers to discharge known toxic industrial chemicals into the ground environment. The defendants used the defence of due diligence, arguing that the legislation was vague and imprecise and contrary to the Canadian Charter of Rights and Freedoms. The company was convicted, as were two of the directors (the third director was acquitted). The court found that the two defendants had not exercised due diligence. The court stated that although it did not expect a board of directors to make all environmental decisions, these decisions were too important to be delegated to subordinates.

Provincial and Territorial Statutes

Province	Transportation	Environment	Other
Alberta	Transportation of Dangerous Goods Act, S.A. 1982	Environmental Protection and Enhancement Act, S.A. 1992	
British Columbia	Transportation of Dangerous Goods Act, S.B.C. 1985	Waste Management Act, S.B.C. 1982/Amended 1990, 1992	
Manitoba	Dangerous Goods Handling and Transportation Act, R.S.M. 1987	Environment Act, S.M. 1987–88/Waste Reduction and Prevention Act, S.M. 1989–90	
New Brunswick	Transportation of Dangerous Goods Act, S.N.B. 1988		
Newfoundland and Labrador	Dangerous Goods Transportation Act, R.S.N. 1990	Department of Environment and Lands Act, R.S.N. 1990/Waste Material Disposal Act, R.S.N. 1990/Water Protection Act, R.S.N. 1990	
Northwest Territories and Nunavut	Transportation of Dangerous Goods Act, 1990, S.N.W.T.		
Nova Scotia	Dangerous Goods Transportation Act, R.S.N.S. 1989	Environment Act (draft)/Litter Abatement Act, S.N.S. 1989	
Ontario	Dangerous Goods Transportation Act, R.S.O. 1990	Environmental Protection Act, R.S.O. 1990 as amended/Environmental Bill of Rights, 1993, S.O. 1993/Ontario Water Resources Act, R.S.O. 1990/Waste Management Act, R.S.O. 1992/Environmental Assessment Act	Gasoline Handling Act, S.O. 1990/Health Protection and Promotion Act, R.S.O. 1990/Municipal Act, R.S.O. 1990/Pesticides Act, R.S.O. 1990/Public Health Act, R.S.O. 1980/Energy Act, R.S.O. 1990
Prince Edward Island	Dangerous Goods Transportation Act, R.S.P.E.I. 1988	Environmental Protection Act, R.S.P.E.I. 1988	
Quebec		Environmental Quality Act, R.S.Q. 1990	
Saskatchewan	Dangerous Goods Transportation Act, S.S. 1984–85–86	Litter Control Act, R.S.S. 1978	
Yukon	Dangerous Goods Transportation Act, R.S.Y.T. 1986	Environment Act, S.Y. 1991	

Transportation of Dangerous Goods

The regulation of environmental hazards, occupational health and safety, and transportation of dangerous goods is not the exclusive domain of either the federal, provincial, or territorial governments. Therefore, the practitioner should be familiar with the statutes relevant to his or her particular jurisdiction. In essence, the environmental and transportation legislation seeks to supply the framework within which society can protect itself from the risk that attends the transportation of inherently dangerous materials.

The federal legislation governing the transportation of dangerous goods applies to all persons who handle, offer for transport, transport, or import any dangerous goods. The provincial or territorial legislation does not always go this far, making it sometimes impossible to determine which statutes apply. Notwithstanding some provincial or territorial limitations, dangerous goods legislation applies to carriers, shippers, and transportation intermediaries such as freight forwarders and customs brokers. Various regulations exist with respect to the identification and placarding of dangerous goods, the control of quantities, and the training and certification of workers. The regulatory wording complements the WHMIS requirements and the OH&S responsibility of employers and supervisors to educate and train workers.

In *R. v. Midland Transport Ltd.* (1991), the New Brunswick Provincial Court made the following observation about the legislation:

> The Transportation of Dangerous Goods Act and the Regulations thereunder with the act fall in the category of legislation which creates public welfare offences. Recognizing the potential dangers, it establishes safety guidelines for the handling of hazardous materials to ensure the protection of the public and the environment.

Corporate Liability

Whereas in the past directors and officers of incorporated entities were responsible solely to the corporation and shareholders, their zone of accountability now extends to the public at large. Environmental and occupational health and safety statutes have been amended to include broad responsibilities for directors and officers. The liabilities that directors and officers now face include the following:

- fines or imprisonment for corporate pollution causing or permitting the discharge of liquid industrial waste into the ground
- cleanup costs associated with a property the corporation owns, controls, or occupies
- fines for failing to comply with regulatory legislation

Canadian jurisprudence has followed the lead of the United States in extending legal responsibility to the boardroom. The executives of a company are no longer permitted to hide behind the laws of incorporation.

Bill C-45 was passed by Parliament in 2003 and became law in March 2004 to deal with issues of corporate liability with respect to both fraud and occupational health and safety. The so-called "Westray Legislation" makes company executives more accountable when workers are killed or injured on the job because of management negligence. It is named after the Westray tragedy in which a mine explosion was attributed to corporate negligence (see Chapter 1). Ultimately, it could lead to a corporation and its management being criminally prosecuted if found negligent in providing an appropriate standard of occupational health and safety in the workplace, resulting in an employee injury or death. This introduces the notion of "corporate homicide" for the first time into the Canadian Criminal Code.

The act makes a company responsible

- for the actions of those who oversee day-to-day operations (e.g., supervisors and mid-level managers)
- for managers (either executive or operational) who intentionally commit, or have employees commit, crimes to benefit the organization

- for managers who do not take action when they become aware of offences being committed
- for the actions of managers who demonstrate a criminal lack of care (i.e., criminal negligence)

Passage of the Westray Legislation substantially raises the stakes for managers and corporations. In addition to introducing criminal liability into the OH&S arena, the act takes away the ability of the company to shift blame to frontline managers. That is, companies are now responsible not only for ensuring that frontline staff know the appropriate rules, regulations, and working procedures, but also that employees follow the procedures. It is no longer possible to claim that employees were derelict in their responsibility—even if true, the company is liable.

Sources: Department of Justice Canada, "Parliament Passes Bill C-45: Stronger Laws Affecting the Criminal Liability of Organizations." Retrieved from http://canada.justice.gc.ca/en/news/nr/2003/doc_31024.html, October 7, 2004; Canadian Centre for Occupational Health and Safety, "Headlines." Retrieved from http://www.ccohs.ca/headlines/text106.html, October 7, 2004; and Canadian Construction Association, "Summary of Bill C-45." Retrieved from http://www.cca-acc.com/news/government/billc45/summary.pdf, October 7, 2004.

Summary

The complexities associated with OH&S legislation in Canada continue to grow. This chapter has outlined the scope of this legislation and the changing climate surrounding it. In particular we focused on some of the duties of each of the major stakeholders under the legislation and the role of joint health and safety committees. The elements composing the Workplace Hazardous Materials Information System were reviewed and some consideration was given to ancillary legislation (e.g., environmental, transportation of dangerous goods).

Key Terms

act, p. 24
constructor, p. 27
guidelines and policies, p. 24

prescribed, p. 27
regulations, p. 24
standards and codes, p. 25

Weblinks

Canadian General Standards Board,
http://w3.pwgsc.gc.ca/cgsb (p. 25)

Canadian Standards Association,
http://www.csa.ca (p. 25)

Standards Council of Canada,
http://www.scc.ca (p. 25)

Underwriters' Laboratories of Canada,
http://www.ulc.ca (p. 25)

American National Standards Institute,
http://www.ansi.org (p. 25)

American Society for Testing and Materials,
http://www.astm.org (p. 25)

International Organization for Standardization,
http://www.iso.ch (p. 25)

Ontario Ministry of Labour, "Joint Health and Safety Committees,"
http://www.gov.on.ca/LAB/english/hs/ohsaguide/ohsag_4.html (p. 30)

Ontario Ministry of Labour, "The Right to Stop Work,"
http://www.gov.on.ca/LAB/english/hs/ohsaguide/ohsag_8.html (pp. 31, 32)

Health Canada, "Workplace Hazardous Materials Information System (WHMIS),"
http://www.hc-sc.gc.ca/hecs-sesc/whmis/(p. 33)

RPC Icons

RPC 2.1 Provides input on matters related to the drafting and/or application of legislation or regulations related to health, safety security, and Workers' Compensation.

- legislation
- process and means of influencing legislative change
- linkages with change agents (e.g., HR Associations, interest groups, politicians, bureaucrats)
- report writing
- Common and statutory law (e.g., employment standard: labour relations)
- Worker Protection (including health and safety and Workers' Compensation)
- Theories and practices for protection of individuals and groups
- Occupational health and safety legislation (e.g., Occupational Health and Safety Act of Ontario, Workplace Safety & Insurance Act—Bill 99, Workplace Hazardous Materials Information System, Transportation of Dangerous Goods legislation, environmental legislation, smoking in the workplace legislation, civil rights legislation)

RPC 2.2 Ensures that security programs and policies minimize risks while considering the obligation of the employer and the rights of employees, union, and third parties.

- nature of the business and physical work environment
- relevant legislation
- industry best practices
- program and policy development
- safety and security equipment in the workplace
- risk assessment/techniques
- cost/benefit analysis

TASK & KNOWLEDGE REQUIREMENTS

- available community resources
- Worker Protection (including health and safety and Workers' Compensation)
- Unions' role in health and safety and in employee involvement
- Occupational health and safety legislation (e.g., Occupational Health and Safety Act of Ontario, Workplace Safety & Insurance Act—Bill 99, Workplace Hazardous Materials Information System, Transportation of Dangerous Goods legislation, environmental legislation, smoking in the workplace legislation, civil rights legislation)
- Emergency preparedness procedures
- Management techniques for OH&S Programs
- Types of employee assistance and wellness programs

RPC 2.3 Establishes a joint responsibility system as required by law, e.g. worker-management Health & Safety committees, investigations, audits, testing and training, to ensure employee safety.

- relevant Occupational Health and Safety legislation
- inspection techniques and procedures
- hazard recognition
- principles of training and development

TASK & KNOWLEDGE REQUIREMENTS

- program and policy development
- audit processes
- Joint Health and Safety Committee functions
- Worker Protection (including health and safety and Workers' Compensation)
- Occupational health and safety legislation (e.g., Occupational Health and Safety Act of Ontario, Workplace Safety & Insurance Act—Bill 99, Workplace Hazardous Materials Information System, Transportation of Dangerous Goods legislation, environmental legislation, smoking in the workplace legislation, civil rights legislation)
- Management techniques for OH&S Programs

RPC 2.4 Responds to any refusals to perform work believed to be unsafe.

- relevant Occupational Health and Safety legislation
- procedure for dealing with work refusals

- policy and program development
- conflict resolution procedures
- emergency procedures
- government inspection agencies such as the Ministry of Labour
- Common and statutory law (e.g., employment standard: labour relations
- Worker Protection (including health and safety and Workers' Compensation)
- Communication theories and techniques
- Concepts and processes of politics and conflict
- Occupational health and safety legislation (e.g., Occupational Health and Safety Act of Ontario, Workplace Safety & Insurance Act—Bill 99, Workplace Hazardous Materials Information System, Transportation of Dangerous Goods legislation, environmental legislation, smoking in the workplace legislation, civil rights legislation)
- Hazard identification and control

RPC 2.5 Implements and evaluates practices in the areas of health, safety, security, and Workers' Compensation.

- investigative techniques
- hazard recognition
- disaster recovery techniques
- relevant legislation
- resource information
- common health and safety practices
- company policies and procedures
- Worker Protection (including health and safety and Workers' Compensation)
- Theories and practices for protection of individuals and groups
- Occupational health and safety legislation (e.g., Occupational Health and Safety Act of Ontario, Workplace Safety & Insurance Act—Bill 99, Workplace Hazardous Materials Information System, Transportation of Dangerous Goods legislation, environmental legislation, smoking in the workplace legislation, civil rights legislation)
- Hazard identification and control
- Management techniques for OH&S Programs

Discussion Questions

1. What are the three fundamental workers' rights that underlie most health and safety legislation?
2. What is the difference between the responsibilities assigned to companies under occupational health and safety and those assigned under environmental legislation?
3. What three components make up WHMIS compliance?
4. Describe the structure and role of joint health and safety committees.

Using the Internet

1. What legislation applies in your jurisdiction? Find the body responsible for occupational health and safety and review the legislation. What are the major provisions and their implications for employers? for employees? for human resource managers?
2. WHMIS training is widely available online. Using a search engine and keywords such as "WHMIS online training," find a local provider of online WHMIS training.

Exercise

1. Health and safety legislation can be crafted following different approaches. One approach is to force compliance through establishing standards, conducting rigorous inspections on a regular basis, and harshly punishing failures to meet the established standards. A second approach is to facilitate self-reliance by providing the parties with the information and resources necessary to monitor and enhance health and safety in their workplaces. What are the relative merits of these two approaches? What advantages and disadvantages accrue under each system? What is the appropriate balance between enforcement and encouragement?

Case 1: Workplace Tragedy

An auto-parts manufacturer employs 500 workers. The plant operates on three shifts, and its various lines include large punch presses, conveyors, paint-spray booths, and overhead cranes. A worker has been killed following an accident on the overhead-crane line. The worker was guiding the load hoisted by the crane when the load slipped, causing a failure of the supporting cables. The worker was killed when the falling load struck him. Although this is the most serious accident, there have been several others at the plant in the past. As plant manager, you are responsible for ensuring the safety of your employees. Outline the steps you plan to take to improve health and safety in the plant.

Case 2: Work Refusal at Regional Hospital

Regional Hospital is a 100-bed acute-care facility providing services to a mid-sized Canadian city. Recently, the hospital took advantage of a special government grant to develop and operate an HIV-treatment ward. Although the ward is now open, there is considerable disquiet among the staff. Two nurses have refused to work their assigned shift on the ward, claiming that it is their right to refuse unsafe work. Moreover, workers have been petitioning their certified representative on the Joint Health and Safety Committee to close the workplace because of the safety standard. As the HR representative for Regional Hospital, what is your planned response? How do you balance the workers' right to refuse unsafe work against the need to staff the ward?

WHMIS Regulations Consulted

Model OH&S Regulations

Alberta	Chemical Hazards Regulation
British Columbia	Workplace Hazardous Materials Information System Regulations
Manitoba	Workplace Hazardous Materials Information System Regulations
New Brunswick	Workplace Hazardous Materials Information System Regulations
Newfoundland and Labrador	Workplace Hazardous Materials Information System Regulations
Northwest Territories/Nunavut	Work Site Hazardous Materials Information System Regulations
Nova Scotia	Workplace Hazardous Materials Information System Regulations
Ontario	Workplace Hazardous Materials Information System Regulations
Prince Edward Island	Workplace Hazardous Materials Information System Regulations
Quebec	An Act to Amend the Act respecting Occupational Health and Safety
Saskatchewan	The Occupational Health and Safety Act 1993, Part IV, Workplace Hazardous Materials Information System
Yukon	Workplace Hazardous Materials Information System Regulations

Endnotes

1. Kelloway, E. K. (2003). Labor unions and safety. In J. Barling & M. Frone (Eds.), *Psychology of occupational safety*. Washington, DC: APA Books.

2. Reilly, B., Paci, P., & Holl, P. (1995). Unions, safety committees, and workplace injuries. *British Journal of Industrial Relations, 33,* 275–288.

3. Weil, D. (1999). Are mandated health and safety committees substitutes for or supplements to labor unions? *Industrial and Labor Relations Review, 52,* 339–361.

4. Weil, D. (1995). Mandating safety and health committees: Lessons from the United States. *Proceedings of the 47th annual meeting of the Industrial Relations Research Association* (pp. 273–281), Madison, Wis.

Chapter 3

Workers' Compensation

Chapter Learning Objectives

After reading this chapter, you should be able to

- outline the goals and methods of Workers' Compensation Boards (WCBs)
- discuss the problems associated with compensating for psychological conditions and occupational illnesses
- describe the assessment methods of WCBs
- with the use of the appendix, understand the methods of calculating injury frequency and severity rates

Type of Injury and Compensation

Donald Martin and Ruth Laseur probably did not intend to rewrite Canadian Workers' Compensation Legislation when they filed their claims. But as a result of a Supreme Court Ruling, they might well have changed the face of compensation law across the country.

Both individuals filed Workers' Compensation claims for chronic pain. Mr. Martin worked as a foreman and sprained his back (a lumbar sprain). Despite several attempts to return to work and completion of a work-hardening and reconditioning program, he was unable to resume his normal job. Ms. Laseur was employed as a bus driver. She injured her back and right hand after falling from the bumper of her bus. Again, despite several attempts to return to work, she continued to suffer debilitating pain. Both claims were denied by the Nova Scotia Workers' Compensation Board. Section 10B of the act limits chronic pain claims to four weeks of functional restoration after which no further entitlement arises.

The parties appealed the decision to the Supreme Court, claiming that the provincial legislation discriminated against their Charter rights and, in particular, violated section 15 of the Charter of Rights and Freedoms, which guarantees equal rights regardless of race, national or ethnic origin, colour, religion, sex, age, and mental or physical disability. The Court awarded Martin extra benefits while determining that Laseur was not entitled to further benefits. The ruling was issued October 1, 2003.

Most important, the Supreme Court ruling means that Workers' Compensation Boards cannot discriminate against a type of injury. In this case, limiting benefits for chronic injury to four weeks was, in effect, discriminating against individuals with chronic pain.

Although the decision is still relatively new, it opens the possibility for compensation for chronic stress or a variety of other conditions that are currently disallowed by Workers' Compensation Boards. In effect, the Supreme Court decision requires the evaluation of every case on its individual merits without recourse to judgments about the type of injury for which compensation is being claimed.

Sources: CBC News, "Top court ruling a victory for chronic pain sufferers." Retrieved from http://www.cbc.ca/stories/2003/10/03/pain_scoc031003, October 9, 2004; Workers' Compensation Board of Alberta, "Chronic pain—Issue overview." Retrieved from http://www.wcb.ab.ca/news/chronic_pain.asp, October 9, 2004; Nova Scotia Department of Environment and Labour, "Chronic pain regulations approved, July 22, 2004." Retrieved from http://www.gov.ns.ca/news/details.asp?id=20040722006, October 9, 2004; and ARCH: A Legal Resource Centre for Persons with Disabilities, "ARCH and client win important case at Supreme Court of Canada." Retrieved from http://www.archlegalclinic.ca/aboutARCH/litigation/cases/oniwg_b.asp, October 9, 2004.

Workers' Compensation is a form of insurance governed by an act of Parliament to help workers who are injured on the job to return to work. Consider the example of a construction labourer who has sustained an injury on the job and is now unable to work because of a disability. Workers' Compensation will ensure that the injured worker receives (1) first-aid treatment, either on the job or at the nearest local treatment facility, (2) benefits while the worker is at home recuperating, and (3) proper treatment for any injuries. If necessary, rehabilitation will be provided to help the worker return to his or her former job or some modified version of it, if circumstances dictate.

Historical Roots

Workers' Compensation has its origin in Germany in 1884 but was not established in Canada until 1914, when the Ontario Workmen's Compensation Act was passed by Parliament. This time lag was something of an advantage, because it allowed for consideration of the American and European experience (the federal Employers' Liability Act was passed in the United States in 1908). In 1900, the Ontario government inquired into the German system. This was followed in 1912–1914 by an intensive and prolonged study of the existing laws in other European countries and in the United States, under the guidance of Sir William Ralph Meredith, Chief Justice of Ontario. On the basis of his findings, the first act in Canada was passed.

Acts were subsequently passed in all provinces and territories, and although they have been amended many times (largely for the purpose of increasing coverage and benefits), they have retained many of the principles set forth in the Ontario act of 1914:

1. collective liability for employers, with some recognition of risk in the amount of contribution paid by individual employers
2. compensation for workers regardless of the financial condition of the employer
3. compensation based on loss of earnings
4. a "no-fault" system
5. a nonadversarial process: little or no recourse to the courts (in Ontario, Schedule 2 can allow legal recourse)

In essence, the implementation of Workers' Compensation systems is a tradeoff for both workers and employers. Workers receive an assurance that they will be compensated for injury without having to undertake expensive and lengthy lawsuits, but in return they accept the authority of the Workers' Compensation Boards to determine the amount of any compensation. Employers take on the obligation of paying for the workers' compensation system but are protected from litigation that could drive them into bankruptcy.[1]

Workers' Compensation in Canada

Administration and Responsibilities

RPC 3.1

RPC 3.2

The provincial and territorial acts throughout Canada are administered by Workers' Compensation Board (WCB) members who are appointed by the lieutenant governor in counsel within each jurisdiction and who hold office at the lieutenant governor's pleasure. The various boards are empowered to fix and collect assessment, determine the right to compensation, and pay the amount due to the injured worker. In all these matters, the Workers' Compensation system has exclusive and final jurisdiction. The Ontario act is representative of the type of legislation that exists in all jurisdictions in terms of its authority and power.

The regulations and responsibilities of Workers' Compensation Boards are as follows:

- The injured worker will receive payment while off work and will have all medical bills paid if the injury happened at work and because of work.
- The injured worker will receive a pension if the disability is or becomes permanent.
- The injured worker will receive benefits if he or she cannot earn the same amount of money earned before the accident.
- The injured worker's immediate family and dependents will be entitled to benefits if the worker is killed or dies as a result of an injury on the job.
- The Workers' Compensation Boards classify employers to ensure consistency.
- The Workers' Compensation Boards decide whether an individual is classified as a worker, a subcontractor, or an employer, as each class has different conditions.
- The Workers' Compensation system can pay benefits if a worker is affected by an industrial disease that has resulted from his or her occupation.

In addition to these regulations and responsibilities, the Board, now the WSIB following the passage of the Workers' Compensation Reform Act in 1998, added a prevention emphasis to the traditional compensation functions.

The addition of prevention to the mandate of Workers' Compensation Boards is increasingly common across Canada. WCBs have focused on prevention by offering premium reductions based on safety records. For example, at the time of this writing, the WCB in Alberta is forecasting a premium reduction of up to 30% (depending on the rate group) for the 2005 fiscal year. More than 80% of employers in Alberta are expected to have reduced premiums in 2005. In addition to the reduction in general premiums, employers in Alberta (and some other provinces—see the discussion in this chapter on the use of experience rating) can achieve

Contact Information for the Provincial and Territorial Workers' Compensation Boards

Workers' Compensation Board of Alberta
P.O. Box 2415
9912-107 Street Edmonton AB T5J 2S5
Tel: 780-498-4000 Fax: 780-498-7875
Home page: http://www.wcb.ab.ca

Workers' Compensation Board of British Columbia
P.O. Box 5350 Vancouver BC V6B 5L5
Tel: 604-273-2266 Fax: 604-276-3140
Home page: http://www.worksafebc.com

Workers Compensation Board of Manitoba
333 Broadway Winnipeg MB R3C 4W3
Tel: 204-954-4321 Fax: 204-954-4968
Home page: http://www.wcb.mb.ca

Workplace Health, Safety and Compensation Commission of New Brunswick
1 Portland Street P.O. Box 160 Saint John NB E2L 3X9
Tel: 506-632-2200 Fax: 506-632-4999
Home page: http://www.whscc.nb.ca

Workplace Health, Safety and Compensation Commission of Newfoundland and Labrador
146-148 Forest Road P.O. Box 9000 Station B St. John's NL A1A 3B8
Tel: 709-778-1000 Fax: 709-738-1714
Home page: http://www.whscc.nf.ca

Workers' Compensation Board of the Northwest Territories & Nunavut
P.O. Box 8888 Yellowknife NT X1A 2R3
Tel: 867-920-3888 Fax: 867-873-4596
Home page: http://www.wcb.nt.ca

Workers' Compensation Board of Nova Scotia
5668 South Street P.O. Box 1150 Halifax NS B3J 2Y2
Tel: 902-491-8000 Fax: 902-491-8002
Home page: http://www.wcb.ns.ca

Workplace Safety and Insurance Board of Ontario
200 Front Street West Toronto ON M5V 3J1
Tel: 416-344-1000 Fax: 416-344-3999
Home page: http://www.wsib.on.ca

Workers Compensation Board of Prince Edward Island
14 Weymouth Street Charlottetown PEI C1A 4Y1
Tel: 902-368-5680 Fax: 902-368-5705
Home page: http://www.wcb.pe.ca

Commission de la santé et de la sécurité du travail
1199 rue de Bleury C.P. 6056 Succursale "centre-ville" Montréal QC H3C 4E1
Tel: 514-873-7183 Fax: 514-873-7007
Home page: http://www.csst.qc.ca

Workers' Compensation Board of Saskatchewan
200, 1881 Scarth Street Regina SK S4P 4L1
Tel: 306-787-4370 Tel: 306-787-2513
Home page: http://www.wcbsask.com

Yukon Workers' Compensation Health & Safety Board
401 Strickland Street Whitehorse YK Y1A 5N8
Tel: 867-667-5645 Fax: 867-393-6279
Home page: http://www.wcb.yk.ca

further premium reductions of up to 20% from the industry rate based on their safety performance. Conversely, organizations with a poor safety record may be charged a surcharge to reflect the increased costs of insurance.

A mandate for prevention also means that WCBs are actively involved in trying to prevent accidents. WCBs provide a wide range of information for employers and employees on safety-related matters. For example, WorkSafe BC maintains a large online library of safety-related publications. The WCB in Alberta offers a Certificate of Recognition (COR) to organizations that have implemented safety programs that meet its standards. In many jurisdictions in Canada, Workers' Compensation Boards provide extensive resources to both employers and individuals interested in health and safety issues.

In relation to most of the industries within the scope of the provincial or territorial acts, the system of compensation is one of compulsory and collective liability. Under collective liability, the various industries are classified according to their size and end product, and each employer is assessed a rate that is a percentage of its payroll. The percentage is determined by the injury cost of its classification. From the accident fund thus collected, payments are made for compensation, medical aid, rehabilitation, accident prevention, and administrative expenses. Each employer is liable for assessment, irrespective of the cost of injuries sustained by its workers. As a result, each is relieved of individual liability. In most jurisdictions, liability is further distributed by a disaster reserve fund.

Public authorities and certain large corporations such as railways and shipping or telegraph companies have a different liability approach from the collective liabilities' scheme and are individually liable for compensation; however, all disputes are settled by the WCB. Such corporations contribute their portion of the cost of administering the various acts.

Most WCBs, at one time, had responsibility for the accident-prevention or OH&S aspects of Workers' Compensation. In the 1970s and 1980s, the combined role was seen as a conflict of interest by some governments, and these WCB functions were placed under a government department in most provinces and territories (e.g., the Department of Labour). Although the OH&S function is separate in most jurisdictions (with B.C. being an exception), all WCBs cooperate with the responsible government department by sharing information. Several WCBs have input into the experience rating or merit/demerit program and work with government in developing programs designed to reduce workplace injuries. Employers or injured workers who disagree with a WCB decision can turn to various appeal bodies and mechanisms. In Prince Edward Island, Saskatchewan, and Yukon, the WCB is the final level of appeal.

Because jurisdictions sometimes provide different benefits, most WCBs within Canada enter into agreements among themselves to avoid duplicate assessments and to assist the worker in claiming and receiving compensation when two or more jurisdictions are involved. These agreements are intended to ensure that the worker receives the best possible benefits and that coverage is extended in a province or territory, often at the request of the injured worker.

The provincial or territorial acts generally cover all employment in industries such as lumbering, mining, fishing, manufacturing, construction, engineering, and transportation. Covered occupations include operation of electrical power lines, employment in waterworks and other public utilities, navigation, operation of boats and ships, operation of elevators and warehousing, street cleaning, painting, decorating, renovating, and cleaning. Those types of employment that are exempted from this list may be admitted at their own request.

Personal injuries resulting from accidents arising out of and in the course of employment are compensated, except in cases in which the accident is attributed to the worker's serious and willful misconduct and does not result in serious disablement. Workers' Compensation systems also compensate for certain specified occupational diseases.

Compensation Rates and Methods

Two standards are in place for determining the rate for payment of compensation. Eight jurisdictions base the payment on a percentage (generally 90%) of **net earnings**; the other four base payments on 75% of average earnings. Jurisdictions like Nova Scotia have used both methods depending on the date of the accident. A worker's average earnings are generally calculated on the basis of his or her earnings during the past 12 months. Since a large number of workers have not worked for the same employer for 12 months, other ways of establishing earnings are sanctioned. Each act also stipulates a maximum amount of earnings that can be used to determine the maximum amount of compensation. Although there are procedural variations across jurisdictions, Workers' Compensation is based on the individual's past salary record—not on the loss or potential loss of future earnings.

One of the underlying premises of Workers' Compensation systems is that people do not want to work.[2] As a result, boards try to provide reasonable compensation without creating an incentive for individuals to stay off work. There is some empirical evidence that raising benefit rates does lead to longer absences from work.[3,4]

The method used to determine the average wage of a worker is the one that gives the best representation of the worker's weekly earnings and seems fair and reasonable. When work is made available and the worker still suffers an earnings loss, the payment for the continuing disability may be adjusted, whether or not the worker accepts the work. A payment for noneconomic loss (functional impairment) is also made in several jurisdictions. This figure is based on such factors as the worker's age, degree of impairment, and number of dependants. For example, a 40-year-old worker with three children would receive a larger payment than a 60-year-old worker with no children.

Compensation may take two forms: cash benefits or wage or earnings loss. Cash allowance is based on the degree of severity of the impairment. Payments continue as long as a disability lasts, in accordance with the entitlement established by the province or territory. In cases of permanent partial impairment, the worker receives a life pension based on rating scales established by the boards. There are allowances for economic losses and noneconomic losses. An injured worker could receive noneconomic loss if he or she were unable to perform some of the things that he or she was able to do before the accident. For instance, if a worker were unable to golf as a result of the accident, a benefit could be paid for that noneconomic loss.

Wage or earnings loss refers to situations in which workers can no longer earn the same amount of money that they were earning before the accident as a result of their impairment. For a worker who was earning $20 per hour

net earnings

salary after mandatory deductions (income tax, Canada Pension, and Employment Insurance)

RPC 3.2

RPC 3.3

before the accident and now, as a result of the injury, is capable of earning only $10 per hour, the potential compensation is $10 per hour. The earnings loss is calculated and paid as long as the worker is unable to return to work paying the same wages as before the accident.

In the event of the death of a worker, the spouse may receive a pension in accordance with the schedules established by the various jurisdictions, and allowances are given to children. In addition, most provincial and territorial boards may allow an immediate lump-sum payment and variable expenses.

Medical Aid and Accident Prevention

ⓇⓅⒸ 3.4

loss of functional capacity
limit of ability or dexterity depending on the seriousness of an injury

Accompanying compensation in all cases is the provision of medical aid. This aid includes medical and surgical care, hospitalization, nursing care, drugs and supplies, physical and occupational therapy, and the provision and maintenance of prostheses. An employee who sustains a work-related injury is compensated not only for loss of earnings but also for **loss of functional capacity.** Workers who, as a result of their injury, are no longer able to perform some of their duties on the job, such as lifting, twisting, or bending, are considered to have suffered loss of functional capacity for which benefits are payable.

Employers within a particular industry may form safety associations and make rules for accident prevention that, on approval of the WCB and the lieutenant governor in council in the jurisdiction, are binding on all employers in that industry. WCBs pay the expenses of these associations out of the accident fund and have the authority to investigate the premises

---

Occupational Health and Safety Today 3.1

Spiralling Disability Costs

An aging workforce and an expanded definition of disabling conditions have resulted in a greatly increased number of individuals receiving disability compensation. Current estimates are that between 8% and 12% of the workforce is on disability (including both Workers' Compensation and private disability plans) at any given time.

Many claims are for musculoskeletal disorders such as chronic back pain and may reflect an aging workforce. Others are for recently recognized disorders such as stress or mental and nervous conditions, which represent approximately one-quarter of claims to insurance plans. Jurisdictions that allow for Workers' Compensation of stress-related disorders (such as California in the U.S.) have seen claim rates skyrocket.

In addition to an increased number of claims, the costs of medical care continue to increase, resulting in disability payments spiralling ever upward. These costs are reflected in increased premium and assessment rates and ever more stringent guidelines for what constitutes a compensable disorder.

Sources: Allen, P. (2004, March 22). Mental health absenteeism threatens to break the disability bank. *Canadian HR Reporter;* and Health Canada, "Economic burden of illness in Canada." Retrieved from http://www.hc-sc.gc.ca/pphb-dgspsp/publicat/ebic-femc93/burd5b_e.html, October 9, 2004.

of employers to ensure compliance with safeguards required by law. The goal of safety associations is to provide training in the area of accident prevention and health and safety.

Social Goals of Workers' Compensation

Workers' Compensation is driven by two main social goals: (1) to provide services intended to prevent injuries or reduce the psychological impact of injuries when they occur, and (2) to provide the training and development necessary to prepare an injured worker to return to work. The various WCBs have come to look on compensation as a means for society to share with the worker the consequences of industrial accidents and to ensure the restoration of the worker to active participation in the life of the community. The focus is more on restoring earning power than paying for its loss. In no sense is compensation considered a reward for being injured.

This social conception of compensation is grounded in the following standard provisions contained in the various acts:

1. unlimited medical aid
2. artificial prostheses
3. a fund to encourage reemployment (known as Second Injury and Enhancement Fund [SIEF] in some jurisdictions)
4. liberal compensation
5. rehabilitation maintenance income

Not only does the compensation system in Canada provide greater benefits than most insurers in other countries, but it also ensures that benefits are not prejudiced by earnings after rehabilitation. In Canada, permanently injured

---

Occupational Health and Safety Today 3.2

Return-to-Work Programs

In response to spiralling disability costs, many firms are adopting an active approach to managing disability and return to work. Such programs typically try to get the individual back to the workforce as soon as possible. Although there is an obvious economic incentive to return individuals to the workforce, there is also a therapeutic incentive. Data from private insurers suggest that the average length of disability is about four-and-a-half years; after the individual has been on disability compensation for two years, the expected length more than doubles to eleven years. These data point to the need for early and effective intervention.

This need is identified under Ontario legislation that requires both workers and employers to maintain contact during the period of recovery from a disability and to cooperate in a return to work. Employees are specifically obligated to cooperate in health care and other return-to-work measures required by the WSIB. Employers are obligated to identify suitable employment consistent with the individual's abilities and, where possible, to ensure a return to preinjury earnings.

Sources: Workplace Safety and Insurance Board of Ontario, "Return to work." Retrieved from http://www.wsib.on.ca/wsib/wsibsite.nsf/public/EmployersESRW, October 9, 2004; and WorkSafe BC, "Understanding return-to-work program." Retrieved from http://www.worksafebc.com/for_health_care_providers/related_information/understanding_return-to-work/default.asp, October 9, 2004.

---

workers draw compensation for life and are able to keep their pensions, even if the sum of their pensions and supplements to earnings amounts to more than their wages before they were hurt. In contrast, many compensation laws in the United States hinder rehabilitation, either by cutting off compensation for permanent injury as soon as workers begin to earn as much money as they did before the injury or by paying compensation for only a limited period, leaving workers stranded before they can be retrained.

(R)(P)(C) 3.5

Provision for Second Injuries

The Canadian Workers' Compensation system provides for a "second injury fund," the purpose of which is to facilitate the reemployment of disabled workers. Without a provision for multiple injuries, employers might be tempted to discriminate against workers with disabilities, as an additional injury could make the employer responsible for a far more serious disability than if the worker had not had a prior injury. Thus, a worker who has lost one arm will be given a total disability rating if he or she loses the second arm. By charging the excess liability resulting from the cumulative effect of a prior disability and the subsequent injury to a disaster reserve fund, the various acts distribute the burden throughout industry as a whole rather than letting it rest on one particular class. In this way, employers are relieved of the extra risks associated with the employment of workers with disabilities.

Rehabilitation

Before World War I, persons with disabilities were left to fend for themselves. Some were placed in poorhouses, while others survived through begging. Gradually, society realized that just because people had disabilities did not mean they could not be productive; however, first attempts at drafting persons with disabilities into the workplace proved to be a difficult and frustrating experience for the workers. Persons with disabilities found that although they were given an opportunity to earn a living, they could do so only by accepting menial jobs that no one else wanted. When thousands of injured soldiers returned from World War I, the need to provide rehabilitation programs was finally recognized. Rehabilitation is a financial necessity as well as a moral and social obligation. Only with the assistance of effective rehabilitation can the future cost of the Workers' Compensation system be maintained at a reasonable level. There are three types of rehabilitation. **Vocational rehabilitation** refers to the steps undertaken by WCBs to help injured workers return to their place of employment or find similar or suitable work elsewhere. Placement services, vocational testing, and retraining or training may all be part of this process. **Physical rehabilitation** refers to the steps taken to restore, whether fully or partially, the worker's physical function. **Social rehabilitation** refers to the psychological and practical services that help workers with severe disabilities cope with daily life (e.g., assistance with cooking, bathing, household chores). A scenario in which the full range of compensation benefits was provided to an injured worker is outlined in Occupational Health and Safety Today 3.3.

vocational rehabilitation

the steps undertaken by WCBs to help injured workers return to their place of employment or find similar or suitable work elsewhere

physical rehabilitation

the steps taken to restore, whether fully or partially, the worker's physical function

social rehabilitation

the psychological and practical services that help workers with severe disabilities cope with daily life

Occupational Health and Safety Today 3.3

Workers' Compensation at Work

In 1987, Mr. X lost his left hand in an industrial accident. Over the previous 10 years, he had risen from the position of delivery-truck driver to plant manager at a small aluminum fabricator in northwest Toronto.

Mr. X recalled the accident. "We were having problems with the alignment. The mechanic was on lunch and repairs had to be made. I had done the same thing a thousand times before. It was a stupid accident. There was a piece of paper on the floor, and I instinctively kicked it out of the way. Unfortunately, I didn't know that the foot pedal was beneath the paper. The press came down in the blink of an eye and my hand was left attached to my wrist by a single tendon."

Mr. X had been thinking about a career change before the accident. In addition to his duties as plant manager, he had begun to do some selling and marketing and found it was something he enjoyed. After the accident, Mr. X knew that he would not be able to work in the plant again, so he began to consider retraining.

After his surgery, Mr. X spent four weeks in hospital recovering. A WCB representative came to see him two days after the accident and initiated his claim so that he could continue to pay his bills. Before Mr. X could be fitted with a prosthesis, his physical wounds had to heal. He spent the next couple of months getting better and receiving treatment.

Around this time, Mr. X decided to pursue a marketing career. Thanks to the sponsorship of the WCB, he enrolled in a marketing program. On graduation, Mr. X received further assistance from a WCB placement adviser. Within months, a job was located. After completing a training program with his new employer, Mr. X began work as a full-time marketing representative.

In this scenario, the full range of compensation benefits was provided, including monetary benefits, medical aid, prosthetic device, vocational rehabilitation, placement services, and counselling in social services.

Occupational Diseases and Workplace Stress

A significant issue facing Workers' Compensation today concerns occupational diseases and the degree to which they are work related. Examples of occupational diseases would include various cancers, skin diseases, and allergic reactions to materials and components within the workplace. Occupational disease compensation has been part of Workers' Compensation ever since six specific diseases were cited in Ontario's act of 1914. The past 30 years have seen a broadening of the definition of "accident" and "injury," which has allowed for greater consideration of occupational disease claims. Today, many occupational disease claims can be considered in the same way as any other claim. The need to isolate the point at which the disease was contracted has given way to a recognition that the disease could be the result of exposure or injury over time. Occupational disease claims, unless very straightforward, are often adjudicated by a special claim unit and may require additional expert medical opinion as well as exposure and employment histories. Some WCBs use separate claim forms for specific occupational diseases. The **latency period** is quite often a major factor in determining the acceptability of the claim.

latency period

the time between exposure to a cause and development of a disease

Stress-related disabilities can be divided into three groups: (1) physical injury or occupational disease leading to a mental disability, (2) mental stress resulting in a physical disability, traumatic occurrence, or series of occurrences, and (3) mental stress resulting in a mental condition. Generally, stress claims in the first group have been dealt with in the same way as any other claims. Those in the second group have been subject to some selection. If the disability (say, a cardiac attack) is acute, it will be considered for compensation. If the disability (say, an ulcer) is a result of accumulated stress, it will likely not be considered for compensation. With respect to the third group, an unusual incident that provokes the mental reaction and results in a disability will probably be considered for compensation; chronic stress resulting in a mental disability is seldom compensated. The adjudication of stress claims is currently receiving a great deal of attention from all insurance parties. The courts and human rights tribunals have been consistent in maintaining that stress-related disorders or other psychological disabilities are to be treated the same as physical disabilities in employment settings.[5] It remains to be seen whether Workers' Compensation schemes can defend their exclusion of some stress-related disorders in the face of this accumulated experience.

Assessments

RPC 3.5

Employers are grouped together according to the type of operation or industry in which they are engaged, and they are assessed on that basis. The groups are referred to as industries, classes, subclasses, or classifications. In some jurisdictions, the terms "unit" and "sector" are used; employers are not grouped by occupation, although occupation may help determine a subdivision of an industry or class.

Occupational Health and Safety Notebook 3.2

Illustrative Industry Assessment Rates

The average Workers' Compensation assessment in Ontario for 2004 was $2.19 for every $100 in insurable earnings with a maximum earning of $66,800. However, there are dramatic differences in assessment across occupational groups. For some sample rates, see table.

Sample of WBC Assessments across Occupational Groups

Rate Group	Description	Assessment per $100 of insurable earnings
031	Logging	$11.36
728	Roofing	$12.34
741	Masonry	$12.21
335	Publishing	$0.60

Source: Workplace Safety and Insurance Board of Ontario, "2004 premium rates table." Retrieved from http://www.wsib.on.ca/wsib/wsibsite.nsf/public/employers2004prtable, October 9, 2004.

Separate accounts are generally used when an employer is involved in more than one industry or when an industry or employer's operation includes several departments. Assessments are determined by the WCB at least once a year when the board sets a percentage or rate to be applied to the payroll of the employer. Payrolls are estimated and then the employer is required to submit a certified payroll statement.

The Workers' Compensation system in Canada is based on the concept of dividing employers into three categories: (1) those who contribute to the accident fund and benefit from its collective liability, (2) those who are individually liable for their own employees' accidents, and (3) those in certain low-risk industries who are excluded under various acts across the country. Employers who pay directly for the accidents of their employees are generally public enterprises such as provincial or territorial and municipal governments and certain transportation and communication companies within Crown corporations.

All employers within a particular industry group are assessed at the same rate based on the injury experience of the group as a whole. In most jurisdictions, within the general accident fund, a provision is made for a rate stabilization and disaster reserve fund. One group by itself cannot sustain the heavy costs associated with a major disaster that might occur in any one year, or with a sharp decline in assessable payroll due to massive layoffs in the industry. Continued financing can be provided by the rate stabilization and disaster funds, which are maintained by the various WCBs.

Experience Rating

Experience rating in Workers' Compensation refers to an accident insurance premium pricing scheme that takes into account the clear cost experience of the individual employer. Under experience rating, the assessment for each firm may be higher or lower than the basic rate for the relative industry group. Firms with lower-than-average accident costs per worker pay lower premiums than firms with above-average accident costs. In essence, experience rating reduces or eliminates the cross-subsidization of relatively unsafe firms by relatively safe firms. Given two otherwise similar firms, a safer employer will face lower Workers' Compensation costs and hence lower production costs. Thus, the primary effect of the experience rating is to create a financial incentive for relatively unsafe firms to begin caring for their workforce.

 3.5

Experience rating is intended to offer an incentive to employers to reduce injuries and to return workers to their jobs as early as possible. In this way, employers benefit because the amount of money spent on compensation is reduced, and workers benefit because they are returned to their job quickly. Experience rating is thus a process of rewarding good performers and penalizing those organizations that are not making efforts to reduce accidents and return workers back to work as quickly as possible.

Generally, if an employer has an experience rating of a three-year average injury cost lower than that of the entire group, that employer will receive a rebate on the annual assessment. Conversely, employers who have an average injury cost higher than the group will receive demerit charges on top of their regular assessments.

One of the most important reasons for mandatory experience rating is the reduction of industrial accidents and injuries and their costs. The profit-maximizing, cost-minimizing firm will respond to incentive by investing in activities that reduce its Workers' Compensation claim costs to the point at which the expected marginal benefits (i.e., incremental reduction in the expected cost of injuries and accidents) equal the marginal cost. Given the existence of workplace risk, and assuming full information about such risk, the firm may allocate resources to safety practices or pay the costs associated with work injury. Profit-maximizing firms operating in competitive markets will strive to minimize some of the costs associated with workplace injuries and accidents, such as Workers' Compensation premium payments (including experience rating service charges/refunds as well as material costs), fixed employment costs, lost production time, and damage to equipment, by preventing accidents (i.e., reducing the probability of a hazardous state) as well as by engaging in activities that minimize costs once accidents do occur. Postaccident employer actions that can result in claim cost reduction include implementing early return-to-work programs and appealing WCB decisions on workers' benefits.

Occupational Health and Safety Notebook 3.3

Experience Rating Programs in Ontario

New Experimental Experience Rating Program (NEER)

NEER automatically applies to companies that pay more than $25,000 per year in premiums and are not in a construction rate group. NEER allows companies to earn rebates on premiums by maintaining a good health and safety record. Alternately, if companies have a poor health and safety record, they will be assessed a surcharge. To establish whether a company's record is better or worse than average, it is compared with similar companies (i.e., a company's costs are compared within its rate group over the past three years). Companies are not penalized for long-term conditions such as hearing loss or asbestosis.

CAD-7

CAD-7 applies to employers in the construction sector whose average annual premiums are more than $25,000. Similar to NEER, a company's claim history is compared with similar firms within a rate group to determine whether a surcharge or rebate is applicable.

Merit Adjusted Premium (MAP) Plan for Small Business

MAP is similar to the foregoing programs but applies to small businesses (those paying between $1,000 and $25,000 in annual WCB premiums). Generally, MAP decreases or increases to premiums do not take effect until after three years of continuous operation (although increases may be applied earlier if a significant number of claims are filed).

Sources: Workplace Safety and Insurance Board of Ontario, "New experimental experience rating program (NEER)." Retrieved from http://www.wsib.on.ca/wsib/wsibsite.nsf/public/NEER, October 9, 2004; Workplace Safety and Insurance Board of Ontario, "CAD-7." Retrieved from http://www.wsib.on.ca/wsib/wsibsite.nsf/public/CAD-7, October 9, 2004; Workplace Safety and Insurance Board of Ontario, "Merit adjusted premium (MAP) plan for small business." Retrieved from http://www.wsib.on.ca/wsib/wsibsite.nsf/public/MAP, October 9, 2004.

The Workers' Compensation Boards in several jurisdictions (e.g., Ontario, Alberta, B.C.) operate experience-rating plans with the goal of creating incentives for firms to reduce their claim rate. That is, the experience rating systems attempt to reward safe firms (through a rebate of assessment premiums) and to penalize unsafe firms (through a surcharge on premiums). Such programs provide some leverage to firms seeking to reduce their Workers' Compensation costs—to the extent that firms can establish and maintain better than average safety records, costs will be decreased.

Empirically then, the question is whether experience rating schemes actually work—that is, do they decrease accidents or injuries in the workplace? This is an exceedingly complex question and there does not appear to be a clear answer thus far.[6] However, the best evidence available to date looked at the incidence of claims before and following the implementation of experience rating plans and suggests that such plans are effective in improving workplace safety.[7]

How Organizations Can Manage Disability

Although minimizing costs, such as Workers' Compensation premiums, is one goal of human resources, another is to ensure that injured workers return to the workplace as quickly as possible. Ensuring a prompt return to work

RPC 3.6

Occupational Health and Safety Today 3.4

Integrated Disability Management

In Canada a clear distinction has been made between programs designed to provide compensation for injuries that occur at work (i.e., Workers' Compensation) and programs designed to provide income to employees who are ill or disabled because of nonoccupational injuries. Nonoccupational illnesses or injuries are typically dealt with through short-term and long-term disability plans paid for by the employer, the employees, or both (i.e., rate-shared plans). Unions and union members may also participate in rate-shared plans. Integrated disability management is based on the belief that rising disability costs can be managed if disability programs (long- and short-term disability, sick leave, and Workers' Compensation) are managed in their entirety.

The costs of disability are staggering:

- The Canadian Life and Health Insurance Association (CLHIA) indicates that health benefit payments of $12.5 billion were paid in 2000.

- Statistics Canada reports that employers pay almost $11.3 billion a year in absence costs.

- The Association of Workers' Compensation Boards of Canada had lost-time injury claims costs of $5 billion in 2001.

The evidence for such integrated programs is convincing. CIBC, for example, saw a 30% reduction in costs as a result of implementing such a program. U.S. data suggest a return of $10 for every $1 spent on implementing integrated disability management programs.

Source: McMahon, K. (1999). Benefits Canada, "Disability management triumphs." Retrieved from http://www .benefitscanada.com/content/legacy/Content/1999/04–99/ ben32.html, October 8, 2004.

helps both the individual and the organization. The individual returns to his or her full income as quickly as possible. The organization minimizes costs associated with replacing employees and retains the valuable skills of current employees.

Not surprisingly, a great deal of attention has been focused on the two issues involved in disability management: minimizing disability-related costs through integrated disability management and ensuring a prompt return to work.

Strategies for managing disability include the following:

1. Create and run an effective corporate culture that values employees and establishes them as an integral part of the workforce. An effective disability management program cannot conflict with the organizational culture. Specifically, it is the culture that makes it easier to create a disability management program. The corporate culture best able to enhance a disability management program is one that includes the following:
   (a) regular collaborative communication between supervisors and employees
   (b) helpful cooperative relationships among coworkers
   (c) training for new managers on how to handle personnel issues effectively, including evaluating employee performance
   (d) favourable work conditions
   (e) opportunities for career growth
   (f) clearly defined and flexible work roles
   (g) a willingness on the part of senior management to invest money up front in order to save money in the near and distant future
   (h) incentive for local managers to make disability management part of their decision-making process

2. Ensure senior management support. To be successful, a disability management program requires support and cooperation from staff at all levels of the company. At times, the most effective way to obtain this cooperation is to enlist senior management support.

3. Intervene early and regularly. All corporations should have a policy of contacting employees early and regularly throughout the disability absence. Contacting employees sooner rather than later produces three distinct benefits:
   (a) Employees tend to come back to work more quickly.
   (b) Employees who return to work tend to stay at work.
   (c) Employees generally return to earn a higher wage.
   The early return and regular contact strategy must be supplemented with an effective return-to-work policy that must be in place before an employee becomes disabled.

4. Develop case management capacities. Case management refers to the coordination of health and social services so that injuries or disabilities receive care that is appropriate, timely, and efficient. The goals of case management are to enhance the injured worker's quality of life and,

if possible, reduce the costs associated with care. Case management should therefore begin early in the process to ensure that injured workers are receiving the most effective and most cost-efficient services available.

5. Create modified and light duty jobs to allow an early return to work. The most cost-saving strategy is to bring employees back to work when they can perform at least some of their tasks. This concept can speed up recovery by giving an employee practical goals to achieve during the rehabilitation process. It can serve as a work-hardening function by gradually strengthening the employee's ability, thereby reducing the risk of injury on the first day back at work.

6. Train supervisors to encourage and facilitate an early return to work. This is perhaps the most difficult step in any disability management program. The company can begin by expanding the role of the supervisors to include assistance for employees with disabilities.

7. Create data systems. An effective disability management system can greatly minimize costs by identifying problem areas, creating a baseline for measuring improvement, and increasing the efficiency with which Workers' Compensation absences are tracked. Companies can obtain a system tailored to individual needs and budgets. Up-to-date data allow a company to track trends and identify problem areas within the corporation.

Return to Work

It is common to classify disability related absence into three stages; acute (1–30 days), subacute (31–90 days), and chronic (91+ days).[8] Clearly the costs of disability increase as a worker progresses through the stages. Return-to-work programs are aimed at getting people back to work early in the process. Even if the individual cannot perform his or her original job, it is possible for the individual to return to work in some capacity.

RPC 3.6

RPC 3.7

One of the first steps in creating an effective return-to-work program is creating the environment. One study found that disability leave was shortened among a sample of 197 workers following carpal tunnel surgery when the organizational culture (manifested in policies and procedures) supported strong interpersonal relations and emphasized safety as a value (e.g., worker training, proactive return-to-work programs, and an emphasis on communication).[9]

Return to work often involves a modified job assignment. Traditionally, injured workers might be assigned to light duties or to some job that they were capable of doing while injured without fear of making their condition worse. Research has consistently identified physical demands of the job as an important predictor of return to work. For example, engaging in heavy physical labour such as construction or work that requires working in awkward positions (e.g., bending, twisting, crouching) is associated with delayed return to work after injury.[10,11] If jobs can be modified to eliminate or reduce the physical demands, then an early return to work may be facilitated. Given these findings, it is not surprising that return-to-work programs that include some ergonomic redesign of the workplace tend to be the most effective.[12]

Occupational Health and Safety Today 3.5

The Duty to Accommodate

Although return-to-work programs are increasingly promoted as a means of managing disability cases, Canadian Human Rights Legislation also imposes obligations on employers to accommodate workers with disabilities. That is, there is a legal obligation to accommodate injured workers to facilitate their return to work. Moreover, case law has increasingly placed the onus on employers to accommodate workers. In the well-known case of *British Columbia (Public Service Employees Relations Commission) v. BCGSEU*, 3 S.C.R. 3, commonly referred to as the "Meiorin decision," the Supreme Court of Canada established that employers had an obligation to accommodate individuals and to be proactive in removing discriminatory workplace practices. Based on a recent review of court cases,[13] the duty to accommodate appears to be defined by 10 general principles:

1. An employer has the obligation to accommodate employees who suffer from a disability to the point of undue hardship.
2. An employee must produce medical or psychological evidence that they are suffering from a disabling condition if they expect to be accommodated by their employer.
3. Disruptive behaviour associated with a disability or failure to perform assigned duties by an employee with a disability is not sufficient cause to terminate the employee, provided he or she makes known the disorder.
4. Failure of an employee to adhere to a medical regimen and therapy that may be prescribed to address the disability may be sufficient grounds for termination of the employee.

5. The risk associated with the position occupied by a person with a disability may mitigate the nature of their accommodation.
6. The severity and stability of the condition can be considered as part of an employee's return to work and accommodation.
7. The employee can make reasonable objections, including economic loss, to the accommodation that is offered by the employer; however, the employee must accept reasonable accommodation offered by the employer, even though that accommodation may not be perfect from the employee's perspective.
8. Accommodation cannot be made on the basis of a stereotype held by the employer about the employee with a disability. The employer must investigate to determine what the individual employee is capable of doing.
9. Large organizations, particularly government departments, will be held to a higher standard with respect to their duty to accommodate employees with disabilities and with respect to the point where undue hardship begins.
10. The BFOR (bona fide occupational requirement) defence outlined in the Meiorin decision will be used to assess any arguments of undue hardship.

Source: Kelloway, E. K., Francis, L., Catano, V. M., Cameron, J., & Day, A. (2004). *Psychological disorders in the Canadian Forces: Legal and social issues. Contractor's report*. National Defence Headquarters, Ottawa, ON: Director Human Resources Research and Evaluation.

In light of our discussion of psychosocial hazards in the workplace (see Chapter 6), it is interesting to note that these factors also affect return to work. As might be expected, low-quality jobs are associated with delayed return to work, where "low quality" refers to high demands, job stress, or a lack of control.[14]

Although employers will generally benefit from return-to-work provisions, employees may resist their implementation. Employees may fear loss of their job (i.e., If I take a modified job, I'll never get back to my real job), fear reinjury or exacerbation of their condition, or may simply feel unable to return to work. Concerns about stigma and threats to career prospects have been identified as barriers to workers taking stress leave.[15] Additionally, coworkers and supervisors who might have to "take up the slack" for the injured individual may accuse him or her of malingering or "working" their injury to get an easy job. The fear of such reactions may delay return to work. For example, fear of discrimination was found to be one factor that inhibited workforce reentry among a sample of individuals with HIV/AIDS.[16] This shows the need to make return to work a standard policy that deals with these concerns up front.

Summary

Workers' Compensation was established in Canada in 1914 with the passage of Ontario's Workmen's Compensation Act. Since then, coverage and benefits have increased, as have the associated costs. The thrust of the Workers' Compensation system today is to create more safety-conscious work environments and to work actively to reduce the number of work-related accidents, disabilities, and diseases. Primary responsibility rests with the employer to ensure that the compensation system is administered efficiently and funded equitably through assessments of employers. The underlying philosophy of Workers' Compensation is that employers are as accountable to their employees as they are for the bottom line.

Key Terms

latency period, p. 61
loss of functional capacity, p. 58
net earnings, p. 57

physical rehabilitation, p. 60
social rehabilitation, p. 60
vocational rehabilitation, p. 60

Weblinks

"Workers' Compensation past, present and future—An historical overview,"
http://wwwtor.activate.net/corpav/wsib/Nov04–02/auditorium/index.asp
(p. 53)

Workers' Compensation Board of Alberta, "Rate setting backgrounder,"
http://www.wcb.ab.ca/pdfs/05_rate_forecast_bgk.pdf (p. 55)

WorkSafe BC,
http://www.worksafebc.com (p. 56)

National Institute of Disability Management and Research,
http://www.nidmar.ca (p. 67)

Workers' Compensation Board of Nova Scotia,
http://www.wcb.ns.ca (p. 69)

RPC Icons

RPC 3.1 Provides input on matters related to the drafting and/or application of legislation or regulations related to health, safety security, and Workers' Compensation.

- legislation
- process and means of influencing legislative change
- linkages with change agents (e.g., HR Associations, interest groups, politicians, bureaucrats)
- report writing
- common and statutory law (e.g., employment standard: labour relations)
- Worker Protection (including health and safety and Workers' Compensation)
- theories and practices for protection of individuals and groups
- Occupational health and safety legislation (e.g., Occupational Health and Safety Act of Ontario, Workplace Safety & Insurance Act—Bill 99, Workplace Hazardous Materials Information System, Transportation of Dangerous Goods legislation, environmental legislation, smoking in the workplace legislation, civil rights legislation)

RPC 3.2 Establishes and implements strategies to minimize compensation costs.

- relevant legislation
- cost/benefit techniques
- Workers' Compensation billing, rate structures, and claims adjudication processes
- industry best practices
- modified return to work program
- ergonomics and physical demands analysis
- training and development
- policy, procedure and program development
- Worker Protection (including health and safety and Workers' Compensation)
- measurement bases and underlying methodologies used in finance departments
- Occupational health and safety legislation (e.g., Occupational Health and Safety Act of Ontario, Workplace Safety & Insurance Act—Bill 99, Workplace Hazardous Materials Information System, Transportation of Dangerous Goods legislation, environmental legislation, smoking in the workplace legislation, civil rights legislation
- ergonomics
- management techniques for OH&S Programs
- types of employee assistance and wellness programs

RPC 3.3 Coordinates Workers' Compensation benefits with other employee benefits (e.g., sick leave, long-term disability, and pension).

- relevant legislation
- employer-sponsored benefits
- statutory benefits
- program/policy development
- the culture of the organization
- conflict resolution
- record keeping and reporting
- technical terminology
- group insurance benefits
- pension plans
- Worker Protection (including health and safety and Workers' Compensation)
- theoretical and applied aspects of compensation functions
- types of employee benefits (e.g., standardized and flexible benefits plans)
- methods of managing compensation systems (including budgeting, cost control, and monitoring, auditing and evaluating effectiveness of pay system)

TASK & KNOWLEDGE REQUIREMENTS
- Occupational health and safety legislation (e.g., Occupational Health and Safety Act of Ontario, Workplace Safety & Insurance Act—Bill 99, Workplace Hazardous Materials Information System, Transportation of Dangerous Goods legislation, environmental legislation, smoking in the workplace legislation, civil rights legislation)

RPC 3.4 Establishes effective programs for accident prevention, incident investigation, inspections, fire and emergency response, and required training.

- relevant legislation
- workplace inspection and accident investigation techniques
- nature of the business and physical work environment
- potential risks and hazards in the workplace
- emergency response planning
- community emergency response services
- training and development
- industry best practices
- Worker Protection (including health and safety and Workers' Compensation)
- training and development program design and administration
- hazard identification and control
- accident investigation procedures
- emergency preparedness procedures
- management techniques for OH&S Programs

RPC 3.5 Analyzes rate grouping costs, early intervention and return to work programs, claims management programs, and claims appeals.

- capability of available resources such as rehabilitation centers, physiotherapists, ergonomists, and medical consultants
- relevant legislation including rate structures (e.g., Workers' Compensation, HR, occupational health)
- cost/benefit methods
- intervention processes
- Workers' Compensation billing and claims processes and guidelines
- industry best practices
- range of job functions within the organization's structure
- company benefit plans and policies
- Worker Protection (including health and safety and Workers' Compensation)
- objectives, processes, and conceptual foundations of financial and management accounting
- issues in identifying relevant costs (e.g., cost accuracy vs. relevance; costs & pricing; irrelevant costs; costing collective; bargaining proposals; cost-benefit analysis)
- the economic, legal, technical, and moral impact of OHS
- types of employee assistance and wellness programs

TASK & KNOWLEDGE REQUIREMENTS
- conceptual definition and implications of occupational stressors (e.g., potential stressors, methods of identifying potential stressors and strain outcomes, response to organizational stressors, and management of employee strain outcomes)

RPC 3.6 Ensures accommodation and graduated return to work programs are in place to meet the needs of disabled employees.

- relevant legislation
- collective agreements

- external factors such as arbitration awards, judicial reviews
- program/policy/procedure development
- best practices outside the organization
- claims and case management
- conflict resolution
- report writing and record keeping
- jobs which may be available for modified work
- physical demands analysis
- ergonomics
- available medical services and outside resources
- the organization's culture
- the economic, legal, technical, and moral impact of OHS
- methods of accommodating employee needs (e.g., flexible hours, job sharing, child care)
- Worker Protection (including health and safety and Workers' Compensation)

RPC 3.7 Ensures that modifications to the work environment are consistent with the nature of worker disability (e.g., total vs. partial and temporary versus permanent).

- relevant legislation
- collective agreements
- arbitration awards, judicial reviews
- industry best practices
- problem solving techniques
- claims and case management
- conflict resolution
- report writing and record keeping
- technical terminology
- physical demands analysis
- ergonomics
- Worker Protection (including health and safety and Workers' Compensation)

TASK & KNOWLEDGE REQUIREMENTS
- methods of accommodating employee needs (e.g., flexible hours, job sharing, child care)
- the economic, legal, technical, and moral impact of OHS
- ergonomics

Discussion Questions

1. Outline the responsibilities of WCBs today. Describe how these responsibilities have changed over the years since the inception of Workers' Compensation in 1914.
2. Imagine that you are a truck driver. An accident on the road has left you with two broken legs and a head concussion. What type of assistance might you expect from Workers' Compensation? What could your manager do to expedite your return to work?

3. If you are employed, talk with the health and safety manager in your organization. (If you are a student, ask to speak to the safety officer at your school.) Obtain information about the organization's sector, assessment, and record of experience ratings.

Using the Internet

1. Check the Workers' Compensation Board in your area. What cost savings are available to firms that improve their health and safety record? What obligations exist to implement return-to-work procedures?
2. Most WCBs publish their current rates online. Pick a single industry and find the appropriate rate group assessment across the provinces and territories. Who pays the highest assessments? Who pays the lowest?

Exercises

1. Various jurisdictions have struggled with how employees should be compensated for stress-related disabilities. Using the Workers' Compensation websites listed in Occupational Health and Safety Notebook 2.2 in the preceding chapter, check to see how the following scenarios are handled in your jurisdiction:

   a. mental/mental—stress at work results in a psychological disorder (e.g., depression)
   b. mental/physical—stress at work results in a physical disorder (e.g., heart attack)
   c. physical/mental—an accident at work results in a psychological disorder (e.g., anxiety attacks)

2. Company X operates one 12-hour shift per day for 220 days per year. They employ 315 people. The company records show a history of accidents and injuries:

   - 3 medical-aid injuries with no days lost
   - 15 property-damage accidents with a total of 35 days lost
   - 11 equipment failures that caused a total of 20 days lost
   - 19 injuries requiring medical attention with a total of 75 days lost

Calculate the following (see the appendix at the end of this chapter for the formulas):

   a. frequency   b. severity

Explain how the company's severity rate can have a significant increase while the frequency rate has a very minor increase.

Case 1: The Employer's Duty

Sulleman has worked for Speedy Courier for the past three years. Last Tuesday, he was loading his truck when he suddenly screamed in pain. Apparently, Sulleman had injured his back while lifting a box that exceeded the weight limits. Sulleman was rushed to the hospital where they could find no evidence of injury other than the pain expressed by Sulleman. Knowing that the lack of hard evidence is common in these types of injuries, you can assume that Sulleman will be off work for a considerable period. As the HR representative for Speedy Courier, you have been charged with fulfilling the company's responsibilities under the act. Moreover, senior management has expressed concern with the number of disability claims and the fact that most recent claims were for extended periods (e.g., several exceeding 12 months). What do you need to do?

Case 2: A Stressful Job

Joan is an emergency room nurse at a busy city hospital. She has always enjoyed the hustle of working with emergencies and the challenges of dealing with the unexpected. Lately, though, Joan has been worried about her own well-being. She has been very abrupt with her coworkers on several occasions and has had difficulty concentrating on her job. Although there have been no problems to date, Joan is worried that her deteriorating performance might cause a problem given the critical nature of her work. Her doctor suggested that she take an extended leave because of her "nerves" and assured her that Workers' Compensation would cover her lost salary. As a HR person, what would you advise Joan?

Appendix

Calculating Injury Frequency and Severity Rates

Copies of the reports of the accident analysis involving injuries should accompany the firm's Workers' Compensation claim forms. Compensation Boards issue injury frequency and severity rates for injuries resulting from accidents in order to determine the assessment for the organization.

Frequency is the number of medical-aid injuries relative to the number of hours worked expressed in a ratio of 200,000. Some firms and jurisdictions use a factor of 1,000,000 rather than 200,000. Using the 200,000 figure, the relationship becomes

$$\text{frequency} = \frac{\text{number of injuries}}{\text{total hours worked}} \times 200{,}000$$

Take, as an example, a company that employs 300 people who work 8-hour shifts for 250 days in one year. The total number of hours worked is

$$250 \times 300 \times 8 = 600,000$$

This company has a record of 6 medical-aid injuries with no lost time, 15 minor injuries with 5 days lost, 3 major injuries with 55 days lost, and 6 property-damage accidents with no lost time. The total number of injuries is

$$(6 + 15 + 3) = 24$$

The frequency is calculated as

$$\text{frequency} = \frac{24}{600,000} \times 200,000 = 8$$

Therefore, this organization has an injury frequency ratio of 8 per 200,000 or 8.

Property-damage accidents are not considered since there is no associated injury.

Severity of work-related injuries is the ratio of the number of days lost due to injuries to a factor of 200,000. Severity is calculated by using the relationship

$$\text{severity} = \frac{\text{number of days lost to injury}}{\text{total hours worked}} \times 200,000$$

The severity based on the total number of days lost due to injury in the above example would be calculated as

$$\text{total lost days} = (5 + 55) = 60$$

$$\text{severity} = \frac{60}{600,000} \times 200,000 = 20$$

The injury severity for this company is 20 or a ratio of 20:200,000. If the company works two or three shifts instead of one as the examples show, then the total hours worked will be increased twofold or threefold and the relationship will be the same.

These figures facilitate comparison between various years of the company and between other companies within the same product and size group. These values can help to identify trends. Records of injuries caused by accidents can also be used as a basis for risk and fault-tree analyses.

Endnotes

1. Roberts, K. (2003). Using workers' compensation to promote a healthy workplace. In D. A. Hoffman & L. E. Tetrick (Eds.), *Health and safety in organizations: A multilevel perspective.* San Francisco, CA: Jossey Bass.

2. Roberts, K. (2003). Using workers' compensation to promote a healthy workplace. In D. A. Hoffman & L. E. Tetrick (Eds.), *Health and safety in organizations: A multilevel perspective.* San Francisco, CA: Jossey Bass.

3. Hyatt, D. E. (1996). Work disincentives of workers' compensation permanent partial disability benefits: Evidence for Canada. *Canadian Journal of Economics, 29*, 289–308.

4. Meyer, B., Viscusi, W. K., & Durbin, D. (1996). Workers' compensation and injury duration: Evidence from a natural experiment. *American Economic Review, 85*, 322–340.

5. Kelloway, E. K., Francis, L., Catano, V. M., Cameron, J., & Day, A. (2004). *Psychological disorders in the Canadian Forces: Legal and social issues. Contractor's report*. National Defence Headquarters, Ottawa, ON: Director Human Resources Research and Evaluation.

6. Roberts, K. (2003). Using workers' compensation to promote a healthy workplace. In D. A. Hoffman and L. E. Tetrick (Eds.), *Health and safety in organizations: A multilevel perspective*. San Francisco, CA: Jossey Bass.

7. Durbin, D., & Butler, R. (1998). Prevention of disability for work-related sources: The roles of risk management, government intervention and insurance. In T. Thomason, J. F. Burton, & D. E. Hyatt (Eds.), *New approaches to disability in the workplace*. Madison, WI: IRRA.

8. Krause, N., & Lund, T. (2003). Returning to work after occupational injury. In J. Barling & M. Frone (Eds.), *The psychology of workplace safety*. Washington, DC: APA Books.

9. Amick, B., Habeck, R. V., Hunt, A., Fossel, A. H., Chapin, A., & Keller, R. B. (2000). Measuring the impact of organizational behaviors on work disability prevention and management. *Journal of Occupational Rehabilitation, 10*, 21–38.

10. Krause, N., & Lund, T. (2003). Returning to work after occupational injury. In J. Barling & M. Frone (Eds.), *The psychology of workplace safety*. Washington, DC: APA Books.

11. Krause, N., Lynch, J., Kaplan, G. A., Cohen, R. D., Goldberg, D. E., & Salonen, J. T. (1997). Predictors of disability retirement. *Scandinavian Journal of Work, Environment, and Health, 23*, 403–413.

12. Krause, N., & Lund, T. (2003). Returning to work after occupational injury. In J. Barling and M. Frone (Eds.), *The psychology of workplace safety*. Washington, DC: APA Books.

13. Kelloway, E. K., Francis, L., Catano, V. M., Cameron, J., & Day, A. (2004). *Psychological disorders in the Canadian Forces: Legal and social issues. Contractor's report*. National Defence Headquarters, Ottawa, ON: Director Human Resources Research and Evaluation.

14. Krause, N., Dasinger, L. K., Deegan, L. J., Brand, R. J., & Rudolph, L. (2001). Psychosocial job factors and RTW after low back injury: A disability phase-specific analysis. *American Journal of Industrial Medicine, 40*, 374–392.

15. Dollard, M. F., Winefield, H. R., & Winefield, A. H. (1999). Predicting work stress compensation claims and return to work in welfare workers. *Journal of Occupational Health Psychology, 4*, 279–287.

16. Martin, D. J., Brooks, R. A., Ortiz, D. J., & Veniegas, R. C. (2003). Perceived employment barriers and their relation to workforce-entry intent among people with HIV/AIDS. *Journal of Occupational Health Psychology, 8*, 181–194.

Chapter 4

Physical Agents

Chapter Learning Objectives

After reading this chapter, you should be able to

- define the numerous terms relating to physical agents
- explain the human reactions to the various agents, particularly noise and radiation
- discuss the management of physical agents
- outline the actions of these agents on human physiology
- with the use of the appendix, understand the methods of calculating noise levels and exposures

Music to Your Ears?

A recent study by researchers at the University of Toronto suggests that one group at high risk for noise-induced hearing loss is high-school music teachers. Based on a sample of 18 music teachers from the Peel School Board, the researchers found that almost 40% of school teachers were at risk for noise-induced hearing loss based on noise exposure. Seventy-eight percent of the teachers experienced a high level of noise exposure over the course of an eight-hour day (85 dB—about the same as a gas lawnmower). Although the noise exposure was below the legislated limit of 90 dB, it is at a level that can still cause damage to hearing. Ironically, some of the steps normally taken to reduce noise (i.e., putting down carpet rather than tile floors) cannot be undertaken in a school environment because of other health and safety concerns (i.e., the possibility of allergens and moulds associated with carpeting). This research illustrates at least four important facts about physical agents in the workplace.

First, such agents may be present in unexpected workplaces. Most discussions of workplace noise focus on heavy machinery and factories—not high school band rooms. Second, exposure to some physical agents may be inherent in the workplace—how does a music teacher teach band without being exposed to loud noise? Third, legislated standards are best viewed as maximum tolerances—not as the "safe" level of exposure but rather as the highest tolerable level. Physical harm (such as noise-induced hearing loss) can occur well below the legislated exposure level. Finally, health and safety issues are often complex and potential solutions have to be evaluated for the risks they may introduce into the environment as well.

Sources: Behar, A., MacDonald, E., Lee, J., Cui, J., Kunov, H., & Wong, W. (2004). Noise exposure of music teachers. *Journal of Occupational and Environmental Hygiene, 4*, 243–247; Study shows music teachers at risk of hearing loss. (2004, June 7). *Canadian Occupational Health and Safety News.*

Ⓡ Ⓟ Ⓒ 4.1

Ⓡ Ⓟ Ⓒ 4.2

Ⓡ Ⓟ Ⓒ 4.3

Ⓡ Ⓟ Ⓒ 4.4

physical agents

sources of energy that may cause injury or disease

ambient

all-encompassing condition associated with a given environment, being usually a composite of inputs from sources all around us

In this chapter we consider the effects of physical agents in the workplace. **Physical agents** are sources of energy that may cause injury or disease. Examples include noise, vibration, radiation, and extremes in temperature and pressure. Each of these agents may be **ambient** or acute (i.e., resulting from a single exposure).

Noise

Noise is defined as any unwanted sound. Technically, it refers to "the auditory sensation evoked by the oscillations in pressure in a medium with elasticity and viscosity" such as air.[1] Noise is a growing health problem in industry.

In British Columbia, for example, approximately 8% of 143,000 workers tested in 2003 showed signs of hearing damage (**early warning change**). In the same year, 2,400 new claims for noise-induced hearing loss were filed.[2]

One major characteristic of the human ear and hearing is that we do not hear everything in a nice, neat way. If sound were measured electronically, the sound spectrum might appear more or less as a straight line. What the human ear hears or perceives is significantly different. The human hearing range of frequencies is approximately 20 Hz to 20,000 Hz. Thus, a person can hear a bass note from a tuba or a shrill note from a piccolo, but not a dog whistle. This has direct implications for human hearing problems. Just because we cannot hear the sound does not mean that it is not present and possibly causing hearing damage.

The response of the human ear is usually represented as a graph that illustrates the threshold of hearing (see Figure 4.1). The term *threshold of hearing* refers to the envelope or range of sound that the human ear can perceive or hear. The standards for the measurement of noise use the unit of a decibel, or dB (also referred to as sound pressure level). When the human response is involved, the unit becomes dB(A) or A-weighted decibel, represented by the graph in Figure 4.1. This response is built into the sound meters used for measuring noise exposure in the workplace.

Human hearing response is conditional on three characteristics: frequency, duration, and loudness. Any noise level investigation must take into account these three elements. Most noise sources and sounds, such as music, are made up of a variety of frequencies that the ear blends to create a pleasant or not-so-pleasant sound. As noted previously, noise beyond the range of human hearing response can be damaging even though not "heard." Similarly, certain

early warning change

a deterioration of hearing in the upper frequency—the earliest detectable sign of noise-induced hearing loss

Figure 4.1

Human Hearing Response Curve

linear curve

A-weighted curve

inaudible range

audible range

Relative hearing response (dB): 0, −5, −10, −15, −20, −25, −30, −35, −40, −45

Frequency f (Hz): 20, 50, 100, 200, 500, 1,000, 2,000, 5,000, 10,000

FIGURE 4.2

The Auditory System

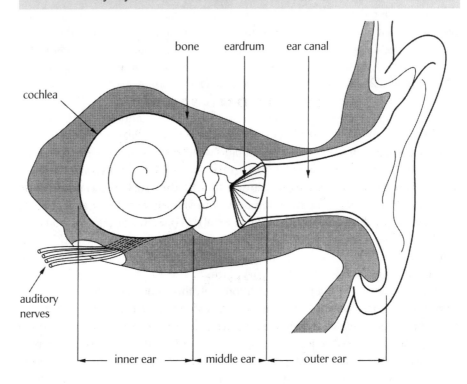

frequencies in a noise that is made up of a variety of frequencies can be extra loud and thus damaging without being noticed, even within the human range. It is important to consider frequency response when dealing with hearing protection.

The duration of the sound is one of those conditions that the human ear responds to in a strange way. A loud noise of very short duration, like a gunshot, is perceived to be "quieter" than the same sound level heard for a longer duration. They can both be damaging, but only the latter one "sounds" like it. The short duration noise is referred to as impact or impulse noise, which has a duration of about 1 millisecond (1/1000th of a second). The third characteristic of human response is loudness. This term is self-explanatory. The louder (volume) the noise, the more problems it can cause.

Types of Hearing Loss

Noise can affect humans in three ways: physiologically, sociologically, and psychologically. In terms of the first effect, physiological damage, there are two basic types of hearing loss. The first is *conductive*, which restricts the transmission of sound to the cochlea or inner ear (see Figure 4.2); the second is *sensorineural* (sometimes referred to as nerve deafness), which affects the cochlea and is usually irreversible. Conductive hearing loss can be caused by wax buildup, infection, or trauma. From an industrial standpoint, it can be caused by the nonhygienic application of hearing protectors or the improper cleaning of these devices.

More prevalent in industry, however, is the sensorineural type of hearing loss. It is interesting to note that exposure to excessive noise first affects frequencies in the speech range—approximately 500 Hz to 3,000 Hz. Two indications of exposure to excessive noise levels at work are ringing in the ears (tinnitus) and raising the volume on radios and television after work. The volume of the radio or television will seem very high the next morning because temporary hearing loss diminishes with rest and removal from exposure. Hearing loss is one of the most insidious of disabilities. It is not uncommon for major loss to occur gradually over 5 to 10 years, depending on the type of exposure.

Gradual hearing loss, known as temporary threshold shift (TTS), can sometimes be reversed by removal from the noise source. Permanent threshold shift (PTS) identifies a hearing disability that is permanent and may not be correctable. In many cases, a hearing aid can bring about some improvement. However, such a device is of little assistance when the hearing loss has been caused by noise exposure or sensorineural loss, because the hair cells in the cochlea have been destroyed.

The second effect of noise is sociological. In the past, companies would sometimes hire workers with hearing loss to work in high-noise areas since it was thought that the damage had already been done. However, it is now known that noise can cause extra-auditory effects, including a startled response to a loud, unexpected noise; cardiovascular, neurologic, endocrine, and biochemical changes; and nausea, malaise, and headaches.[3] Other laboratory and field studies have also demonstrated **vasoconstriction, hyperreflexia,** fluctuations in hormonal secretions, and disturbances in equilibrium and visual functions.

vasoconstriction

the process of causing a constriction of the blood vessels

hyperreflexia

the condition of unusually quick reaction by the nerves to some external stimulus

The third effect deals with human psychology. Many people are affected and disturbed by certain sounds that are not loud enough to present any serious physiological problem. These are day-to-day noises that tend to bug us, such as a patron talking during a movie, a helicopter flying overhead, or a tap dripping. Although the actual noise level may be well below acceptable standards and may not be measurable with a sound level meter, it is nonetheless very real (often referred to as "selective hearing") and can cause stress and other possible nonauditory effects.

Noise Exposure Standards

Noise exposure standards vary across provinces and territories in terms of their relative stringency. The standards are based on worker exposure during a defined time frame. This relationship is referred to as *dose*, which describes the amount of noise absorbed by or impinged on an organ (the ear or the body) in a given unit of time. The noise standard or threshold limit value (TLV) in Ontario allows for an eight-hour exposure of 90 dB(A) without hearing protection. Most other jurisdictions use a standard of 85 dB(A) for eight hours. The 5 dB(A) difference between the two standards represents a difference of twice the noise energy, the 90 dB(A) standard being greater. The exposure limits in Canadian jurisdictions are presented in Table 4.1. The 5 dB increments noted in the table are referred to as a 5 dB exchange rate. The **exchange rate** represents the doubling of the sound power, which in turn requires the halving of the exposure time.

exchange rate

represents the doubling of the sound power

TABLE 4.1

Noise Level Exposure Limits in Canadian Jurisdictions

JURISDICTION	MAXIMUM ALLOWABLE 8 H EXPOSURE
Federal	87 dB(A)
Alberta	85 dB(A)
British Columbia	85 dB(A)
Manitoba	90 dB(A)
New Brunswick	85 dB(A)
Newfoundland and Labrador	85 dB(A)
Northwest Territories and Nunavut	85 dB(A)
Nova Scotia	85 dB(A)
Ontario	90 dB(A)
Prince Edward Island	85 dB(A)
Quebec	90 dB(A)
Saskatchewan	85 dB(A)
Yukon	85 dB(A)

The above standards are based on continuous noise, such as an air compressor or machine running. Impact or impulse noises, such as a punch press operating with more than a one-second interval between strokes, have a totally

Occupational Health and Safety Notebook 4.1

Noise in the Workplace: Signs and Levels

Given the noise exposure limits presented in Table 4.1, some comparisons are useful:

normal conversation at 1 metre	55 dB(A)
passenger car at 20 metres	65 dB(A)
diesel truck at 20 metres	85 dB(A)
lawnmower at 1 metre	92 dB(A)
handheld circular saw at 1 metre	115 dB(A)

Although nothing will replace accurate measurement of noise levels in the workplace, the Canadian Centre for Occupational Health and Safety suggests that a workplace might be too noisy if

a.   people have to raise their voices to be understood

b.   employees have ringing in the ears at the end of the workday

c.   employees find they have to turn their radio up on the drive home (compared with the volume on the way to work)

d.   individuals who have worked in the workplace for years have difficulty understanding conversations at parties or restaurants

If any of the above statements are true, a noise assessment or survey of the workplace should be undertaken.

Source: Canadian Centre for Occupational Health and Safety. Retrieved from http://www.ccohs.ca, October 8, 2004.

Hearing Protection for Fire Fighters

Although we recognize the many hazards involved in firefighting, we might not think of noise as a particular concern for fire fighters. However, fire fighters use power tools, work around noisy fire engines and pumpers, and, of course, are close to loud sirens. Although this seems like a clear case calling for hearing protectors, it is also important that fire fighters be able to communicate with one another. One solution is an earmuff-type hearing protector with a built-in microphone and headset. These commercially available devices allow fire fighters to communicate with one another while protecting hearing.

However, this is not a total solution as there is now evidence that hearing protection may be less effective when worn in conjunction with hard hats, eye protection, and respirators—all equally essential to the fire fighters' role.

Sources: Abel, S. M., Sass-Kortsak, A., & Kielar, A. (2002). The effect on earmuff attenuation of other safety gear worn in combination. *Noise & Health, 5,* 1–13; also Fire Fighters' Association of Ontario, "Issue: Hearing protection during emergency operations." Retrieved from http://www.ffao.on.ca/section21old1.htm#hearing, October 9, 2004.

different method of measurement based on the number of impacts per day. Another widely applied or referenced set of standards is that established by the American Conference of Governmental Industrial Hygienists (ACGIH). ACGIH recommends a noise TLV of 85 dB(A) for eight hours. This organization's standards are updated annually.

Noise exposure tests can be done by an outside specialist or a trained person on staff using a **sound pressure level meter**, an **octave band analyzer**, a **dosimeter**, or an **audiometer**.

Noise Control

Noise can be controlled by using logical methods. The process for control follows the source–path–human strategies used by health and safety professionals. The first strategy used to reduced noise is to make the *source* quieter. There are a number of possible approaches. If the problem consists of a noisy machine, for instance, it may be possible to make the machine quieter by adding sound-absorbing materials, placing vibration padding under it, redesigning the operation so that the machine performs in a different manner, isolating the machine in a separate room or sound-deadening enclosure, or purchasing a new machine. All these alternatives can be expensive and may not be enthusiastically endorsed. However, a cost-benefit analysis, which takes into account such factors as noise-based illness, absenteeism, and Workers' Compensation costs, may paint a more positive and dramatic picture.

The second strategy—*path*—involves moving the worker away from the source or erecting sound barriers between the noise and the worker, or both. Based on the physics of noise, as the distance from the sound source is doubled, the noise level will drop by a fixed amount. For example, if a noise level of 90 dB is measured 5 metres away from a machine (a point source) and the distance is increased to 10 metres, the noise level will be **attenuated** or lowered by 6 dB.

sound pressure level meter
measures gross noise level

octave band analyzer
measures the noise level in each frequency range

dosimeter
measures a person's exposure to noise as a percentage for one shift

audiometer
an instrument used to determine the sensitivity of a person's hearing or degree of hearing loss

attenuated or attenuation
reduction of noise at one location compared to another farther from the source

Choosing Hearing Protectors

For each application and to be properly fitted for maximum protection, there are ten factors to consider when deciding on the most effective hearing protection.

1. *Comfort*. Earmuffs in particular can be hot in warm conditions. The spring band can generate a feeling of the head being squashed. Workers who are claustrophobic may experience feelings of confinement.

2. *Visibility*. It is important that hearing protection be visible, so that supervisors can ensure that the worker is wearing the protection and using it in the required manner.

3. *Size*. People have heads of different sizes and shapes. It is imperative that hearing protective devices be fitted properly. Additional types of paraphernalia such as face shields used in conjunction with hearing protection must also be examined.

4. *Weight*. Generally, the lighter the protection, the greater the comfort.

5. *Ease of donning*. A device that is easy to put on will gain more acceptance among workers.

6. *Cost*. The actual dollar cost will depend on the application, the required degree of attenuation, and the style of device. Earmuffs are more costly than earplugs. The specific noise protection required could necessitate both plugs and muffs.

7. *Effective attenuation*. Most modern hearing protection devices use a noise reduction rating (NRR) system to indicate the degree of attenuation based on laboratory evaluation. The NRR value is usually accompanied by a chart showing attenuation by octave band frequencies. Generally, the higher the number, the greater the level of attenuation. A good rule of thumb relationship is expressed with the equation below:

$$NRR = L_{actual} - L_{standard} + 7$$

where L_{actual} is the noise level measured in the workplace, and $L_{standard}$ is the noise standard for an eight-hour period. Thus, if a worksite has a noise level of 97 dB(A) and the standard is 90 dB(A) for eight hours, the required NRR for hearing protectors would be $97 - 90 + 7$ or 14 dB(A).

8. *Hygiene*. This requirement is the most critical and most abused. It is not uncommon to observe a hearing protection device hanging from a hook in a dirty environment. Care must be taken to keep the personal item clean and stored in a sanitary location to avoid ear infections, which could cause more damage than the noise does.

9. *Useful life*. Disposable plugs or inserts do not last long but require no maintenance, while muffs last longer but require maintenance.

10. *Maintenance*. All nondisposable hearing protection devices require ongoing maintenance and care. They must be cleaned regularly with soap and warm water, not alcohol, and checked periodically for wear. The foam seal pads on circumaural units must be regularly maintained because skin oils and sweat will cause embrittlement and surface failure. Once the seal is damaged, the attenuation effectiveness is reduced.

Sources: Berger, E. H., Ward, W. D., Morrill, J. C., & Royster, L. H. (Eds.). (1988). *Noise and hearing conservation manual* (4th ed.). Akron, Ohio: American Industrial Hygiene Association; Chandler, H. (2004). "An earful of sound advice," *Occupational Health and Safety Canada*. Retrieved from http://www.ohscanada.com/SafetyPurchasing/HearProt.asp, October 9, 2004; Canadian Centre for Occupational Health and Safety, "What is personal protective equipment?" Retrieved from http://www.ccohs.ca/oshanswers/prevention/ppe/designin.html, October 9, 2004.

This is called a "free field effect," which simply means that nothing like walls is around to reflect the sound back on the worker. Objects such as the walls of the building and other machines will cause reflections that can reduce the amount of attenuation from this fixed amount. Nevertheless, the principle is still valid, and this process is usually less costly than the source approach.

The third strategy—*human*—involves the use of personal protective equipment. This approach is the least costly and the one that is most commonly used. It is not always the best method, but many companies are not well enough informed to undertake other approaches such as job rotation, relocation, isolation, automation, rest periods, and site design. The two basic classes of hearing protection available are earplugs, which are inserted into the ears, and circumaural muffs or earmuffs, which are worn over the ears. A description of the various types of industrial hearing protection is provided in Table 4.3 in the appendix. It should be noted that whatever strategies are used to decrease noise exposure, personal protective devices may still be necessary in conjunction with other methods.

Vibration

Vibration refers to the oscillating motion of a particle or body moving about a reference position.[4] Vibration has a number of mechanical causes, including the dynamic effects from machine tolerances, clearances, rolling or rubbing contact, and out-of-balance conditions with rotary or reciprocating parts. Vibration can be accidental (a car wheel that is out of balance) or intentional (a vibrating feeder on a dry bulk material conveyor).

Vibration is a health hazard for three reasons. It can cause whole body vibration, segmental vibration, and noise. As with noise, vibration is transmitted through a medium, although in this case the medium is usually solid (e.g., steel or brick). The health effects will vary depending on the frequency and amplitude of the vibration. At low frequencies, say up to 15 Hz, the body will experience what is known as **whole body vibration**. In this instance, the complete human body will "shake" with the source. We have all experienced this condition in an automobile or on board a ship—the condition is called car- or seasickness. As the frequency of the vibration increases, parts of the body—not the whole body—will be affected by a process called **segmental vibration**.

One term that frequently comes up in discussions of vibration is **resonance**, which refers to the effect that occurs when an object reacts strongly to some particular frequency. If you sing in a tiled shower stall, you will occasionally hear a note that sounds louder than most, which means that the space is resonant to that note. Parts of the human body can resonate when exposed to some lower frequencies. For instance, the head and shoulders can resonate at 20 Hz to 30 Hz, while the eyeballs resonate at 60 Hz to 90 Hz.[5] If your vision becomes blurry when you have been working with a power tool such as a belt sander, you are experiencing minor levels of eyeball resonance, which is harmless unless prolonged.

Vibrations are classified into two categories: low frequency (discussed above) and high frequency. Vibrating effects fall into two separate conditions. As noted, the first concerns low-frequency vibrations. The second deals with higher frequency vibrations that can happen so fast that the body cannot respond. When the higher frequencies occur, the effects of wave velocity and acceleration take precedence. Vibratory effects are evaluated using measurements of velocity and acceleration caused by the source using a vibration meter, which is often a variation on a sound level meter.

whole body vibration
affects the whole body as a unit

segmental vibration
affects only parts of the body

resonance
the effect that occurs when an object reacts strongly to some particular frequency

Occupational Health and Safety Notebook 4.3

Hand-Arm Vibration Syndrome (HAVS)

Working with hand-held power tools (particularly in cold weather) can result in vibration-induced white finger (VWF) or more generally, hand-arm vibration syndrome.[6] HAVS results from changes in blood circulation and the nervous system associated with vibration and is characterized by

- tingling in the fingers
- loss of sensation in the fingers (numbness)
- loss of sense of light touch

- whitening (blanching) of the fingers when exposed to cold
- loss of grip strength
- development of cysts in fingers and wrists

HAVS is a progressive disorder and is also known as Raynaud's phenomenon.

Source: Mason, J. (2003). Bad vibrations. *Occupational Heath*, *55*(7), 24.

---

necrosis

death or decay of tissue

decalcification

loss of lime salts (calcium) in the bones

The health effects of whole body vibration include inhibition of muscular reflexes, impaired or blurred vision, and alterations of brain electrical activity. Segmental vibration effects include sore neck and shoulder muscles and sore joints; Raynaud's phenomenon, or white fingers, caused by restricted blood circulation in the fingers; neuritis and degenerative alterations of the central nervous system; fragmentation, **necrosis**, and **decalcification** of the carpal bones; and muscle atrophy and tenosynovitis.

The frequency response associated with vibrating systems is directly related to the mass of the system. In the simplest terms, if the mass or weight is increased, the effects of vibration can be lowered through a dampening action. An example would be the increased weight on the outer flange of a flywheel that smoothes out much of the machine vibration. Using a flywheel is one method of control to reduce the health effects.

Whole body vibration effects can result from driving a motorcycle, truck, or tractor, or working near large machines such as air compressors or punch presses. Segmental vibration effects are caused by using vibrating tools such

Occupational Health and Safety Notebook 4.4

Controlling Vibration

Strategies for whole body and segmental vibration control include

- avoiding the source by revising the task
- using equipment that produces lower vibrations
- adding dampening devices to equipment to reduce vibrations

- decreasing worker exposure time
- isolating the worker from the source

Source: Canadian Centre for Occupational Health and Safety, "How can you measure vibration?" Retrieved from http://www.ccohs.ca/oshanswers/phys_agents/vibration/vibration_measure.html, October 9, 2004.

as riveters, sanders, saws, air hammers, or hammer drills. The most serious segmental effects are those associated with hand-arm vibrations. Using vibrating hand tools produces a Catch-22 situation. To properly control a vibrating hand tool, it is necessary to grip it securely; however, the tighter the hand grips the tool, the more severe the effects of segmental damage from vibration. The human resource professional should also be aware that vibration has chronic effects that must be managed.

Thermal Stress

Thermal stress conditions involve cold and hot temperature extremes, usually coupled with high humidity. The human body can be seen as a machine that takes in chemical energy (food) and converts it to mechanical energy (muscles) and heat (see Figure 4.3). The balance of this heat generation, referred to as **homeostasis**, is the basis for examination of the effects of heat and cold on the body. Simple thermodynamic theory shows that temperature, like water, flows from the high point to the low point. Thus, in cold climates, heat will flow from the body into the surrounding environment, thereby making the person feel cold. Similarly, in hot climates, heat will be absorbed by the body, making the person feel hot. Adding physical work to either of these situations will increase body heat and shift the thermal balance. When an imbalance occurs, the body is stressed thermally. This body thermal balance can be illustrated by the mathematical model below:[7]

homeostasis
the balance of heat generation

$$S = (M - W) \pm R \pm C \pm V - E$$

where S is the body heat storage or loss, M is the metabolic heat production of the body, W is the work output, R is the radiative heat gain or loss, C is the convective heat gain or loss, V is the respiratory heat gain or loss, and E is the evaporative heat loss.

Figure 4.3

The Body as a Machine System

INPUT ENERGY
Chemical
- food
- air
- water

HUMAN
- a constant temperature process (thermoregulatory)
- internal energy
- heat generated (metabolism)

OUTPUT ENERGY
Mechanical
- sit, stand
- walk, run, jump
- work – push
           – pull

Heat rejected to environment (loss)

When there is heat, the body will gain heat if R, C, and V are positive; similarly, if there is heat loss, then R, C, V, and E are negative. In medical terms, heat gain is referred to as hyperthermic; heat loss is referred to as hypothermic; and a condition of neither gain nor loss is known as balance.

There are three methods of heat transfer that apply to the body, as well as to any other thermal condition. The first method, **conduction**, occurs when two surfaces are in contact (e.g., the skin touches a hot stove, resulting in a local burn). The second method, **convection**, occurs when one surface adds heat to the surroundings (e.g., the skin is close to air flow emanating from a flame or a heater). The third method, **radiation**, occurs when energy is transmitted by electromagnetic waves (e.g., the skin is exposed to sunlight).

The body has remarkable temperature control, with the blood system and the skin being the major players. As body heat increases, blood flow increases, capillaries move closer to the surface of the skin (they actually open up), and sweating increases, thereby allowing increased heat exchange to the atmosphere. As body heat decreases, blood flow slows and the capillaries withdraw from the skin surface, thus reducing the amount of heat transferred to the atmosphere.

The effects of heat and cold on health are well recognized by anyone who spends a lot of time outside in summer and winter. The focal point of most thermal stress and control is at the body core—from the neck to the groin and

conduction

heat transfer occurring when two surfaces are in contact

convection

heat transfer occurring when one surface adds heat to the surroundings

radiation

heat transfer occurring when energy is transmitted by electromagnetic waves

Occupational Health and Safety Today 4.2

Beat the Heat

Occupational health and safety legislation such as that in British Columbia now obligates employers to pay close attention to the dangers of heat exposure. If workers are at risk of heat-related disorders, employers are required to conduct a heat-stress assessment. If it is not possible to reduce the level of heat or to implement engineering controls, the employer must either (a) adjust work-rest schedules to reduce exposure or (b) provide personal protective equipment such as air-cooled or water-cooled vests. Employers must also ensure a supply of cool drinking water near the worksite.

Tips for reducing the adverse consequences of working in the heat include the following:

- Drink cool water at least every 15–20 minutes (remember that thirst is not a good indicator of fluid loss).

- Wear personal protective gear such as cooled vests or bandanas when working in high temperatures on a regular basis.
- Use sunblock and wear a hat.
- Wear suitable eye protection.
- Schedule work-rest regimens.

Similar controls also apply to cold exposure.

Source: WorkSafe BC, "Preventing heat stress at work." Retrieved from http://www.worksafebc.com/publications/ health_and_safety_information/by_topic/assets/pdf/ heat_stress.pdf, October 9, 2004.

Measuring Thermal Stress

Thermal stress is measured using the wet bulb globe temperature (WBGT) index. This index measures the effect of heat and humidity on a worker.

WBGT °C	Description
< 27	No complaints of heat discomfort
27–29	Varying complaints
> 29	Sedentary work for unacclimatized workers
> 31	Continuous work suspended; work-rest schedules implemented
> 38	Threshold limit value; no work without protection

Source: Workers' Compensation Board of BC, "WCB of BC occupational health and hygiene issue sheet: *Issue—Heat stress measurement standards."* Retrieved from http://www.bcpsea.bc.ca/public/ohs/OHandSManual/Gen_Hazard_Requirements/07_Noise_Vibration/Heat_Stress/WCB_Issue_Sheet_Heat_Stress_Measurement.html, October 9, 2004.

between the shoulders. The body core temperature range is 35°C to 38.5°C, with "normal" being 37°C. When the core temperature goes outside this range, serious problems can result. Heat-related illnesses include heat stroke (the body loses control of its thermal balance), heat hyperpyrexia (the body temperature rises), heat syncope (heat-induced fainting), heat exhaustion, heat cramps, heat rash, and heat fatigue. Cold-related illnesses include chilblains, caused by reduced circulation in the extremities; trench foot, caused by cold, wet conditions; frostbite, caused by local freezing of tissue; and hypothermia, which occurs when cold causes the body's thermal regulation to fail.

Radiation

Radiation is divided into two distinct groups—ionizing and nonionizing. These two types of radiation are identified primarily by wavelength range—short for ionizing and long for nonionizing—and by their action on tissue. This section will be general since any worker employed by a company involved in radiative processes or materials must undergo extensive, specialized training.

Ionizing Radiation

Ionizing radiation is any form of electromagnetic energy capable of producing ions through interaction with matter. Types of ionizing radiation include X-rays, gamma rays, alpha particles, beta particles, and neutrons. X-radiation is most commonly found in medical facilities. The other forms of ionizing radiation are commonly found in nuclear operations or research companies. All of these forms, except X-rays, occur naturally as well as in manufactured states. Natural radiation is found in ground-grown food, cosmic bombardment, building materials such as concrete, and fertilizers such as phosphorous. Most of these sources are measurable with very sensitive instruments but are insignificant from a health standpoint. Some harmful ionizing radiation, which might occur in basements and mines, is radon gas.

Radiation exposure or dosage is usually measured in a unit called a rem (*r*oentgen *e*quivalent *m*an). Natural radiation is approximately 125 mrem (millirem) per year. A dose of approximately 75 rem (75,000 mrem) per year can cause serious health effects.

Manufactured ionizing radiation can be found in a number of products or operations other than nuclear energy. Most home smoke detectors use a source that emits alpha particles, which are harmless; older "glow-in-the-dark" watch faces were painted with very low radioactive paint. In industry, ionizing radiation can be found in bulk-material measuring devices, high-voltage electronic devices, and medical equipment such as X-ray machines or scanners; none of these poses a health hazard to the general population.

The biological effects of equal amounts of different radiations depend on several factors, including whether the exposure is whole body or local (for example, the arm), acute or chronic. Genetic effects can include cell mutation, burns, and radiation sickness. Control of exposure will include regular monitoring, shielding, job rotation, protective equipment, and extensive training. This is why the dentist places a lead apron over your body and neck when taking X-rays.

Occupational Health and Safety Notebook 4.6

Effects of Nonionizing Radiation

Specific health effects of nonionizing radiation forms can be itemized as follows:

1. Ultraviolet radiation (originating from mercury vapour lamps and fluorescent tubes): conjunctivitis and keratitis (inflammation of the cornea), reddening of the skin (sunburn), skin cancer.
2. Infrared radiation (originating from incandescent, fluorescent, high-intensity discharge lights, and hot metals and glass): corneal and retinal burns, overheating of the iris, cataracts, skin burns.
3. Microwave radiation (originating from microwave ovens, radar, induction heating equipment, and diathermy equipment): deep tissue damage (cooking), surface skin rash, cataracts and eye lens opacities, biochemical changes and central nervous effects, pacemaker interference.
4. Radio waves (originating from radio and television broadcasting, most electronic devices—e.g., video-display terminals [VDTs] and power lines): a number of conditions, including tumours, none of which have been conclusively proven.

Sources: Ontario Ministry of Labour, "Radiofrequency and microwave radiation in the workplace." Retrieved from http://www.gov.on.ca/LAB/english/hs/guidelines/radiation/, October 9, 2004; Manitoba Department of Labour, "Work Safe bulletin: Radiation, July 1997, Bulletin #180." Retrieved from http://www.gov.mb.ca/labour/safety/pdf//bltn180.pdf, October 9, 2004.

Nonionizing Radiation

Nonionizing radiation refers to electromagnetic radiation that does not have energies great enough to ionize matter. Types of nonionizing radiation include ultraviolet radiation, visible (white light) radiation, infrared radiation, microwave radiation, and radio waves. The sun can be a source of all these radiations. The eye is the primary organ at risk from nonionizing radiation (see Figure 4.4).

Control of nonionizing radiation exposures usually includes isolation or separation, protective equipment, and training. With respect to separation, a pregnant computer worker should be offered another job where she is not exposed to a VDT. Even though there is no hard evidence of fetal risk, and such a move may be impractical in a small firm, the company should not put itself in the position of subjecting one of its employees to a possible health risk.

FIGURE 4.4

General Absorption Properties of the Eye for Electromagnetic Radiation

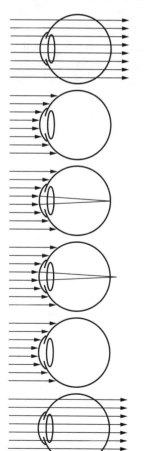

High energy X-rays, gamma rays; 99% pass completely through the eye. 1% is absorbed.

Short UV; absorption principally at cornea. (Intermediate UV; absorption at cornea and lens.)

Long UV, visible; transmitted through eye and focused on retina.

Near IR; partially absorbed by lens, iris, and media; partially focused at retina.

Far IR; absorption localized at cornea for sharp H20 absorption wavelengths; other wavelengths absorbed also by lens and iris.

Microwave; generally transmitted with partial absorption in all parts of the eye.

Occupational Health and Safety Today 4.3

Is Your Cell Phone a Physical Agent?

The proliferation of cell phones for personal and business use has given rise to concerns that cell phones may pose a risk factor for diseases such as brain cancer. The concern emerges from the observation that cell phones are essentially radio transceivers that emit and receive electromagnetic signals.

Laboratory studies with animals have not resolved these concerns. In some studies, rats exposed to electromagnetic signals developed tumours while others had a decreased rate of tumours. Although exposure to microwave energy can cause human tissue to "heat up," there is no evidence that cell phones have been associated with such effects.

Currently, there are no exposure limits for cell phones and it is unlikely that such guidelines will come in the near future. The Canadian Centre for Occupational Health and Safety suggests limiting the use of cell phones in favour of "regular" telephones or car phones, "just to be on the safe side."

Sources: BC Centre for Disease Control, "Health concerns of cellular and PCS telephones." Retrieved from http://www.bccdc.org/content.php?item=55&PHPSESSID=3b9eb77aaeb578035ba3b397a0b8899f, October 9, 2004; Canadian Centre for Occupational Health and Safety. Retrieved from http://www.ccohs.ca, October 9, 2004.

Summary

This chapter has focused on four physical agents that are commonly encountered in industry—noise, vibration, thermal stress, and radiation. Industries in which agents like ionizing radiation are encountered have implemented extensive, specialized training programs and procedures. In most situations, however, simple prevention policies and programs are adequate for reducing and controlling worker exposure to physical agents.

Key Terms

ambient, p. 82
attenuated or attenuation, p. 87
audiometer, p. 87
conduction, p. 92
convection, p. 92
decalcification, p. 90
dosimeter, p. 87
early warning change, p. 83
exchange rate, p. 85
homeostasis, p. 91

hyperreflexia, p. 85
necrosis, p. 90
octave band analyzer, p. 87
physical agents, p. 82
radiation, p. 92
resonance, p. 89
segmental vibration, p. 89
sound pressure level meter, p. 87
vasoconstriction, p. 85
whole body vibration, p. 89

Weblinks

CBC News, "Noise,"
http://www.cbc.ca/consumers/market/files/home/noise/ (p. 83)

National Research Council Canada, "Noise Control in Buildings,"
http://irc.nrc-cnrc.gc.ca/bsi/85_E.html (p. 84)

Hearing Center Online, "Name that sound—What does hearing loss sound like?"
http://www.hearingcenteronline.com/sound.shtml (p. 85)

American Conference of Governmental Industrial Hygienists,
http://www.acgih.org (p. 87)

WorkSafe BC, "Part 7 Noise, Vibration, Radiation and Temperature,"
http://regulation.healthandsafetycentre.org/s/Part7.asp (p. 89)

Ontario Paramedic Asociation, "Public Service Announcements,"
http://www.ontarioparamedic.ca/communications/service_announcements.html (p. 91)

The Radiation Safety Institute of Canada, "Issues in Radiation Safety,"
http://www.radiationsafety.ca/Issues.htm (p. 93)

RPC Icons

RPC 4.1 Analyses risk to the health and safety of employees and determines appropriate preventative measures, including training, provision of required safety equipment, and administrative practices.

- relevant legislation
- nature of the business and physical work environment
- hazard recognition
- workplace inspection techniques
- safety programs, equipment, and emergency procedures
- ergonomics
- functions of the JHSC
- training and development/presentation techniques
- industry best practices
- relevant technical terminology
- the collective agreement
- services and equipment available in the community
- Worker Protection (including health and safety and Workers' Compensation)
- Training and development program design and administration

TASK & KNOWLEDGE REQUIREMENTS
- Occupational health and safety legislation (e.g., Occupational Health and Safety Act of Ontario, Workplace Safety & Insurance Act—Bill 99, Workplace Hazardous Materials Information System, Transportation of

Dangerous Goods legislation, environmental legislation, smoking in the workplace legislation, civil rights legislation)
- hazard identification and control
- emergency preparedness procedures
- management techniques for OH&S Programs
- types of employee assistance and wellness programs

RPC 4.2 Implements and evaluates practices in the areas of health, safety, security, and Workers' Compensation.

- investigative techniques
- hazard recognition
- disaster recovery techniques
- relevant legislation
- resource information
- common health and safety practices
- company policies and procedures
- Worker Protection (including health and safety and Workers' Compensation)
- theories and practices for protection of individuals and groups
- Occupational health and safety legislation (e.g., Occupational Health and Safety Act of Ontario, Workplace Safety & Insurance Act—Bill 99, Workplace Hazardous Materials Information System, Transportation of Dangerous Goods legislation, environmental legislation, smoking in the workplace legislation, civil rights legislation)
- hazard identification and control
- management techniques for OH&S Programs

RPC 4.3 Analyses risk to the health and safety of employees and determines appropriate preventative measures, including training, provision of required safety equipment, and administrative practices.

- relevant legislation
- nature of the business and physical work environment
- hazard recognition
- workplace inspection techniques
- safety programs, equipment, and emergency procedures
- ergonomics
- functions of the JHSC
- training and development/presentation techniques
- industry best practices
- relevant technical terminology
- the collective agreement
- services and equipment available in the community
- Worker Protection (including health and safety and Workers' Compensation)
- training and development program design and administration

TASK & KNOWLEDGE REQUIREMENTS
- Occupational health and safety legislation (e.g., Occupational Health and Safety Act of Ontario, Workplace Safety & Insurance Act—Bill 99,

Workplace Hazardous Materials Information System, Transportation
of Dangerous Goods legislation, environmental legislation, smoking
in the workplace legislation, civil rights legislation)
- hazard identification and control
- emergency preparedness procedures
- management techniques for OH&S Programs
- types of employee assistance and wellness programs

**RPC 4.4 Ensures due diligence and strict liability requirements are met,
e.g. records are kept and formal procedures established.**

- relevant legislation and common law
- company policies and procedures
- industry best practices
- program and policy development
- training and development techniques
- risk analysis
- common and statutory law (e.g., employment standard: labour relations)
- Worker Protection (including health and safety and Workers'
  Compensation)
- theories and practices for protection of individuals and groups

Task & Knowledge Requirements
- Occupational health and safety legislation (e.g., Occupational Health
  and Safety Act of Ontario, Workplace Safety & Insurance Act—Bill 99,
  Workplace Hazardous Materials Information System, Transportation
  of Dangerous Goods legislation, environmental legislation, smoking in
  the workplace legislation, civil rights legislation)
- management techniques for OH&S Programs

Discussion Questions

1. Workers in a manufacturing division in your jurisdiction have made a
   formal complaint that three machines are too noisy. Noise measurements
   are taken: the results are 83 dB, 87 dB, and 88 dB. Do the workers have a
   legitimate complaint?
2. Name three sources of UV radiation in an office. Then describe the
   effects of UV radiation on health.
3. All jurisdictions in Canada have access to the same science. Yet
   jurisdictions vary in legislated standards (e.g., for noise exposure
   see Table 4.1). Why might different standards apply in different
   jurisdictions?
4. Many occupations involve an inherent exposure to a physical agent
   resulting in excessive exposure to noise, vibration, thermal conditions,
   and so on. Outline the steps an employer can take to protect employees
   when avoiding the exposure is not possible.

Using the Internet

1. Working outside in the Canadian winter can be a hazard for many workers. Using Internet resources, determine the health and safety regulations and guidelines for outdoor work in your jurisdiction. Compare regulations across several provinces or territories. Which jurisdictions have developed the most extensive sets of guidelines for outdoor work?

Exercise

1. Occupational health and safety legislation establishes standards for exposure to various forms of physical agents in the workplace. Think of common forms of after-work entertainment (e.g., movies, bars, restaurants, malls). What physical agents are present in these settings? What risks do they pose for customers? for employees of these establishments?

Case 1: Monty's Problem

The newly appointed corporate medical director, a physician, paid an initial visit to one of the branch plants of the company. For the first time, he met the occupational health nurse, an RN and recent CCOHN, who had been appointed from the local community some years previously. Occupational hygiene and safety at the plant was the responsibility of one of the senior production engineers, a P.Eng., who had been at the plant for many years. Neither of these individuals had received any formal instruction in occupational health nursing or occupational health and safety, respectively, since such training had not been available when they were appointed to these positions. The director was disturbed to note that medical records maintained by the nurse appeared to be available to the personnel department and that there was no defined occupational health and safety program. The manager of the plant was absent on the day of the director's visit and therefore unavailable to discuss these concerns.

On returning to corporate headquarters, the physician sent a directive to the occupational health nurse instructing her that medical records were to be regarded as private and that information was not to be released without his express permission. He also asked the occupational health and safety person to purchase a simple class 2 sound level meter and to carry out a survey of noise levels at the branch plant. This information was to be available for discussion when the director next visited the operation.

Unfortunately, these requests caused considerable difficulties. The nurse had an argument with the personnel department over the availability of medical records and this led to intense internal friction. The production engineer/health and safety specialist resented the interference of the physician and complained to the plant manager, whom he had known personally for many years. The plant manager, Monty James, called head office to ensure that the director did not visit the plant without his permission or at least giving notification so that Monty would be available.

In reply, the physician pointed out that the noise levels at the site were clearly excessive and that the so-called occupational health and safety specialist was not capable of carrying out his duties.

When Monty James heard this response, he telephoned his superior, the general manager at corporate. If you were Monty, what would you say to your superior and how would you go about resolving the situation?

Case 2: Expensive Jewellery

As a newly hired HR specialist, you are touring the floor of the manufacturing plant. You are surprised to see that many workers are wearing their hearing protectors around their neck like a necklace instead of covering their ears. Moreover, the style seems to be to wear safety glasses perched on top of the head rather than in a position that would protect eyes. Employees working with acids are doing so in street clothes and barehanded despite the fact that rubber gloves and safety aprons are hanging on hooks next to the workstation. Even from your brief tour, it is clear that the company has invested in the best personal protective equipment available. Yet workers do not seem to use the equipment to protect themselves. One of your new responsibilities is health and safety programming. What do you do?

Appendix

This appendix illustrates some of the techniques and calculations for noise and hearing protection that could prove useful to the HR practitioner when examining workplace conditions, adding new noise-generating equipment, or working with a consultant, government inspectors, or certified members of the Joint Health and Safety Committee. Noise calculations deal with the combining of noise levels from various operating machines or purchase of new equipment. Some of this material may be required as defined in the specific course of study of the academic institution involved.

Calculating Noise Levels

Noise level is measured in units of decibels or dB. This is a unit of measure of sound pressure level (SPL), which is the technical name for noise level or the "amount" of noise that we hear. This relationship can be mathematically expressed as

$$dB = 20 \log (p/p_0) \qquad \text{(equation 5.1)}$$

where dB is the sound pressure level (SPL), p is the sound pressure, and p_0 is a reference pressure, usually 0.00002 Pascal (N/m^2) or 0.0002 microbars.

Although equation 5.1 has little practical application other than identifying the basics of noise, a variation of it can assist in noise-level evaluation. The variation is expressed as

$$\text{total dB} = 10 \log (10 \text{ dB}^{1/10} + 10 \text{ dB}^{2/10} + \ldots + 10 \text{ dB}^{n/10}) \quad \text{(equation 5.2)}$$

where the various dB values are for any number of machines or noise sources in an area. For example, one manufacturer had a machine with a noise level, or SPL, of 88 dB. The manufacturer decided to purchase an additional machine. The supplier insisted that the noise level of the new machine was 85 dB, below the current noise standard. However, when the values for each of these machines were entered into the relationship expressed in equation 5.2, the result was the total dB $= 10 \log (10^{88/10} + 10^{85/10}) = 89.8$ or 90 dB, which reached the current limit and could possibly create some hearing problems. Any other ambient noise in this workplace could cause the noise level to exceed the safety standards. This calculation can be used for decibels (dB) as above, or A-weighted decibels [dB(A)].

An easier way to make this same calculation is shown in Table 4.2. In our example, the difference in noise level between the two machines is 88−85, or 3 dB. Using the table, find the line that shows a difference of 3. The line at

TABLE 4.2

Measuring Noise Levels

Difference Between High and Low Noise Levels	Amount to be Added to Higher Noise Level	Difference Between High and Low Noise Level	Amount to be Added to Higher Noise Level
0.0 to 0.1	3.0	4.1 to 4.3	1.4
0.2 to 0.3	2.9	4.4 to 4.7	1.3
0.4 to 0.5	2.8	4.8 to 5.1	1.2
0.6 to 0.7	2.7	5.2 to 5.6	1.1
0.8 to 0.9	2.6	5.7 to 6.1	1.0
1.0 to 1.2	2.5	6.2 to 6.6	0.9
1.3 to 1.4	2.4	6.7 to 7.2	0.8
1.5 to 1.6	2.3	7.3 to 7.9	0.7
1.7 to 1.9	2.2	8.0 to 8.6	0.6
2.0 to 2.1	2.1	8.7 to 9.6	0.5
2.2 to 2.4	2.0	9.7 to 10.7	0.4
2.5 to 2.7	1.9	10.8 to 12.2	0.3
2.8 to 3.0	1.8	12.3 to 14.5	0.2
3.1 to 3.3	1.6	14.6 to 19.3	0.1
3.4 to 3.6	1.5	19.4 to ∞	0.0
3.7 to 4.0	1.5		

which the difference ranges from 2.8 to 3.0 gives a factor of 1.8, which is to be added to the highest noise level. Thus, 88 + 1.8 gives a total of 89.8, or 90 dB, as before.[8]

This table can be used for more than two sound sources. When there are more than two, the sound sources must be dealt with in pairs. For example, there are four machines in an area that are running and causing noise. The ratings are 82 dB, 85 dB, 88 dB, and 88 dB. Take these noise levels in pairs, 82 and 85, 88 and 88. In the first instance, the difference is 3 dB, which from the table, as above, gives a factor of 1.8, which is added to the highest value. Thus 85 + 1.8 = 86.8. Perform this same operation with the second pair, 88 and 88. The difference between these is 0. From the table for 0.00 to 0.1, the factor is 3.0, which when added to the highest value gives 88 + 3.0 = 91.3. Now we have two new pairs—86.8 and 91.3. The same operation is again performed. The difference is 4.5. From the table for 4.4 to 4.7, the factor is 1.3, which is added to the higher of the two values. Thus 91.3 + 1.3 = 92.6. The total noise level in this example becomes 92.6 dB, which by any standard is too high.

If equation 5.2 is used, then

$$\text{total dB} = 10 \log (10^{82/10} + 10^{85/10} + 10^{88/10} + 10^{88/10}) = 92.4 \text{ dB}$$

Shift Adjustment for Noise Exposure

All of the TLV values for chemical and noise exposure are based on an 8-hour shift. If the shift is longer, say 12 hours, or shorter, say 4 hours, then the time weighted average (TWA) should be adjusted. This adjustment for noise uses the equation:

$$L_{eq'} t = L_{eq} - 10 \log T_1/T \qquad \text{(equation 5.3)}$$

where L_{eq} is the noise exposure level limit for an 8-hour shift; $L_{eq'} t$ is the noise exposure level limit for the time exposure t; T_1 is the time period worked; and T is the nominal time period.

Example: If a worker works a 12-hour shift at a location where the limit for an 8-hour period is 85 dB(A), then the exposure limit for the 12-hour shift will be

$$L_{eq'} 12 = 85 - 10 \log 12/8 = 83.2 \text{ dB(A)}$$

In a similar fashion, if the worker only spent 4 hours at the job, then the new TWA will become

$$L_{eq'} 4 = 85 - 10 \log 4/8 = 88.0 \text{ dB(A)}$$

Although these calculations are mathematically correct, conditions such as long-term exposure, physical condition, and a 40-hour workweek must be considered.

Hearing Protection Types or Classifications

The early part of this chapter noted that there were two basic styles of hearing protection devices—plugs and muffs. The following table shows a more detailed breakdown of the styles and their designations.

TABLE 4.3

Types of Industrial Hearing Protection

CLASS	TYPE	DESCRIPTION
Earplugs	A1	Pre-formed earplug, the fitting of which should be done professionally.
	A2	User-formable earplug made of soft sponge-like materials that the user rolls between the fingers for insertion into the ear canal.
	B1	A stethoscope configuration with the spring headband holding earplugs in position in the ears. Easy to observe, and the band may be worn in several positions on the head.
Circumaural	D1	An earmuff that surrounds the complete ear with a headband that sits only on the top of the head. Often best for comfort and optimum attenuation.
	D2	An earmuff similar to D1 but with a headband system that can be worn in many positions on the head. Attenuation may vary with headband position.
	D3	An earmuff attachment for a hardhat, which can be permanently attached or field applied. Usually used in construction settings.
Nonlinear Protectors	F1	A specialty device with an electronic amplifier. A system that allows only certain sound levels and frequencies to pass unimpeded.
	F2	A specialty device with a mechanical "ear valve" on each ear that responds to impact noise and causes attenuation.
Combination		Many of the above types may be used in combination.

Endnotes

1. Berger, E. H., Ward, W. D., Morrill, J. C., & Royster, L. H. (Eds.). (1988). *Noise and hearing conservation manual* (4th ed.). Akron, Ohio: American Industrial Hygiene Association.

2. WorkSafe BC Health and Safety Centre. *Hearing conservation in British Columbia–2003*. Retrieved from http://hearingconservation.healthandsafetycentre.org/s/Statistics.asp, August 5, 2004.

3. Key, M. M., Henschel, A. F., Butler, J., Ligo, R. N., Tabershaw, I. R., & Ede, L. (1977). *Occupational diseases: A guide to their recognition* (rev. ed.). Cincinnati, OH: U.S. Department of Health, Education, and Welfare.

4. Broch, J. T. (1980). *Mechanical vibration and shock measurements* (2nd ed.). Nærum, Denmark: Brüel and Kjær.

5. Soule, R. D. (1973). Vibration. In *The industrial environment—Its evaluation and control*. Cincinnati, Ohio: U.S. Department of Health, Education, and Welfare.

6. Mason, J. (2003). Bad vibrations. *Occupational Health, 55*(7), 24.

7. Hammer, W. (1989). *Occupational safety management and engineering* (4th ed.). Englewood Cliffs, N.J.: Prentice Hall.

8. Michael, P. L. (1988). Physics of sound. In *The industrial environment—Its evaluation and control* (2nd ed.). Cinninnati, OH: U.S. Department of Health, Education, and Welfare.

Chapter 5

Chemical and Biological Agents

Chapter Learning Objectives

After reading this chapter, you should be able to

- define the numerous terms relating to chemical and biological agents
- explain the interactions of various chemical and biological groups
- discuss the management of chemical and biological agents
- describe the monitoring requirements and instrumentation used
- outline the actions of chemical and biological agents on human physiology
- explain the health and safety risks of airborne respirable contaminants and aerosols
- discuss the methods of measuring airborne contaminants

WHEN WORK MAKES YOU SICK

A laboratory technologist is the latest of 17 employees to claim that working in New Waterford Consolidated Hospital has made her sick. Carol Brewer worked at the hospital for 30 years. The complaint stems from renovations that began in 2002 and took 14 months to complete. The provincial Occupational Health and Safety Act requires that workplace air be free of dust or gas that could endanger health. When such impurities are known to be in the air, workers should be provided with protective gear. During the renovations, construction workers wore respirators and masks to protect themselves, but hospital employees were not provided with such protection.

Staff at the hospital claim to have tested positive for arsenic and lead. At least one physician has been off work for more than a year, attributing his tremors and headaches to high levels of heavy metals in his system ingested at his workplace. Although an external consultant found no evidence of heavy metals in the workplace on January 23, 2004, a recent case-control study compared hospital employees with a control group and noted elevated levels of metals in the urine of the hospital employees on August 7, 2004. At the time of this writing, the debate over the cause of the workers' symptoms and whether compensation will be forthcoming rages on. One more report, expected to be delivered in September 2004, is anticipated to be the final word on the subject. As of this writing, the report has not been made public.

Sources: CBC News, "We need answers, sick workers plead." Retrieved from http://novascotia.cbc.ca/features/2003/dec12.html, October 9, 2004; "Results show no signs of trace elements in NS hospital," *OHS Canada*, April 5, 2004. Retrieved from http://www.ohscanada.com, September 10, 2004; Smith, L. F. (2004). "New Waterford Consolidated Hospital review of the investigations of indoor air quality with special reference to claims of metal poisoning." Report prepared for the Nova Scotia Department of Health. Retrieved from http://www.gov.ns.ca/health/downloads/New%20Waterford%20District%20Hospital.pdf; "NS health authority testing for trace elements in hospital," *OHS Canada*, December 1, 2003. Retrieved from http://www.ohscanada.com, October 9, 2004.

RPC 5.1

RPC 5.2

RPC 5.3

RPC 5.4

Most occupational health and safety legislation, as noted in Chapter 2, now includes specific sections dealing with chemical and biological agents. Chemical and biological agents are also dealt with under WHMIS regulations. Virtually all occupational diseases, such as asbestosis, silicosis, various types of dermatitis, and respiratory problems, and many occupational injuries, such as chemical splashes, spills, and burns, are related to chemical or biological exposures. The results of these exposures can range from minor irritation to death. Dealing with these materials requires complete training. There have been too many deaths, among young people in particular, to ignore these facts. This chapter will provide an overview of the problems associated with chemical and biological substances and the requirements for management and control. The term **chemical agents** is used to describe hazards that are created by any one or any combination of a very large number of chemicals and their physical reactions. A biological agent or **biohazard** can be as subtle and as deadly as some chemical agents. Biological agents include hazards such as mould, fungus, bacteria, and viruses. Each of these agents may be **ambient** or acute (i.e., a single exposure).

chemical agents

hazards created by one or more chemicals

biohazard

hazard created by exposure to biological material

ambient

all-encompassing condition associated with a given environment, being usually a composite of inputs from sources all around us

Chemical Agents

More than 70,000 different chemicals are currently in use in North America, and approximately 800 new ones are introduced every year. No toxicity data is available for about 80% of the chemicals that are used commercially.[1] Increasingly, physicians are seeing patients who complain of physiological reactions to low-level chemical exposures in the environment, such as headaches, dry nasal passages, and nausea, to name but a few. These complaints have been variously labelled as multiple chemical sensitivity (MCS), twentieth-century disease, total allergy syndrome, and environmental illness.[2] Certain industrial chemicals have been linked to cancer, lung disease, blood abnormalities, nervous-system disorders, birth defects, sterility, and skin problems. The specific effects of some chemicals are well documented, while those of many others are still unknown.

For example, vapours entering the atmosphere from solvents such as paint thinners are included in the chemical-reaction category, because the vapours from the solvents can have a reaction to such things as heat and pressure. Airborne particulates (e.g., dust created by mechanical means such as sanding or grinding) are included in the physical-reaction category in that the contaminant is caused by an expenditure of energy or work. These categories account for most of the health hazards found in industry and at home.[3]

Although such agents may be a hazard in and of themselves, they can also interact synergistically with other lifestyle or environmental factors. Synergistic effects occur when the result of two factors taken together is greater than the sum of the two. For example, a lifestyle factor such as smoking can have a synergistic effect on some materials. An asbestos worker is four times more likely to develop lung cancer than is a non-asbestos worker; the probability rises to 80 to 90 times more likely if the asbestos worker smokes.

It has been estimated that 80% of all occupational illnesses are the result of chemical exposures.[4] Health problems created by chemical exposures are more prevalent in the workplace than in any other location.

Deadly Fires Burning: Fire Fighters at High Risk for Occupational Cancer

Each day Canadian fire fighters risk their lives in flaming buildings as a service to their community. Although the immediate risk of death from an injury sustained during an active fire is obvious, other health risks associated with firefighting may not be as obvious. In reality, fire fighters are also at high risk for certain types of cancer because of long-term exposure to carcinogenic chemical fumes and smoke. For instance, the chemical fumes released from burning plastic are toxic. In fact, some relatively rare forms of cancer are far more common among fire fighters than among the general population. For instance, glial blastoma, a primary brain cancer, is three times more likely among fire fighters than it is in the general population.

Some provincial and territorial jurisdictions recognize particular forms of cancer as an occupational illness stemming from fighting fires. In 2002, Manitoba became the first province to pass legislation linking cancer to full-time firefighting. Under an amendment to the Workers Compensation Act, if a past or present fire fighter is diagnosed with one of five types of cancer—brain cancer, bladder cancer, kidney cancer, non-Hodgkin's lymphoma, or leukemia—the illness will be presumed to be caused by employment as a fire fighter. This amendment means that fire fighters who suffer these conditions and their families are qualified to receive Workers' Compensation.

Manitoba set a high bar for other jurisdictions. Since the Manitoba legislation passed, other provinces have followed with legislation linking firefighting to certain forms of cancer.

The availability of financial compensation for fire fighters suffering from cancer is certainly a large move forward—in fact, the Manitoba legislation follows years of lobbying on the part of the Manitoba Professional Firefighters Association. However, fire fighters are also focused on the prevention of occupational cancers. In terms of chemical exposure, the most dangerous time is when the flames have been put out, but the fire is smouldering and fire fighters are engaged in site cleanup. This is a time when individuals may be less vigilant about the use of protective breathing apparatus. Education programs about the importance of protective equipment may help reduce the incidence of these deadly cancers.

Sources: McLauchlin, D., & Bartlett, S. (2002, Summer). Deadly duties. *Media Magazine*. Retrieved from http://www.caj.ca/mediamag/summer2002/award-radio.html, August 5, 2004; Tomlinson, A. (2002, June 17). Manitoba recognizes firefighting cancer risks. *Canadian HR Reporter*, p. 2; and Legislative Assembly of Manitoba. (n.d.). Bill 5, "The workers compensation amendment act." Retrieved from http://web2.gov.mb.ca/bills/37–3/b005e.php, August 5, 2004.

Although for the sake of simplicity this chapter will discuss single chemical exposures, most of the exposures that take place in the workplace are more complex.

To understand chemical agents, we must be familiar with the associated hazards each possesses. The hazard associated with a material is defined as the likelihood that it will cause injury in a given environment or situation. The potential degree of seriousness of the hazard is determined by its **toxicity** (i.e., its ability to cause injury to human biological tissue) or its explosive properties, which are defined in terms of flammability and reactivity. The extent to which a potentially toxic substance is an actual health hazard will depend on other factors, such as the concentration of the chemical and the length of time the employee is exposed to it.

toxicity

ability to cause injury to human biological tissue

Occupational Health and Safety Notebook 5.1

Types of Contaminants

Listed below are seven types of contaminants:

1. *Dust:* Airborne respirable particulate that is solid particles generated by some mechanical means such as grinding, crushing, or sanding. The heavier particles tend to settle out of the air under the influence of gravity. The lighter or smaller the particle, the longer or greater the **settling rate**.

2. *Fume:* Airborne respirable particulate formed by the evaporation of some solid materials (e.g., steel where the parent metal will vaporize on the application of weld-level heat and the vaporized metal will condense on contact with cooler ambient air. This condensed particulate is a fume. (This term is often confused with vapour.) Particle size is usually less than one **micron** or micrometre in diameter. Other examples of fume include plastic extrusion and automobile exhaust, which can include fumes (from the metallic additives) and vapours (from the unburned fuel).

3. *Smoke:* Airborne respirable particulate originating from the products of combustion, usually less than 0.1 micron in size. An example would be tobacco smoke or smoke from a fire.

4. *Mist:* Airborne respirable particulate in the form of liquid droplets generated by condensation from the gas state or by the breaking up of a liquid into a dispersed state of finely divided droplets. Spray paint and hair spray are two sources of mist generation.

5. *Vapour:* The airborne respirable particulate in a gaseous form of any substances that are normally in the solid or liquid state at room temperature and pressure. Usually caused by evaporation. An example would be the airborne contaminant present above any solvent.

6. *Gas:* An airborne respirable particulate that is one of the three states of matter created where the temperature is above the boiling point. Carbon dioxide and oxygen are two examples.

7. *Liquid:* Chemicals are sometimes found in a liquid form that, although not airborne respirable particulate, can come in contact with the skin and the eyes, when there is a splash or spill during manual mixing or pouring operations, for instance.

Source: Olishifsky, J. B. (1995). Overview of industrial hygiene. In B. A. Plog (Ed.), *Fundamentals of industrial hygiene* (4th ed.). Chicago, Ill.: National Safety Council.

All chemicals have different melting, freezing, and boiling points. In most situations, more than one of these states is present at the same time. Consider an open container of boiling water: The water is in the liquid state, while the steam is the water entering the gas state. Similarly, ice will feel hard (solid), be wet (liquid), and actually have evaporated water surrounding it (vapour). The majority of chemical-related health problems result from contact with chemicals in the liquid and gas or vapour states. Most of the negative effects of exposure are derived from airborne respiratory contaminants known as **aerosols**.

A workplace health hazard is posed by exposure to one or more of these airborne respirable particulate forms. For instance, the white cloud that rises from a welding operation usually consists of fumes resulting from the condensation of the parent metal and the weld rod metal and coating, smoke resulting from the combustion of oil and other surface contamination, and vapours resulting from the evaporation of some of the oils and solvents on the metal surface.

settling rate

the time in seconds that it takes for an airborne particle to fall one foot; the larger the suspended particle, the lower the settling rate

micron

one-millionth of a metre

aerosols

airborne respirable contaminants, such as liquid droplets or solid particulate, dispersed in air, that are of a fine enough particle size (0.01 micrometres to 100 micrometres) to remain suspended for a time

Occupational Asthma: The Case of Snow Crab Workers

If we asked you to think about someone with a shellfish allergy, you would likely recall a person with a food allergy that was diagnosed in childhood, rather than a person with an adult-onset occupational illness. However, this less well known reaction to shellfish is a reality for many people who work in snow crab processing plants. Snow crab processing employees are at risk for developing a specific type of occupational asthma called crab asthma. This form of asthma may develop following exposure to airborne fumes and dust that materialize when processing (cooking, crushing, or cutting) crab. SafetyNet, a community research alliance on health and safety in coastal and marine work, led by Memorial University of Newfoundland researchers Dr. Barbara Neis and Dr. Stephen Bornstein, has launched a long-term research program on crab asthma.

The symptoms have two major categories: asthma symptoms and allergy symptoms. The asthma symptoms include coughing, wheezing, tightness of the chest, and shortness of breath. The allergy-type symptoms include itchy, watery eyes, running nose, and skin rash. These symptoms are strongest while at work but can persist when the person goes home at night or takes vacations.

Although not all processing workers develop crab asthma, it can be a devastating diagnosis for those who develop the condition. The symptoms, which can occur anywhere from a few weeks after starting work in a plant to a few years after exposure, can mean the individual has to leave the job. In many coastal communities, the crab processing plant may be the only employment option. As such, alternative employment is difficult to find and unemployment may follow. Due to this, some individuals with crab asthma may continue to work in crab processing plants while their condition worsens. As an occupational illness, crab asthma is a compensable claim.

Sources: SafetyNet: A Community Research Alliance on Health and Safety in Coastal and Marine Work. Retrieved from http://www.safetynet.mun.ca/, August 5, 2004; Newfoundland and Labrador Workplace Health, Safety and Compensation Commission. "Crab asthma." Retrieved from http://www.whscc.nf.ca/pubs/pdf/brochures/CrabAsthmaBrochure.pdf, August 5, 2004; and Howse, D., Neis, B., & Horth-Susin, L. (2003, October). All out of breath and nowhere to go: The social, economic and quality of life impacts of occupational asthma to snow crab. Paper presented at the SafetyNet Conference, St. John's, NL.

Toxicology: An Overview

routes of entry

respiration (inhalation), skin absorption, ingestion, and skin penetration

Toxicology is the scientific study of poisons. For the purposes of this chapter, toxicology will refer to the study of chemical-related occupational illnesses.

Chemicals may enter the body by one of four routes, referred to as **routes of entry.** In order of risk and normal contact, they are respiration (inhalation), skin absorption, ingestion, and skin penetration.

Respiration (Inhalation)

An average-sized human breathes approximately eight litres of air per minute while at rest; this quantity increases with any activity.[5] Most human exposure to chemicals comes from breathing airborne contaminants. The respiratory system, illustrated in Figure 5.1, does a very efficient job of distributing these contaminants throughout the body during the normal air exchange process.

FIGURE 5.1

The Respiratory System

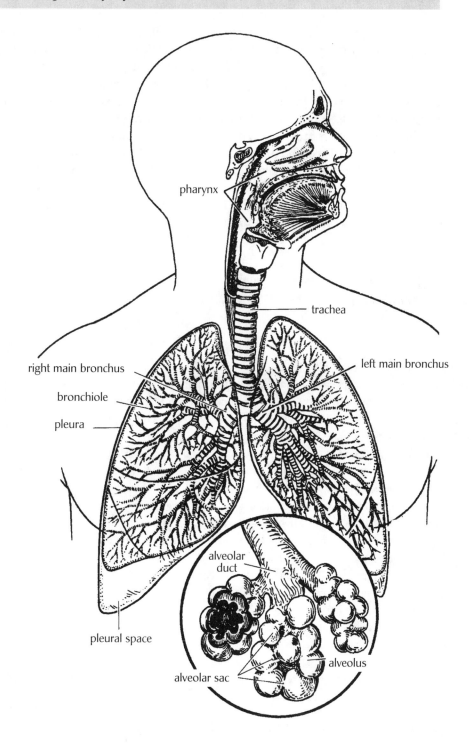

turbinates

spiral or spongy sections of the respiratory system that have a centrifugal effect to help remove aerosols

alveoli

tiny air sacs

There are five basic levels of protection or defence within the respiratory tract. The first level of defence is the nose. The nose, or upper respiratory tract, is lined with hairs, or cilia, that act as a coarse filter medium. The interior of the nasal passage is the second level of defence; here **turbinates** are found, which act as a humidification and heat exchange source. The third level of defence is further back in the throat where the hairs or cilia are coated with a thick fluid called mucus. This mucus/cilia system will entrap the finer particulate. The trapped contaminant is removed by blowing the nose and/or clearing the throat. Everyone has experienced these conditions after cleaning the garage, dusting a room, or sanding wood for refinishing. The fourth level of defence is the aerodynamic characteristics of the lung passages such as the bronchi and the bronchiole. Here, the flow of air and its turbulence from breathing will allow much of the larger particulate that bypassed the earlier defences to be expelled with normal exhalation. The fifth level of defence consists of myriad tiny air sacs, called **alveoli**, that are located at the ends of the lung's

Occupational Health and Safety Today 5.3

Good Scents?

Environmental illness (EI) involves seemingly healthy individuals experiencing long-lasting symptoms of physical distress in their work settings. EI contaminants are estimated to exist in 20% to 30% of all work settings in North America. This illness has generally been associated with newly constructed and renovated buildings designed for energy efficiency and, until recently, was thought to be related solely to the inadequacy of mechanical ventilation systems. Recent findings suggest that other factors contribute to poor indoor air quality (e.g., car exhaust fumes from indoor garages, and heat and chemicals released by laser printers, computers, and photocopiers).

The effects of EI are variable and nonspecific, affecting building occupants both physically and psychologically. Physical symptoms include mucous-membrane irritation affecting the eyes, nose, and throat; skin ailments; and unpleasant odour and taste perceptions. Other commonly reported symptoms include fatigue, headaches, nausea, confusion, and dizziness, as well as asthma-like symptoms. Typically, symptoms increase with exposure to the affected environment, but usually dissipate once the occupant leaves the building (i.e., evenings, weekends, and holidays). In some cases symptoms do not abate. They

may recur on exposure to chemicals found in home products and in nonwork environments. Moreover, an increasing number of individuals have developed sensitivities to fragrances such as perfumes, scented deodorants, and hair spray.

In recognition of this growing phenomenon, an increasing number of organizations are adopting scent-free policies. Typically, workplaces post notices requesting both employees and visitors to refrain from using scented products while on the premises. Although aimed at a health and safety issue, such policies can be quite controversial, with some individuals maintaining their right to wear fragrances of their choice. Adopting a scent-free workplace policy should be preceded and accompanied by an educational campaign pointing out the reality of EI chemical/fragrance sensitivities and the types of physical symptoms some individuals experience when exposed to such fragrances.

Source: Canadian Centre for Occupational Health and Safety, "Can scents cause health problems?" Retrieved from http://www.ccohs.ca/oshanswers/hsprograms/scent_free.html, October 9, 2004.

Illnesses Linked to Asbestos Exposure

Asbestos exposure is killing Canadian workers. Diseases stemming from asbestos exposure dominate occupational illness claims processed by the Workers' Compensation Boards across the country. For example, from 1992 to 2001 in B.C., 18.9% of the fatality claims accepted by the WCB were related to asbestos. All other occupational diseases combined accounted for only 12.9% of the claims.

What is asbestos? The term actually describes a class of strong and flexible mineral fibres. It was the strength and flexibility of asbestos that made it a popular component for building and construction materials. In fact, before the 1970s asbestos was widely used in building materials such as cement and insulation. However, as the long-term health consequences of asbestos exposure have become known, its use has become increasingly controlled and limited. Nonetheless, products containing asbestos do remain on the market. Today, asbestos products are bonded with other materials, thus reducing the health threat. However, damage to these products, such as automotive brakes or some floor tiles, may release dangerous particles into the air.

Individuals who work in certain industries are at particular risk of asbestos-related illness. For example, petrochemical workers in Sarnia, Ontario, are dealing with an unprecedented outbreak of asbestos-related disease.[6] However, since asbestos was used historically in construction, individuals who work in older buildings may also be at risk. For example, this type of asbestos exposure was implicated in the deaths of two professors at the University of Manitoba.

The first signs of asbestos-related illness tend to arise many years after exposure. Some of the conditions that have been linked to asbestos include the following:

- *Asbestosis.* A scarring of the lung tissues that arises 10 to 15 years following exposure to airborne asbestos. This condition is characterized by respiratory difficulty. The damage is irreversible. This condition can result in respiratory failure and ultimately death.
- *Mesothelioma.* A form of cancer that attacks the linings of the chest cavity, lungs, and abdomen. It spreads rapidly and survival following diagnosis is very rare. The only known cause of mesothelioma is asbestos exposure.
- *Lung cancer.* Asbestos is an acknowledged cause of lung cancer. Even though it takes years to develop, changes to the lungs start soon after exposure to asbestos.

Sources: Glenn, W. M. (2002). What's killing Canadian workers? *OH&S Canada*, pp. 18, 20; Workers Health and Safety Centre, "Resource lines: Asbestos (2001, Spring)." Retrieved from http://www.whsc.on.ca/Publications/hazardbulletins/spring2000/asbestos.htm, August 5, 2004; Mittelstaedt, M. (2004, July 10). The voice of sick workers. *The Globe and Mail.* Retrieved from http://www.theglobeandmail.com/servlet/ArticleNews/TPPrint/LAC/20040710/KINART10/TPObituaries/, August 6, 2004; and Loewen, C. M. (2003, February 26). Asbestos still a serious concern on campus. *The Manitoban.* Retrieved from http://www.umanitoba.ca/manitoban/20030226/news_index.shtml, August 6, 2004.

air passage, called the alveolar ducts. These sacs (which are the source of oxygen transfer from the lungs to the bloodstream) contain small cells called macrophages (Greek for "big eater") that dispose of any impurities via the lymph system.

Skin Absorption

In many workplaces and at home, chemical contact with the skin is a common occurrence. Many fat-soluble chemicals can be readily absorbed and most gases can pass through the skin very quickly. Chlorinated solvents such as carbon tetrachloride can pass through the skin into the blood and eventually reach the liver, where tissue damage may occur. Dimethyl sulphoxide can be absorbed through the skin in less than a minute following contact, and most people can detect a garlic-like taste in the back of the throat from this exposure.

The ability of a chemical to easily pass through the skin is often closely associated with its level of toxicity. For example, the toxicity of DDT is about the same for insects and humans when it is injected. However, it is much less toxic to a person when applied to the skin, because it is poorly absorbed through the skin. Other pesticides are much more rapidly absorbed through human skin. Many agricultural workers have died following skin absorption of pesticides, particularly the organophosphate insecticides.

Chemicals that are not rapidly absorbed through the skin may produce a localized irritation (dermatitis) at the point of contact through a process called defatting, which causes the skin to become white and dry (e.g., when cleaning your hands with paint remover) and thus more permeable to water vapour, leading to tissue water loss and cracking. Burns or blisters can result from contact with acids or alkalis (chemical action). Skin disorders can result from contact with certain plants (biological action). Skin damage can result from contact with radiation or heat (physical action).

Occupational Health and Safety Notebook 5.3

Toxicity Terminology

Dose. The degree of exposure and possible reaction with time. The dose is usually the basis for the values that are developed for threshold limit values (TLV), which are used as a control measure in the workplace. For example, the TLV for carbon dioxide is 5,000 parts per million (ppm), based on an 8-hour exposure time.

Acute toxicity. An effect that manifests itself immediately following exposure or very shortly thereafter. Burning your hand on a hot surface, for example, results in immediate pain and discoloration, and, later, blisters.

Chronic toxicity. An effect that manifests itself some time after the exposure (possibly months or even years). Some examples are cirrhosis of the liver from prolonged alcohol exposure; sensitization from isocyanates; occupational cancer, such as leukemia, from benzene exposure; or mesothelioma from asbestos exposure.

Local toxicity. The effect of an exposure at the point of contact. Cleaning your hands with paint thinner will cause dry, grey skin at the point of contact; this will be an immediate reaction.

Systemic toxicity. An effect that occurs at some location remote from the point of contact. For example, inhaling a chlorinated solvent such as trichloroethylene can cause damage to the liver, or inhaling carbon monoxide, which interrupts oxygen transfer to the blood, can cause asphyxiation and death.

Sources: University of Alberta, WHMIS Training, Environmental Health and Safety, "Chemical safety: Toxic substances." Retrieved from http://www.ehs.ualberta.ca/WHMIS/Chemicals/toxic.asp, October 9, 2004; and ACGIH. (1994). *Threshold values for chemical substances and physical agents in the workplace.* Cincinnati, Ohio: American Conference of Governmental Industrial Hygienists.

Ingestion

For many solvents, entry through the mouth and digestive system is not as important as entry through the skin or the lungs. Poor personal hygiene can contribute to poisoning, as can eating, drinking, or smoking in an area where solvents are used. Ingestion of most solvents will cause damage to the lining of the digestive system. The ingested solvent may also be absorbed into the bloodstream and carried to **target organs**, where it will produce toxic effects. Worse still, the ingested solvent may be aspirated into the lungs where it can destroy the **surfactant layer**, cause a chemical pneumonitis, and collapse the alveoli.[7]

Penetration

Penetration occurs when the skin is cut or punctured by any sharp object. The type of contamination on the source, such as a knife or needle, will determine the possible trauma or illness. Cuts can occur when contact is made with sharp metal, glass materials, or other pointed instruments. Workers such as

target organs

tissues or organs that are most affected by exposure to a particular substance

surfactant layer

layer of liquids in the digestive tract and elsewhere (e.g., the cardiovascular system) that modify or reduce the surface tension within the conductors—intestine, blood vessels—to allow material—blood, food, stools, and so on—to move easily

---

Occupational Health and Safety Notebook 5.4

Classification of Toxic Substances

Toxic materials are many and varied and have a variety of health effects on humans. In this section, organic and inorganic solvents are enumerated, because they are common at home and at work, and they can have widespread health effects based on their properties. The overall effects of toxic materials can be grouped under the following 12 classifications.

1. *Irritants.* Irritants, sometimes referred to as "primary irritants," produce tissue or other damage at the point of contact. They are divided by route of entry into two groups:
   a. *Inhaled irritants.* Inhaled irritants refer to **airborne respirable contaminants** or aerosols (including vapours, gases, and solid particulate) that are inhaled into the lungs causing damage wherever they settle. Ammonia is dissolved into body fluids and absorbed by the mucous membranes of the upper airways, and can result in symptoms such as headache, nausea, salivation, and burning of the throat. Bronchitis may follow a very severe exposure, if the patient survives.
   b. *Contact irritant.* A contact irritant is any material that causes some sort of irritation, such as a rash or itch,

at the point of contact. An example would be using Varsol to clean paint from your hands or coming into contact with poison ivy. In most cases, the skin is the organ most affected.

2. *Asphyxiants.* Any material that interferes with the oxygen supply to the blood and body tissues is referred to as an asphyxiant. Normal air contains approximately 21% oxygen and 79% nitrogen. The average person uses about 3% of the oxygen in air when breathing. If the oxygen content of the air falls below 15%, the body will be asphyxiated. There are two major types of asphyxiants:

   a. *Simple asphyxiants.* Any airborne respirable chemical that reduces the quantity of oxygen in the inhaled air by displacement is referred to as a simple asphyxiant. Examples are methane, propane, and nitrogen.

   b. *Chemical asphyxiants.* If an airborne and inhaled chemical interferes with the transport of oxygen by the blood hemoglobin or with the ability of the body cells to use oxygen, it is called a chemical asphyxiant. Examples of such chemicals are carbon monoxide, which interferes with the ability of the hemoglobin to transport oxygen and can result in tissue **hypoxia**

(continued)

Classification of Toxic Substances (continued)

and death, and hydrogen sulphide (rotten gas), which can interfere with the ability of the body cells to use oxygen and can result in immediate coma with acute exposure and possible death.

3. *Anesthetics and narcotics*. Any chemical that affects the central nervous system (CNS) can be considered to belong to this class. Most of these chemicals can, on exposure, cause headaches, interfere with the ability to concentrate, and act as a depressant. Examples include ethyl alcohol, acetylene, acetone, and toluene. In fact, all organic solvents can produce narcotic effects. Many of us have experienced some of these symptoms after consuming alcohol.

4. *Systemic poisons*. Systemic poisons can cause damage to one or more internal organs, as well as cell and **neuron** damage. Chlorinated materials such as DDT, endrin, chloroform, or trichloroethylene can cause damage to the liver and kidneys, usually as a result of chronic exposure. Benzene can cause damage to the blood-forming cells (the homeopathic system). Carbon disulphide is believed to damage the neurons. Other common systemic poisons include heavy metals such as lead, cadmium, and mercury, and chemicals such as arsenic and fluoride.

5. *Liver toxicants*. This grouping includes any chemical that will cause direct damage to the liver. The toxic action may be chemical (caused by alcohol) or **metabolic** (caused by benzene). In most instances, slight damage can be repaired. Cirrhosis is the most common disease.

6. *Kidney toxicants*. Kidney toxicants, like liver toxicants, include chemicals that cause damage to the kidneys, usually through the process of **metabolic transformation** whereby harmless chemicals are rendered harmful or vice versa. Heavy metals such as lead, cadmium, and mercury, in addition to some solvents, can have this effect.

7. *Neurotoxins*. As the name indicates, these chemicals can cause damage to the nerves in the body. Hexane, a component of gasoline, can produce a condition called peripheral neuropathy—a disease affecting the nerves of the extremities—that can result in numbness and loss of feeling. This condition is dose-related.

8. *Sensitizers*. Sensitizers, whether chemical or biological, cause the body's immune system to respond abnormally and produce antibodies against chemicals such as isocyanates and poison ivy. The result is an allergy to the specific chemical in which even casual exposure to the material will cause an allergic reaction. Workers thus affected may have to change jobs, if not employers. Although sensitization is usually a chronic process, a very large acute exposure can sometimes bring it on. Farmer's lung, humidifier fever, nickel itch, and nickel fume fever are some common examples of sensitization.

9. *Lung toxicants*. Toxic chemicals that can affect the lungs include irritant gases such as hydrogen chloride and ammonia, vapours such as isocyanates, and respirable solids such as asbestos, platinum, and silica. These materials can cause a variety of diseases, from simple **pneumoconiosis** (an accumulation of dust in the lungs and the tissue reaction to the presence of such dust) to cancer.

10. *Mutagens*. Any chemicals that can lead to changes or mutations in DNA. The actions of chemicals like lead, nickel, zinc, and manganese usually cause the death of cells but may in some cases allow the distorted cell to multiply and create a potentially malignant tumour.

11. *Teratogens*. Chemicals such as lead, DDT, and PCB can cause damage to germ cells or create defects in a developing fetus. The most infamous chemical—thalidomide—is well known to cause gross abnormalities or birth defects in the fetus.

12. *Carcinogens*. Carcinogens are agents that cause or promote the formation of cancers. Well-known carcinogens include vinyl chloride, which can cause a liver cancer called angiosarcoma; benzene, which can result in leukemia; and asbestos, which can lead to mesothelioma. Following exposure to the carcinogenic chemical, there can be a latency period of 5 to 15 or more years.

Sources: Key, M. M. et al. (Eds.). (1977). *Occupational diseases: A guide to their recognition* (rev. ed.). Cincinnati, Ohio: U.S. Department of Health, Education, and Welfare; and WorkSafe Saskatchewan, *Ontario's Basic Certification Training Program Participant's Manual* (Chemical hazards chapter). Retrieved from http://www.worksafesask.ca/files/ont_wsib/certmanual/ch_08.html?noframe, October 9, 2004.

doctors, nurses, and veterinarians can easily be punctured by a hypodermic needle. The disorders range in seriousness from low-grade infections to HIV (human immunodeficiency virus).

Characteristics and Properties of Solvents

Solvents were created, for the most part, by the science of organic chemistry, and they are the most prevalent of products that we use both at work and at home. There are eight general characteristics or properties that make solvents effective but at the same time hazardous and toxic.

1. *Low surface tension*. This property allows a solvent to spread evenly and quickly and to provide excellent wetting of the contact surface. The higher the wetting factor, the better the wetting effect. But the wetting factor allows a spilled solvent to flow into cracks and joints and remain there, creating vapours that may be toxic. It also allows for more effective skin absorption.

2. *High vapour pressure*. The fact that vapour pressure increases with temperature increases the volume or concentration of a generated vapour or gas. This solvent property allows efficient cleaning in processes such as degreasing systems because of the high vapour generation at the high operating temperatures. It can, however, create an inhalation hazard, the risk of which increases with temperature. This is not considered a problem as long as the container is kept closed. In a fire situation, the pressure increase can cause an explosion.

3. *Low boiling point*. The lower the **boiling point**, the greater the rate of evaporation or generation of vapours from a liquid. This property is useful when cleaning or painting because the solvents can evaporate quickly at room temperature allowing the article to dry or tack off efficiently. The lower the boiling point, the greater the health risk since vapour can be generated at lower temperatures. Chemicals with boiling points close to room temperature or lower, such as ammonia (BP = −2 °C) or hydrogen cyanide (BP = 25 °C), can be a special problem since they can evaporate readily and are very toxic.

4. *Low heat of vaporization*. This characteristic defines the amount of heat or energy that is required to change a liquid into a gas or vapour. The less heat required, the less costly the process is in an industrial environment. Similarly, the lower the amount of heat necessary, the greater the risk of exposure if the material is not properly controlled.

5. *High volatility*. The main test of a solvent's effectiveness is the speed at which it will evaporate. The greater the volatility, the faster the evaporation, the greater the health and fire risk.

6. *Ability to dissolve fats*. The more effectively a solvent dissolves fats or oils, the more useful it can be. However, when solvents are in contact with the skin, the skin's surface oils are dissolved. The unprotected skin then becomes susceptible to infection and other trauma. Skin contact with solvents is one of the major causes of **dermatitis**.

airborne respirable contaminants
refers to very fine airborne contaminants that can reach the alveoli

hypoxia
the partial reduction in oxygen concentration supplied to the cells or tissues

neuron
the structural and functional unit of the nervous system, consisting of the nerve cell body and all its processes

metabolic
the stable reduction/ oxidation that turns living tissue into waste products— destructive metabolism— of a simpler chemical composition

metabolic transformation
the process whereby harmful chemicals that are introduced into the body are rendered harmless for easy disposal

pneumoconiosis
an accumulation of dust in the lungs and the tissue reaction to the presence of such dust

boiling point
temperature at which the vapour pressure of a liquid equals atmospheric pressure

dermatitis
the inflammation of the skin from any cause

7. *Flammability*. It is one of the main hazards associated with solvent use since all organic solvents are flammable. Care must be taken to ensure that there are no sources of ignition present during use. Chemical specifications usually list four characteristics that relate to flammability.

   (a) *Flash point*. Defined as the lowest temperature at which a liquid gives off enough vapour to form an ignitable mixture with air and produce a flame with a source of ignition. If the flash point is close to room temperature, the danger of ignition can be very great.

   (b) *Lower explosion limit* (LEL) also known as lower flammability limit (LFL). Defined as the smallest fuel-air mixture that is ignitable, expressed as a percent. Carbon monoxide has an LEL of 12.5% by volume, which is equivalent to 125,000 parts per million (ppm). The upper exposure value for health exposure is 50 ppm, as shown in various standards. If the exposure to carbon monoxide in the workplace is maintained well below the health limit, there is no risk of ignition to that source.

   (c) *Upper explosion limit* (UEL) also known as the upper flammability limit (UFL). Defined as the highest fuel-air mixture that is ignitable, expressed as a percent. Carbon monoxide has a UEL of 74% by volume or 740,000 ppm. The LEL and UEL spread indicates that carbon monoxide could be ignited through a wide range of fuel-air mixtures, which could be an advantage if the gas was to be used for some heat application.

   (d) *Auto-ignition temperature*. Defined as the lowest temperature at which a flammable fuel-air mixture will ignite from its own heat source. An example is spontaneous combustion in moist hay in a barn or in paint-soaked rags stuffed in a pail.

8. *Vaporization*. Most solvents will form very large volumes of vapour from a small amount of liquid. For instance, turpentine can form 112 litres of vapour for each litre of liquid at standard temperature and pressure conditions.

Inorganic Solvents

Inorganic solvents fall into two classes: acids and bases. These are the simplest of chemical groups and are the oldest known forms. The difference between an acid and a base is expressed in terms of pH, a unit that notes the degree of acidity or alkalinity of a solution, having a scale of 1 to 14. A pH value of 7 is considered as neutral (i.e., neither an acid nor a base). A pH of 1 indicates extreme acidity, while a pH of 14 indicates extreme alkalinity.

1. *Acids*. Materials such as hydrochloric acid (HCl), sulphuric acid (H_2SO_4), and chromic acid (H_2CrO_4) are some of the most common. All are very corrosive and are used for refining and processing metals. The plating process makes extensive use of these acids.

The health effects are predominantly burns resulting from inhalation and skin contact. The eyes are the most susceptible body part, and are exposed usually as a result of splashing. Chromic acid is a known carcinogen and a sensitizer. The most common sign of chromic acid exposure is the presence of chrome holes in the surface of the skin. These are ugly, black holes left when the skin has been corrosively attacked. Their size depends on the amount of exposure and personal hygiene practices.

2. *Bases*. Sometimes referred to as alkalines, these chemicals include potassium hydroxide (KOH), sodium hydroxide (NaOH), and sodium chloride (NaCl) or table salt. Sodium chloride in its refined state is a requirement of a normal diet. In its less refined form, it is used to keep roads free of ice. The other two alkalines are used to etch or dissolve a variety of materials. All are toxic in certain concentrations.

Organic Solvents

Organic solvents, which are petrochemically based, are manufactured by combining the carbon atom with a great many other elements. These solvents can be identified by their molecular structure and can be grouped under 10 classifications, as shown in Table 5.1.

 5.5

Biological Agents

Biological agents or biohazards are natural organisms or products of organisms that present a risk to humans. Two of the better-known diseases resulting from biological agents are Legionnaires' disease (*Legionella pneumophilia*) and AIDS (acquired immunodeficiency syndrome). Although exposure to biohazards is not as common as exposure to chemical agents, the results can be just as deadly. The acute and chronic exposure effects described previously for chemical agents apply to biohazards as well, although the sources of exposure are different and the physiological reactions vary. The majority of exposures occur through inhalation.

Most biohazards encountered in the workplace fall into BSL 1. Viral agents such as hepatitis B would be included in BSL 2. People most at risk of exposure to biohazards are employed in unique or specialized fields, such as medicine, research, and farming. In the case of salmonella food poisoning, however, members of the general public could be at risk through food contamination (see Table 5.2).

biological agents

natural organisms or products of organisms that present a risk to humans

Control of Exposures

 5.1

The safe use and handling of chemical and biological agents can be ensured only through the active employment of a variety of control measures. Figure 5.2 outlines the various control measures used to ensure the safe handling of solvents. Controls for low-level biohazards can follow similar measures. These controls are the subject of the sections that follow.

TABLE 5.1

Organic Solvents

Number	Classification	Example	Toxic Effects	Uses
1	Aliphatic hydrocarbons	Paraffin, acetylene, methane	Simple asphyxiants, CNS, irritants	Fuels, refrigerants, dry cleaning, propellants
2	Aromatic hydrocarbons	Benzene, toluene, xylene	CNS, dermatitis, leukemia (benzene)	Plastics, resins, dyes, pharmaceuticals
3	Halogenated hydrocarbons	Chlorine, iodine, fluorine, carbon tetrachloride	CNS, dermatitis, cancer (carbon tetrachloride)	Fire extinguishers, fumigants, aerosol propellants
4	Nitro-hydrocarbons	Nitroglycerin, pitric acid	Irritants, skin sensitizers	Explosives
5	Esters	Methyl acetate, banana oil	Irritants	Plastics, resins, artificial flavours, perfumes
6	Ethers	Ethylene oxide	Irritants, anesthetics, nausea, respiratory difficulties	Antifreeze, chemical synthesizers, cancer treatment (ethyl ether–anesthetic)
7	Ketones	Acetone, methyl ethyl ketone (MEK)	Narcotic, irritants, vertigo, nausea	Acetate rayon, artificial silk, lubricants
8	Alcohols	Ethyl alcohol (grain alcohol), methyl alcohol (wood alcohol)	Narcotic, dermatitis, headache, nausea, tremors, blindness	Ethyl–liquors; methyl–solvent for inks, embalming fluids
9	Glycols	Ethylene glycol, cellosolve	Intoxication; blood, brain and kidney disorders	Antifreeze, disinfectants, drugs
10	Aldehydes	Formaldehyde	Sensitizers, CNS, allergic response	Dyes, perfumes, flavourings, vinegar

Classification of Biological Agents

All biological agents are classified in four groups on the basis of their degree of risk to humans. The higher the class number, the greater the risk.

- *Biosafety Level 1 (BSL 1)*. Agents of no or minimal hazard that can be handled safely using techniques for **nonpathogenic** materials and are harmless to healthy humans. An example is E. coli K12. Effective control is maintained through cleanliness and ventilation in which air is conducted through a high-efficiency particulate air (HEPA) filter in a **biological safety cabinet** (a well-ventilated room or space in which a worker is isolated from contact with biological agents). The degree of sophistication of the biological safety cabinet depends on the biosafety level.
- *Biosafety Level 2 (BSL 2)*. Agents that may produce diseases of varying degrees of seriousness through accidental skin penetration for which preventative or therapeutic interventions are often available. Examples are bacteria such as salmonella, legionella, and streptococcus; fungi; parasites; and viruses such as hepatitis A, B, C, and D. Control involves the use of a well-ventilated, sealed, filtered space with an air wall to keep workers from contacting the biohazard.
- *Biosafety Level 3 (BSL 3)*. Agents involving special hazards that require special conditions for containment. Agents are indigenous or exotic with potential for infection following aerosol transmission. Agents are associated with serious or lethal disease for which preventative or therapeutic interventions may be available. These agents can pose a high risk to the individual but not the community. Examples include rabies, yellow fever, and HIV types 1 and 2. Containment involves specialized facility design and equipment, with cabinets with HEPA filters externally exhausted back to the room with the plena under negative pressure.
- *Biosafety Level 4 (BSL 4)*. Organisms that are extremely dangerous or exotic, that pose a life-threatening disease, and for which preventative or therapeutic interventions are usually not available. Examples include Lassa fever virus, Ebola virus, and tickborne encephalitis virus. Containment locations are rare and usually involve a totally enclosed room that is gas-tight and well ventilated. OH&S practitioners should not be involved at this level.

Sources: DiNardi, S. R. (ed.). (1997). *The occupational environment–its evaluation and control.* Fairfax, VA: AIHA Press; Canadian Council on Animal Care, "Biosafety guidelines and levels of containment." Retrieved from http://www.ccac.ca/english/educat/Module12E/module12-15.html, October 9, 2004; and Office of the Auditor General of Canada, "Biosafety and laboratory containment levels." Retrieved from http://www.oag-bvg.gc.ca/domino/reports.nsf/html/9807xe01.html, October 9, 2004.

Engineering Controls

One of the best ways to reduce the risks associated with handling solvents is to find alternatives. A thorough investigation should be conducted to ensure that the proposed substitute meets the intended purpose, does not contain dangerous properties, and is compatible with existing materials in use. However, if solvents are being used, areas should be properly enclosed to prevent or minimize the escape of vapours, and an effective exhaust system should also be in place. Because some of the chemicals used may be a source of ignition, it is equally important to ensure that appropriate fire-extinguishing equipment is on hand and that combustibles are isolated from sources of ignition. Materials should not be stored adjacent to highly reactive chemicals.

nonpathogenic
an agent that is not capable of producing a disease

biological safety cabinet
a well-ventilated room or space in which a worker is isolated from contact with biological agents

TABLE 5.2

Biological Agents

Agent Group	Agent	Source	Occupation
Bacterial	Anthrax (bacillus anthracis)	Direct contact with infected animals, hides, and wool	Veterinarians, farmers, butchers, wool workers
	Brucellosis (brucella species)	Exposure by ingestion or cuts from excretions or secretions of infected animals	Livestock handlers, meat inspectors, farmers, microbiology lab workers
	Salmonellosis (salmonella species)	Oral exposure, usually from unsanitary food conditions (food poisoning)	Travellers, patient-care workers, amateur chefs
	Staphylococcal food poisoning (staphylococcus species)	Ingestion of improperly stored or leftover food or food infected by workers	Food workers, health care workers, home storage
	Lyme disease (borrelia burgdorferi)	Tick bites	Outdoor workers
Chlamydiae	Psittacosis or ornithosis (chlamydia psittaci)	Inhalation or exposure to infected bird droppings	Zoo workers, taxidermists, pet owners
Rickettsia	Q fever (coxiella burneth)	Contact with sheep, cattle, goats, birth by-products, and contaminated dusts	Farmers, veterinarians, slaughterhouse workers, laboratory workers
	Rocky Mountain spotted fever (rickettsia rickettsii)	Tick bites	Outdoor workers— lumberjacks, ranchers
Viruses	Cat scratch disease	Breaks in skin, usually from animal scratch	Pet owners and breeders
	Serum hepatitis (hepatitis B virus–HBV)	Direct contact with infected material by puncture, abraded skin, or onto mucous membrane surfaces	Hemodialysis workers, surgeons, dentists, health care workers
	Infectious hepatitis (hepatitis A virus–HAV)	Fecal-oral transmission (from contaminated water)	Travellers, primate handlers, dentists
Fungal	Dermatophytosis (trichophyton species)	Contact with people infected by soil, animals, or humans	Gardeners, military personnel (athlete's foot), farm workers (cattle ringworm), health care workers
	Histaplosmosis (histoplasma capsulatum)	Inhalation or ingestion of dust from areas that have been bat or bird habitats	Construction workers, bird or chicken farm workers

Farmer's lung (*aspergillus* species)	Inhalation or ingestion of dusts containing spores from mouldy hay or grain or compost piles	Mushroom workers, brewery workers, bird hobbyists
Humidifier lung (*penicillium* species)	Inhalation of airborne spores from sources of mould such as cheese, wood, HVAC system water	Cheese workers, HVAC (heating, ventilating, and air-conditioning) workers, tree cutters

Work Practices and Procedures

All employees must be properly trained in the identification and handling of dangerous substances. Senior management must ensure that policies and procedures are accompanied by an appropriate discipline system for dealing with those employees who willfully choose to neglect these practices. Standards must be communicated, in writing, to all employees. (This is also a requirement of WHMIS.)

Good housekeeping is essential when handling, storing, or using **agents**. If containers are leaking, they must be transferred immediately to sound containers. Spills must be cleaned up properly, and employees who may be exposed to the hazard must wear protective equipment. Solvent-soaked rags

agents

any substances—chemical, biological, or physical—to which a human may be exposed at work or at home

Occupational Health and Safety Today 5.4

Needlestick Injuries: A Spreading Health and Safety Concern

Needlestick injuries have been a health and safety concern for many years. A needlestick injury occurs when a sharp object, such as a needle, that is potentially carrying blood-borne pathogens punctures the skin of a care provider. For example, a nurse changing an intravenous (IV) may inadvertently stick the used needle in her own hand. It is estimated that more than 800,000 needlestick injuries occur each year in North American health care systems—approximately 30% of such injuries carry the potential of transmitting diseases such as hepatitis or HIV.

Health care workers have developed procedures for handling and disposing of "sharps" that minimize the chance of a needlestick injury. However, the potential for needlestick injuries has now spread to a new occupation—workers at recycling centres.

Many communities have adopted recycling programs that involve (at least in part) individuals working

at a recycling centre sorting through various types of recyclable material (e.g., glass, plastic, etc.). Items such as syringes are frequently discarded in the recycling bins, and recycling plant workers run the risk of a needlestick injury as they sort through the material to identify what can be recycled.

The solution to the problem lies in both prevention and protection. First, communities with recycling programs must educate citizens in the proper procedures for disposing of needles and similar items. Second, employees should be provided with protective gear (e.g., heavy leather gloves over latex) to offset the exposure to needles.

Source: Canadian Centre for Occupational Health and Safety, "What are needlestick injuries?" Retrieved from http://www.ccohs.ca/ohsanswers/diseases/needlestick_injuries.html, October 9, 2004.

FIGURE 5.2

Engineering, Work Practices, and Medical Control Measures

should be disposed of in airtight, all-metal containers and removed daily. Each municipality has its own guidelines for the disposal of wastes, and employees must be familiar with the guidelines that apply to them.

Preventive maintenance must be conducted regularly to ensure that no potential dangers exist. For example, air filters on exhaust or ventilation equipment may become damaged or plugged and pose a potential danger in an enclosed area in which solvents or biohazards are used. Employees should understand the procedures for maintaining equipment and documenting all repairs.

Thorough record keeping is essential. Although provinces and territories vary in terms of record-keeping requirements, all demand that records be kept of employee exposure, workplace air monitoring, and equipment breakdowns and repairs.

Administrative Controls

Perhaps the single most important administrative function is the education and training of all employees in safe work practices. Employees should receive training in safe operating and emergency procedures, in the use and care of personal protective equipment, and in the handling and control of agents. Training must be conducted on an ongoing basis, given the fact that new solvents and other agents are constantly entering the workplace. Finally, workers must be familiar with all aspects of Workplace Hazardous Materials Information System (WHMIS) legislation, which was discussed at length in Chapter 2.

Personal Protective Equipment

Personal protective equipment (PPE) is specifically designed to protect workers from particular hazards. PPE should be used only when there is no feasible or practical way to enclose a process, provide local exhaust, or apply other control measures. *PPE must not be used as an alternative to putting in the proper controls.*

Because inhalation is the most common and hazardous route of entry, the most commonly used protection device is a respirator. Respiratory protection is more specialized for biohazards than it is for chemical agents, since a biological airborne contaminant can be much smaller than a chemical one. PPE for hands, face, and other body parts must be provided where necessary. No single protective device, such as a facemask, will adequately address all conditions for all workers. Each device must be matched to the chemical or biological exposure, and it is imperative that the device be properly fitted to the individual. (One size does not fit all!)

Personal Hygiene Practices

The ingestion of chemicals or biological particulate is often due to poor hygiene practices. Individuals who handle agents without wearing proper protective gear, such as gloves, are at risk of food contamination. In other such instances, chemicals that are not adequately removed at the workplace can be transferred to the worker's home. To ensure that this and similar types of incidents do not occur, individuals who handle toxic substances must adhere to the following:

- Remove outer protective clothing and clean hands, arms, face, and nails before entering rest areas or lunchrooms.
- Avoid touching lips, nose, and eyes with contaminated hands.
- Wash hands before eating, drinking, or smoking, and eat, drink, and smoke only in designated areas.
- Remove work clothes and wash or shower before leaving work.

Medical Surveillance

Medical surveillance programs, an administrative control, are implemented to ensure that employees who are exposed to agents are not subjected to situations in which their health will be jeopardized. To be effective, pre-employment and preplacement medical examinations should be conducted to establish a baseline of the employee's health or exposure to agents in previous workplaces. Follow-up medical examinations should be conducted periodically. Examinations may include chest X-ray, pulmonary function tests, and blood workups. Finally, record keeping is an important aspect of the medical surveillance program. The types of exposures employees face and their health records before and after exposure should be included in this process.

Summary

Chemical agents and, to a lesser extent, biological agents, are the major causes of occupational diseases. Despite their associated risks, these agents are easily controlled if guidelines such as those provided in the WHMIS and OH&S legislation are rigorously followed. This chapter has focused on the types, characteristics, measurement, and control of chemical and biological agents. All workers who are exposed to these agents should be knowledgeable about their potential health effects as well as trained in their proper use and handling.

Key Terms

aerosols, p. 109

agents, p. 123

airborne respirable contaminants p. 117

alveoli, p. 112

ambient, p. 107

biohazard, p. 107

biological agents, p. 119

biological safety cabinet, p. 121

boiling point, p. 117

chemical agents, p. 107

dermatitis, p. 117

hypoxia, p. 117

metabolic transformation, p. 117

metabolic, p. 117

micron, p. 109

neuron, p. 117

nonpathogenic, p. 121

pneumoconiosis, p. 117

routes of entry, p. 110

settling rate, p. 109

surfactant layer, p. 115

target organs, p. 115

toxicity, p. 108

turbinates, p. 112

Weblinks

Toxicology Resources,
http://home.nas.net/~dbc/cic_hamilton/toxic.html (p. 110)

Saskatchewan Agriculture, Food, and Rural Revitalization, "Pesticide Safety Handbook,"
http://www.agr.gov.sk.ca/DOCS/crops/integrated_pest_management/ general/pesticidesafety.asp (p. 114)

Later's Pest Solutions for Canada, "Poison Control Centres of Canada,"
http://www.laters.com/poiscntr.htm (p. 115)

WorkSafe BC, "Resources—Fungi and Microorganisms,"
http://indoorair.healthandsafetycentre.org/s/FungiandMicroorganisms.asp
(p. 119)

Office of Health and Safety, "The 1, 2, 3's of Biosafety Levels"
http://www.cdc.gov/od/ohs/symp5/jyrtext.htm (p. 121)

RPC Icons

RPC 5.1 Analyses risk to the health and safety of employees and determines appropriate preventative measures, including training, provision of required safety equipment, and administrative practices.

- relevant legislation
- nature of the business and physical work environment
- hazard recognition
- workplace inspection techniques
- safety programs, equipment, and emergency procedures
- ergonomics
- functions of the JHSC
- training and development/presentation techniques
- industry best practices
- relevant technical terminology
- the collective agreement
- services and equipment available in the community
- Worker Protection (including health and safety and Workers' Compensation)
- Training and development program design and administration

TASK & KNOWLEDGE REQUIREMENTS
- Occupational health and safety legislation (e.g., Occupational Health and Safety Act of Ontario, Workplace Safety & Insurance Act—Bill 99, Workplace Hazardous Materials Information System, Transportation of Dangerous Goods legislation, environmental legislation, smoking in the workplace legislation, civil rights legislation)
- hazard identification and control
- emergency preparedness procedures
- management techniques for OH&S Programs
- types of employee assistance and wellness programs

RPC 5.2 Implements and evaluates practices in the areas of health, safety, security, and Workers' Compensation.

- investigative techniques
- hazard recognition
- disaster recovery techniques
- relevant legislation
- resource information
- common health and safety practices

- company policies and procedures
- Worker Protection (including health and safety and Workers' Compensation)
- theories and practices for protection of individuals and groups
- Occupational health and safety legislation (e.g., Occupational Health and Safety Act of Ontario, Workplace Safety & Insurance Act—Bill 99, Workplace Hazardous Materials Information System, Transportation of Dangerous Goods legislation, environmental legislation, smoking in the workplace legislation, civil rights legislation)
- hazard identification and control
- management techniques for OH&S Programs

RPC 5.3 Analyses risk to the health and safety of employees and determines appropriate preventative measures, including training, provision of required safety equipment, and administrative practices.

- relevant legislation
- nature of the business and physical work environment
- hazard recognition
- workplace inspection techniques
- safety programs, equipment, and emergency procedures
- ergonomics
- functions of the JHSC
- training and development/presentation techniques
- industry best practices
- relevant technical terminology
- the collective agreement
- services and equipment available in the community
- Worker Protection (including health and safety and Workers' Compensation)
- training and development program design and administration

TASK & KNOWLEDGE REQUIREMENTS
- Occupational health and safety legislation (e.g., Occupational Health and Safety Act of Ontario, Workplace Safety & Insurance Act—Bill 99, Workplace Hazardous Materials Information System, Transportation of Dangerous Goods legislation, environmental legislation, smoking in the workplace legislation, civil rights legislation)
- hazard identification and control
- emergency preparedness procedures
- management techniques for OH&S Programs
- types of employee assistance and wellness programs

RPC 5.4 Ensures due diligence and strict liability requirements are met, e.g. records are kept and formal procedures established.

- relevant legislation and common law
- company policies and procedures
- industry best practices
- program and policy development
- training and development techniques
- risk analysis
- Common and statutory law (e.g., employment standard: labour relations)

- Worker Protection (including health and safety and Workers' Compensation)
- Theories and practices for protection of individuals and groups

TASK & KNOWLEDGE REQUIREMENTS
- Occupational health and safety legislation (e.g., Occupational Health and Safety Act of Ontario, Workplace Safety & Insurance Act—Bill 99, Workplace Hazardous Materials Information System, Transportation of Dangerous Goods legislation, environmental legislation, smoking in the workplace legislation, civil rights legislation)
- management techniques for OH&S Programs

RPC 5.5 Contributes to policy on the workplace environment (e.g., smoking, workplace violence, scent-free, communicable diseases, and addictions).
- relevant legislation
- program and policy development
- the culture of the organization
- conflict resolution
- record keeping and reporting
- technical terminology
- environmental hazards
- Common and statutory law (e.g., employment standard: labour relations)
- Worker Protection (including health and safety and Workers' Compensation)
- Theories and practices for protection of individuals and groups
- Occupational health and safety legislation (e.g., Occupational Health and Safety Act of Ontario, Workplace Safety & Insurance Act—Bill 99, Workplace Hazardous Materials Information System, Transportation of Dangerous Goods legislation, environmental legislation, smoking in the workplace legislation, civil rights legislation)
- management techniques for OH&S Programs
- trends in occupational health and safety

Discussion Questions

1. This chapter lists the types of contaminants found in industrial workplaces. Consider the typical office setting—what types of chemical hazards might office workers be exposed to?
2. Explain the concept of a "synergistic effect" as used in this chapter.
3. What are the major ways of controlling the potential adverse effects of exposure to chemical and biological agents?

Using the Internet

1. Using a search engine, such as Google, find reports of the SARS outbreak in Canadian cities (especially Toronto) during 2003. What procedures did workplaces (i.e., hospitals) implement to minimize exposure or reaction to this biological hazard?

2. Cases of environmental illness or environmental sensitivity seem to be becoming more common. Search out contemporary cases in which employees have been exposed to chemical or biological agents with long-term consequences. Could these exposures have been prevented? Could the workers have been protected?

Exercise

1. Although exposure to various workplace hazards is never a good thing, some individuals may be more sensitive to some exposures than others. For example, pregnant women may be more at risk when exposed to certain chemicals than are other employees. To what extent can we use HR tools such as selection and placement to offset this problem? Is it appropriate to refuse to hire women of childbearing age to work in environments in which exposures are possible?

Case 1: Mass Hysteria?

It's the first week of the semester in the new school building and already Principal LeBlanc is ready to quit. For years, parents in her district have been campaigning for a new school and teachers have been complaining about out-dated classrooms. Now they have a new multimillion-dollar building with all the latest technology.

"You'd think that everyone would be happy," groused LeBlanc to her vice principal, "but all I've heard all day are complaints."

"What kind of complaints?"

"Well, for starters, we have five teachers off sick claiming that they get migraines every time they enter their classrooms. And now parents have started to complain that their kids have sore eyes and are feeling nauseated all the time they're in the building."

"Maybe they're really sick," stated the concerned vice principal.

"Yeah, sick of school," replied LeBlanc. "At least that's what I think."

As a health and safety expert what do you think? What actions would you take?

Case 2: Unexpected Gas

A man was killed by an explosion when another worker attempted to cut through the top of one of two old steel drums using a hand-held grinder. Both barrels had contained a fruit concentrate but were never cleaned. The sparks generated by the grinder ignited hydrogen gas that had been generated from the contents' residue after standing for many years. Because there was a defective sterile coating separating the walls of the drum from the concentrate, the acid in the fruit concentrate reacted with the metal of the drum and formed hydrogen gas. The gas accumulated and the pressure caused the drum ends to bulge. This deformation made it impossible to open the drum with the drum opener and a hole was punched into the top of each drum. One worker was attempting to add water to one drum in order to displace the remaining gas, while another worker attempted to open the other drum with a grinder. Sparks ignited the hydrogen gas, causing an explosion and a fire. The fire was extinguished, but one worker lost his life. The defective drums had been recalled years before by the supplier, and only three remained unaccounted for before the accident.

What steps would you take to ensure that this event was never repeated?

Endnotes

1. Workplace Safety and Insurance Board of Ontario. (2000). *Annual Report*. Toronto: WSIB.

2. Genesove, Dr. L. (1995). *Multiple chemical sensitivity syndrome*. Toronto: Healthwise, Accident Prevention.

3. DiNardi, S.R. (Ed.) (1997). *The occupational environment— Its evaluation and control*. Fairfax, VA: AIHA Press.

4. Workplace Safety and Insurance Board of Ontario. (2000). *Annual Report*. Toronto: WSIB.

5. Williams, P. L., & Burson, J. L. (Eds.). (1985). *Industrial toxicology—Safety and health applications in the workplace*. New York: Van Nostrand Reinhold.

6. Pilger, C. W. (1994). *Toxic solvents*. 23rd Intensive Workshop in Industrial Hygiene, Toronto.

7. Pilger, C. W. (1994). *Toxic solvents*. 23rd Intensive Workshop in Industrial Hygiene, Toronto.

Chapter 6

Psychosocial Hazards

Chapter Learning Objectives

After reading this chapter, you should be able to

- describe and distinguish among the concepts of stressor, stress, and strain
- explain the transactional model of stress and its implications
- identify major sources of stress in the workplace
- discuss the psychological, physiological, behavioural, and organizational consequences of stress
- describe and distinguish among primary, secondary, and tertiary stress interventions
- discuss violence, injustice, technology, and sexual harassment as emerging workplace stressors

VIOLENCE AT WORK

On October 15, 2002, shortly after being fired, Dick Anderson entered his former place of work, B.C.'s Environmental Protection Agency, armed with a handgun. He fatally shot James McCracken, his boss, who had delivered the news of his dismissal, and union steward David Mardon before turning the weapon on himself and committing suicide. This double homicide-suicide is an extreme example of the problem of violence in the workplace.

During a Workers' Compensation Board inquiry following this murder-suicide, employees of Mr. Anderson testified that he had been under considerable stress at work. Funding cutbacks meant that he had to lay off staff members and manage an increasingly heavy workload. It appears that he was unable to handle this degree of work stress and was temperamental and abusive with staff. The inquest concluded that Mr. Anderson's dismissal came as a surprise to him, and the shock of being fired without notice prompted his act of extreme violence.

Exposure to violence at work is also an occupational hazard. We can imagine that individuals who were present on the day of Mr. Anderson's outburst were extremely frightened by the event. These individuals now likely fear the possibility of future violent events at work. Such anxiety can contribute to health concerns such as trouble sleeping and gastrointestinal problems.

The Workers' Compensation Board's inquiry resulted in several recommendations pertaining to violence at work. One such recommendation was that organizations should review procedures for employee dismissal. Workers should receive regular performance information to avoid a situation in which termination comes as a shock. Additionally, the report offered recommendations regarding the need for organizations to better document incidents of violence, acknowledge and act on implied or expressed threats of violence, and provide workplace violence training programs.

Sources: CBC, "Coroner's jury focuses on threats of violence," May 30, 2003. Retrieved from http://vancouver.cbc.ca, November 15, 2003; "Broaden workplace violence rules," *The Globe and Mail*, May 30, 2003. Retrieved from http://www.theglobeandmail.com, November 21, 2003.

In 1990, the United States' National Institute of Occupational Safety and Health (NIOSH) declared occupational stress to be one of the 10 leading causes of workplace death, and it is now common to speak of occupational stress as an epidemic.[1] Indeed, it is a problem costing U.S. businesses an estimated $150 billion per year.[2] In Canada, the Conference Board of Canada has estimated that workplace stress costs the Canadian economy $12 billion dollars annually. Although we recognize that estimates of the cost of work stress involve considerable guesswork, it is clear that workplace stress is a large and growing problem with considerable consequences for individuals and organizations. So, what exactly is stress?

One way to discuss stress is in terms of the **psychosocial model of health**. The term *psychosocial* is used to highlight the importance of both the social environment and the psychological or individual factors that affect a person's health and well-being. Social factors that may influence a person's health include supportive family members, exposure to violence, and workplace policies. Psychological factors that affect a person's health include self-esteem, anxiety levels, and ability to cope with pressure.

In everyday conversation, we use the term *stress* in several different ways. We talk about feeling stress and about stress as something we're exposed to. Even the scientific literature demonstrates considerable confusion over the precise meanings of stress-related terms.[3] Most researchers now agree on a general stress model that distinguishes among three closely related terms: stressors, stress, and strain.

Stressors

A **stressor** is an objectively verifiable event occurring in the environment that has the potential to cause stress. For example, congested traffic would constitute a stressor. Stressors, then, exist outside the individual and reflect some of the social factors that affect a person's health. Stressors may vary along several dimensions: frequency of occurrence, intensity, duration, and predictability (time of onset).[4] The combination of these dimensions has led researchers to distinguish among four categories of stressors: acute stressors, chronic stressors, daily stressors, and catastrophic stressors (see Table 6.1).

Acute stressors have a specific time onset (i.e., you know exactly when it began), are typically of short duration and high intensity, and have a low frequency. For example, a traffic accident is an acute stressor. In terms of the work environment, a performance review meeting or a conflict with a supervisor may be acute stressors. In contrast, a *chronic* stressor has no specific onset, may be of short or long duration, repeats frequently, and may be of

psychosocial model of health

approach to the study of health that highlights the importance of both the social environment and psychological factors

stressor

an objectively verifiable event that occurs outside the individual that has the potential to cause stress

TABLE 6.1

Categories of Stressors

Type	Frequency	Duration	Intensity	Time of Onset
Acute	Rare	Short	High	Specific
Chronic	Frequent	Short or long	Low or high	Non-specific
Daily	Infrequent	Short	Low	Specific
Catastrophic	Very rare	Short or long	Extremely high	Specific

either low or high intensity. Many individuals today are experiencing job insecurity as a chronic stressor. Most cannot point to a specific event or time that triggered the insecurity, but the nagging worry that their job is at risk is always with them.

Daily stressors have a specific onset, are of short duration, are low in intensity, and are typically infrequent. Getting caught in a traffic jam is an example of a daily stressor. To use a work-related example, dealing with a broken piece of office equipment may be a daily stressor for some employees. Finally, we need to recognize the existence of *catastrophic* stressors or disasters. Much like acute stressors, catastrophic stressors have a specific onset, occur infrequently, have a high intensity, and may be of either long or short duration. The main distinction between acute and catastrophic stressors is in the intensity of the stressor. Catastrophic stressors typically involve a direct threat to life, loss of life, or major property damage. Again, the complexity of categorizing stressors is indicated by the observation that catastrophic stressors can become chronic stressors over time. For example, the disaster at the Three Mile Island nuclear plant in March 1979 has had long-term consequences for workers because of the ongoing uncertainty about the effects of exposure to radiation.

Stressors in the Workplace

Although the categorization of stressors presented above provides a general overview of stressors, other researchers have focused on defining the content or sources of stressors that exist in the workplace.[5] The NIOSH model identifies the following major categories of workplace stressors.

- *Workload and work pace*. This category refers to the amount of work that has to be completed and the speed at which employees have to work to complete their tasks.
- *Role stressors* (conflict, ambiguity, and interrole conflict). Role conflict exists when individuals face incompatible demands from two or more sources. Role ambiguity reflects the uncertainty employees experience about what is expected from them in their jobs; the opposite of role ambiguity is role clarity. Interrole conflict exists when employees face incompatible demands from two or more roles. The most common form of interrole conflict is work-family conflict, in which the demands of work conflict with the role of parent or spouse.
- *Career concerns*. This category includes worries about job security, fear of job obsolescence, underpromotion and overpromotion, and, more generally, concerns about career progression.
- *Work scheduling*. Working rotating shifts or permanent night shifts results in a disruption of physiological circadian rhythms, as well as a disruption of social activities.
- *Interpersonal relations*. Poor interpersonal relations in the workplace are consistently identified as a source of stress. Conversely, having well-established sources of social support (i.e., receiving support from coworkers and supervisors) may actually reduce the effects of other workplace stressors.

- *Job content and control.* Jobs that are highly repetitive or do not make use of a variety of workers' skills or give workers a measure of control over how and when they complete their tasks can be a source of stress.

Stress

Although stressors are objective events, the individual's response to or evaluation of these events also has an important role to play. Researchers have typically referred to this response or evaluation as **stress.** Stress, then, reflects some of the psychological factors that affect a person's health. In contrast to the objective stressors we have discussed, stress is an internal event that is subjectively defined. Stress is a consequence of any action, situation, or event that places special demands on a person. The stress response is an adaptive reaction to these demands and is influenced by differences between people.

Stress is an adaptive response. The stress response is our way of mobilizing resources to deal with stressors in the environment. Viewed in an evolutionary context, stress is the product of millions of years of evolution. The **general adaptation syndrome** (stress response) is the body's way of gearing up for fight or flight (i.e., to confront or run away from a predator).[6] The syndrome has three stages: alarm, resistance, and exhaustion. The alarm phase begins when a person is confronted with a stressor (i.e., the body prepares for fight or flight). Resistance is the body's attempt to restore homeostasis (i.e., to return to normal). Exhaustion occurs if the stressor is not dealt with and strain reactions set in. Some of the physiological changes that occur as the body prepares for fight or flight include increased blood supply to the brain and major muscle groups, decreased blood supply to the digestive system and skin, increased heart rate and breathing, and increased activity in the stomach, bowels, and bladder. If the stress reaction is prolonged, the resulting symptoms include headaches, dry mouth, skin rashes, heartburn, hypertension, stomach ulcers, and asthma.

stress
an individual's response to, or evaluation of, stressors

general adaptation syndrome
the body's way of gearing up for fight or flight (i.e., to confront or run away from a predator)

Stress is moderated by individual differences. Psychologists have recognized for many years that our responses to events in the environment are largely determined by our interpretation of the events. Some people are less vulnerable to stressors in their environment than others. In fact, one of the most popular models of stress, the transactional model, is based on the notion that individuals may perceive and respond differently to the same stressors.[7] According to this model, people appraise the stressors in their environment and assess their ability to manage them. For example, a person may determine that although he or she has heavy work demands, he or she can manage the workload by setting up a comprehensive "to do" list and delegating some of the tasks to coworkers. Stress occurs when an individual realizes that a pertinent stressor is present and that he or she does not have the resources or ability to manage that stressor. Thus, it is clear that stress does not always follow exposure to a stressor; rather, it results when an appraisal process indicates that the stressor is indeed an unmanageable threat to the person's well-being.

Researchers often talk about stressors as events that have the potential to cause change, harm, or loss, or to pose a threat or a challenge. Even events that are viewed as positive can be stressors. For instance, a promotion can be a stressor because it involves considerable change (e.g., in job duties), challenge (e.g., increased job responsibilities), and threat (e.g., the potential to be a failure in the new job). Stress is the body's way of coping with the environment, and the response is the same whether these demands are positive or negative.

Stress Moderators

Many factors affect people's evaluations of stressors as well as how they react to them (degree of stress experienced). We often call these factors **moderators**. A moderator is a variable that changes the relationship between two other variables. Some moderators *aggravate* or increase the effects of stressors. These types of moderators are called **risk factors** for stress. Other moderators can *protect* an individual from the adverse effects of stressor. Because of their role in breaking the chain of response, these moderators are sometimes referred to as stress **buffers**.

Two well-accepted general classes of moderators in the stress process are the enduring properties of the individual (i.e., personality characteristics) and the social context (i.e., social support, individual relationships). We will consider each type of moderator.

The Individual—Personality

A considerable amount of research has examined the role of personality in stress. Personality is the relatively stable set of characteristics, responses, thoughts, and behaviours of a given individual.[8] Two personality characteristics of particular relevance in a consideration of stress are the **Type A behaviour** pattern and negative affectivity.

TYPE A BEHAVIOUR Type A individuals are people who try to achieve increasingly more in increasingly less time. Their struggle is chronic and, if necessary, is carried out against the will of others.[9] Individuals who exhibit Type A behaviour

moderator

a variable that changes the relationship between two other variables

risk factor

a variable that increases the negative effects of stress

buffer

a variable that protects people from the negative effects of stress

Type A behaviour

action-emotion complex that can be observed in any person who is aggressively involved in a chronic, incessant struggle to achieve increasingly more in increasingly less time are hard-driving, competitive, and time-urgent. There are two components of Type A behaviour: achievement-striving and impatience-irritability.[10] An individual who is high on achievement-striving is typically very goal directed and action oriented. Individuals high on impatience-irritability are typically very time conscious, hostile, impatient, and irritable. In general, achievement-striving is associated with performance but not health outcomes. That is, those high on achievement-striving perform well, but this aspect of themselves is not related to their health. Conversely, impatience-irritability is associated with health outcomes. Those high on impatience-irritability experience more stress and have poorer health, but this aspect is not related to their work performance.[11]

NEGATIVE AFFECTIVITY **Negative affectivity** is a mood factor that reflects persistent individual differences in the experience of negative emotion. A simpler way to interpret this is the difference between an optimist and a pessimist. The latter demonstrates negative affectivity across situations; that is, some individuals seem predisposed to see the negative side of everything. Such individuals may seem to react negatively or adversely to all stressors, and it is in this sense that negative affectivity may serve as a risk factor in the stress process.

negative affectivity
a dispositional dimension reflecting persuasive individual differences in the experience of negative emotion

The Social Context—Social Support

Although the preceding discussion has focused on the qualities and personality traits of the individual, a considerable body of evidence also suggests the importance of social relationships as a moderator of the stress process. Having sources of support can help reduce a person's vulnerability to stressors.[12] In other words, having people who provide support is a buffer for stress. Alternatively, a lack of social support can intensify the impact of stressors and may be a potential risk factor for stress.

Support can come from a number of sources, including supervisors, coworkers, and family members. Support can also be offered in a number of ways. For instance, a coworker may provide tangible support by giving a new employee needed information about a job task. This same coworker might also show emotional support by offering positive feedback and encouragement to the new hire.

Strain

The result of stress is **strain**. When people encounter a stressor and experience persistent stress, ultimately strain will result. We will discuss four categories of strain reactions: psychological, physical, behavioural, and organizational.

strain
the result of stress; it is classified into four categories of reactions: psychological, physical, behavioural, and organizational

Psychological Strain

Psychological strain reactions typically include either a disturbance in affect (e.g., mood) or a disturbance in cognition (e.g., concentration). Feeling irritable, anxious, overwhelmed, moody, depressed, and angry are all common *affective* strain reactions. Indeed, we often describe these moods as "feeling stressed out."

Although most people recognize affective or emotional reactions to stress, cognitive reactions often go unnoticed. Typical strain-related cognitive disturbances include difficulty in making up your mind (often on trivial matters), difficulty in concentrating and staying with one task, not being able to remember people's names even though you know them quite well, and other small mistakes. These small mistakes are generally not very important, but they can be devastating for an individual under considerable strain. For instance, in some situations, making even small mistakes in the workplace can have negative consequences for employee safety and performance.

Physical Strain

Many physical strain reactions have been identified throughout this chapter (e.g., stomach upsets, headaches). Some of these symptoms may seem quite trivial, but considerable evidence now suggests that stress is implicated in more serious physical conditions. Most prominently, coronary heart disease (CHD) has been consistently linked to increased stress, as has high blood pressure (hypertension), strokes, ulcers, asthma, and even some forms of cancer.

The mechanisms through which strain manifests itself physically are not yet clearly understood, although well-documented changes in hormone and enzyme secretion occur under stress. Moreover, stress may play a dual role as a cause of serious physical illness. First, individuals exposed to a stressor may experience stress and ultimately develop a physical strain response—illness (e.g., you are constantly under pressure to meet deadlines and make clients happy; as a result, you have developed hypertension). Second, increased strain may also lower the body's resistance (by impairing the immune system), thereby opening the door to physical illness. In fact, recent evidence suggests work-related stress is a risk factor for the common cold, such that those experiencing heavy psychological job demands reported increased incidence of colds.[13]

Behavioural Strain

Behavioural strain reactions can take a variety of forms. Individuals under increased stress may develop nervous habits (e.g., nail biting or nervous tics). Other forms of behavioural strain reactions may include avoidance of certain situations, or a reduction in individual involvement, either because of a lack of interest or as a means of reducing the demands on the individual's time. Evidence also suggests that individuals may increase their smoking, consumption of alcohol, or reliance on psychotherapeutic drugs under periods of increased stress.[14] Given the known health outcomes associated with smoking, excessive alcohol consumption, and overmedication, these are very dangerous ways of coping with increased stress.

Organizational Strain

Stress researchers interested in organizations identify increased absenteeism, decreased performance, disturbances of interpersonal relationships at work, and an increased likelihood of looking for alternative employment as some

Psychosocial Hazards at Work

Information gathered during a recent General Social Survey (GSS) conducted by Statistics Canada reveals that workplace stress is a staggering reality in our nation. In fact, one-third of Canadians between the ages of 25 and 44 identified themselves as workaholics, and fully half of the individuals in this age group indicated that they don't have enough time to spend with friends and family. Thirty-four percent of Canadians surveyed in the GSS conducted in 2000 indicated that the primary cause of stress at work was too many work demands and hours. Other commonly mentioned stressors included having poor interpersonal relations in the workplace (15%) and having to learn new computer skills (10%).

The 2001 Canadian Mental Health Survey, conducted by the Canadian Mental Health Association, revealed that 50% of those surveyed view their workplaces as a major source of stress in their lives, up from 39% in 1997. However, Canadians are giving their employers higher ratings when it comes to helping them manage workplace stress. In 2001, 60% of respondents indicated that their employer was either very or somewhat effective in helping them to deal with workplace stress. That's up from 44% for the same question in 1997.

Sources: Statistics Canada, "Sources of Workplace Stress," *The Daily*. Retrieved from http://www.statcan.ca/Daily/English/030625/d030625c.htm, August 5, 2004; and Canadian Mental Health Association, "The 2001 Canadian Mental Health Survey." Retrieved from http://www.cmha.ca/english/research/compas_survey.htm, August 5, 2004]

of the most common organizational outcomes of stress. Consistent evidence suggests that increased stress is also associated with an increased risk of workplace accidents. This increased risk may be a consequence of other strain reactions (e.g., increased cognitive failures, impaired ability to concentrate). We should also note that the causal direction of this relationship is not certain. Although accidents and increased stress are certainly correlated, it may be that working in a dangerous or risky environment is, in itself, a stressor.

Managing Psychosocial Hazards

It is clear that work-related stressors, stress, and strain have substantial negative consequences for both employees and organizations. Fortunately, individual employees and organizational management can work together to offset or avoid these negative outcomes by using an approach known as **preventive stress management**. The basic principle of preventive stress management is that the health of an organization and the health of its employees are interdependent.[15] In other words, organizations whose employees are in good health are more likely to be successful. Alternatively, employees who work for organizations that provide pleasant working conditions are more likely to be healthy, productive individuals.

Ideally, stress management programs will include both organizational and individual interventions that are designed to reduce exposure to stressors, reduce the experience of stress when stressors are unavoidable, and swiftly provide treatment options to those individuals who are experiencing the negative consequences of stress. In the following paragraphs, we describe

R P C 6.1

R P C 6.2

preventive stress management

an approach to managing stress in the workplace that emphasizes that the health of an organization and its employees are interdependent; it encourages the reduction of stressors in the workplace as well as the recognition and management of occupational stress and strain three categories of interventions (primary, secondary, and tertiary) and provide illustrative examples of organizational and individual efforts to manage stress in the workplace for each type of intervention.

Primary Interventions

Primary interventions involve the reduction or removal of the actual stressors and are highly effective in reducing work-related stress and strain.[16] The logic of this approach is that the removal of sources of stress from the workplace should reduce employee stress and strain. Despite the supporting evidence, primary prevention strategies are not broadly implemented in Canadian organizations. Some have suggested that organizational decision makers presume that the cost and logistics of primary preventive strategies would be excessive; therefore, they prefer to focus on interventions that target the employees' ability to cope with existing stressors.[17] However, the costs associated with primary preventive efforts can be reasonable and, given resulting reduction in employee stress, worth the effort involved in their implementation. Tables 6.2 and 6.3 provide examples of primary stress prevention strategies at the individual and organizational levels.

RPC 6.3

RPC 6.4

RPC 6.5

Secondary Interventions

Secondary interventions focus on minimizing negative outcomes once a person is feeling stress. Techniques such as stress management and relaxation training help people to identify the negative health effects of stress and teach effective coping strategies, with the intention that appropriate strategies for managing stress can lessen the negative effects of stress on health.[18] Common examples of secondary intervention programs are relaxation training, stress management training and counselling, physical

TABLE 6.2

Stress Intervention Strategies: Individual Level

LEVEL OF INTERVENTION	EXAMPLES
Primary	Avoid taking on an overload of work.
	Take adequate leisure time.
	Try to reduce Type A behaviour.
Secondary	Talk with friends and coworkers.
	Make time to exercise.
	Use relaxation techniques.
Tertiary	Seek medical treatment.
	Participate in psychological counselling.

TABLE 6.3

Stress Intervention Strategies: Organizational Level

LEVEL OF INTERVENTION	EXAMPLES
Primary	Redesign particularly demanding jobs.
	Respect employees' opinions in management decision-making process.
	Provide flexible working conditions.
Secondary	Provide comprehensive benefits programs that include provisions for such options as employee assistance programs (EAPs), personal leave, massage therapy.
	Offer on-site fitness centres.
	Ensure balanced nutrition on the cafeteria menu.
Tertiary	Offer benefits packages with sick days and leave options.
	Provide counselling services following major stressors, such as a violent episode at work or major acts of terrorism.
	Support employee efforts to find appropriate medical or psychological care.

fitness programs, and balanced nutrition. Secondary interventions are more widely used than primary preventive techniques. However, secondary strategies are less desirable than primary approaches because they target stress only after it has occurred. See Tables 6.2 and 6.3 for examples of ways that organizations and individuals can engage in secondary stress interventions.

Tertiary Interventions

Tertiary interventions include strategies such as psychological therapy and medical attention that are used after the fact to help those individuals who have not been able to effectively manage workplace stress and are now experiencing symptoms of strain.[19] In the "best of all organizations, primary and secondary prevention would be enough to manage the demands of work life."[20] However, in the event that stressors and stress are not adequately dealt with via primary and secondary efforts, it is important to consider potential tertiary intervention strategies that organizations and individuals can use to treat their symptoms of strain. What is important at the tertiary level is that individuals experiencing strain are aware that the symptoms are a real threat to their overall health and well-being and seek treatment. The organization can facilitate tertiary interventions by providing education about strain-related illnesses for employees. Tables 6.2 and 6.3 outline the individual and organizational strategies that contribute to successful tertiary stress interventions.

tertiary interventions

stress intervention techniques that are used to help those individuals who have not been able to effectively manage workplace stress and are now experiencing symptoms of strain

🅡🅟🅒 6.6

🅡🅟🅒 6.7

Emerging Stressor: Workplace Violence

Workplace violence is a critical health and safety issue facing North American organizations. Homicide, the most severe form of violence, is the second leading cause of death in American workplaces, exceeded only by motor vehicle–related deaths.[21] On average, 20 employees in the United States are murdered each week while at work or on duty.[22] Although occupational homicide occurs more frequently in the United States, Canadian organizations are not immune from this phenomenon. For example, in 1999 a former employee of Ottawa-Carleton Transpo shot and killed four transit workers and seriously wounded two others. Less severe forms of workplace violence such as pushing and shoving occur more frequently than homicide. In Ontario, for example, the most frequent forms of workplace violence are hitting, kicking, and biting. Recent evidence suggests that Canadians may be even more likely than are Americans to experience assault at work. In a survey conducted by the International Labour Organization (ILO), almost 4% of men and 5% of women in Canada reported being assaulted in the last year while at work, compared with 1% of men and 4.2% of women in the United States.[23]

Workplace violence has been categorized into four major types based on the assailant's relationship to the workplace.[24] These categories are described in Table 6.4. By far the most common type of workplace violence is that where the perpetrator has no legitimate business relationship with the targeted workplace and enters the work environment to commit a criminal act (e.g., robbery). Most workplace homicides are robbery related.[25] Individuals at risk include taxicab drivers, convenience store employees, and gas station attendants. The type of workplace violence in which a "disgruntled employee" threatens a coworker or supervisor for what is perceived as unfair treatment captures a large amount of media attention. Only a small portion, 4% to 7%, of workplace homicides occurs between coworkers.[26]

Researchers have attempted to identify the job characteristics that increase the risk for violence from both members of the public and coworkers. In 2002, LeBlanc and Kelloway developed a risk assessment instrument that

TABLE 6.4

A Categorization of Workplace Violence Incidents

CATEGORY	RELATIONSHIP OF THE ASSAILANT TO THE ORGANIZATION
Type 1	Member of the public with no legitimate relationship to the organization, usually committing a criminal act
Type 2	Member of the public who receives legitimate service from the organization (e.g., client, patient)
Type 3	An employee or former employee of the organization
Type 4	The spouse or partner of an employee

focused on occupational characteristics.[27] Some of the job characteristics that they found placed people at a high risk to experience workplace violence included, but were not limited to, the following:

- *Interacting with the public*
- *Denying the public a service or request*
- *Making decisions that influence other people's lives* (e.g., an HR manager terminates an employee or a teacher assigns a student a failing grade)
- *Supervising others*
- *Exercising physical control over others* (e.g., law enforcement officers and private security personnel)
- *Handling firearms and similar weapons* (e.g., law enforcement, retail workers who sell guns)
- *Working alone* (particularly working alone at night or working alone with money as is the case with taxi drivers)
- *Handling cash* (e.g., retail jobs)
- *Collecting or delivering items of value* (e.g., armoured car drivers)
- *Contact with individuals who are under the influence of mind-altering substances* (e.g., bartenders)
- *Caring for the physical needs of others* (e.g., health care workers)
- *Going to clients' homes* (e.g., home care health workers)

Consequences of Workplace Violence

The immediate consequences of workplace violence (i.e., someone is physically injured or killed) are obvious. However, it is becoming increasingly apparent that the consequences of violence in the workplace may be even

---

Occupational Health and Safety Notebook 6.1

Tips for Dealing with Workplace Violence

The Canadian Centre for Occupational Health and Safety offers workers the following tips for dealing with threats of workplace violence:

1. Know the risks involved in your job.
2. Trust your instincts.
3. Be ready to respond.
4. Remain calm.
5. Report all incidents.

These tips point to the need for individuals to recognize that workplace violence can and does happen. Individuals need to be prepared for potential violence. Similar cautions apply to employers. The legal requirement of due diligence and the experience of companies that have dealt with workplace violence suggest the following tips for employers.

1. Know the risk factors present in the workplace; minimize risk whenever possible.
2. Have a written policy prohibiting violence and ensure that employees are trained in the application of the policy.
3. Have a plan—know how to respond to actual or threatened violence.
4. Take all threats of violence seriously.
5. Stay within your area of competence; get the proper authorities involved.

Source: Canadian Centre for Occupational Health and Safety, "Violence in the Workplace." Retrieved from http://www.ccohs.ca/oshanswers/psychosocial/violence.html, October 5, 2004.

---

more widespread. Research on the consequences of workplace violence has identified a wider circle of victims than originally thought. Research on disasters and other serious trauma shows that their impact extends beyond the primary victims. In fact, secondary victims—those who witness or hear about the events—also exhibit stress and strain reactions. Similar findings have been noted in research on workplace violence—the vicarious exposure to workplace violence (i.e., witnessing workplace violence or hearing about a violent incident in the workplace) may also have long-term consequences for individuals.[28]

Exposure to violent episodes in the workplace seems to have more long-lasting consequences for the individuals involved and their employing organizations than originally thought. Numerous research studies show that exposure to workplace violence results in individuals fearing the recurrence of violence. We might describe this fear of future incidents of violence as stress. In turn, that fear results in both personal strain (i.e., impaired mental and physical health) and organizational strain (i.e., decreased commitment, increased intent to leave the organization, neglect of job duties).[29]

Emerging Stressor: Sexual Harassment

RPC 6.8

RPC 6.9

Several studies have identified sexual harassment as a workplace stressor of increasing importance. Most forms of sexual harassment involve unwelcome, intrusive sexual attention and verbal comments. A recent estimate, based on an evaluation of numerous research studies, is that 58% of women have experienced behaviours that are potentially harassing and 24% of American women agree that they have experienced sexual harassment in the workplace.[30] Data collected in Canada suggest similar exposure rates: 56% of working women who responded to a large survey on sexual harassment indicated that they had experienced sexually harassing behaviour in the previous year.[31] The most commonly reported behaviours in the Canadian survey were insulting jokes and staring. Physically violent actions such as rape do occur in the workplace but only rarely.[32]

Section 247.1 of the Canada Labour Code prohibits sexual harassment and defines sexual harassment as any conduct, comment, gesture, or contact of a sexual nature

> (a) that is likely to cause offence or humiliation to any employee; or
> (b) that might, on reasonable grounds, be perceived by the employee as placing a condition of a sexual nature on employment or on any opportunity for training or promotion.[33]

sexual harassment

intentional, persistent, and unwelcome sexual conduct or remarks that occur despite resistance from the victim

Sexual harassment, then, is any intentional, persistent (i.e., repeated), and unwelcome sexual conduct or remark that occurs despite resistance from the victim. Note that in cases of severe misconduct (e.g., sexual assault) a single incident meets the definition and constitutes sexual harassment. The act or conduct must be deliberate and intentional. In other words, the offender must be aware that the behaviour is offensive. To alleviate the potential loophole of offenders who could say during a sexual harassment hearing that they were unaware that their behaviour was offensive, tribunals use what they call the "reasonable person" test. Basically, this test determines whether a reasonable person would be aware that the behaviour is offensive.

This description of sexual harassment seems to point to two different types of sexual harassment.[34]

1. *Sexual coercion* (or "quid pro quo" harassment) is an attempt to extort sexual cooperation. This extortion can take the form of subtle or explicit job-related threats (e.g., job loss, loss of promotion), or the form of promising job-related rewards (e.g., promotions, raises). The Ontario Human Rights Code specifically prohibits job-related rewards or punishment in exchange for sexual favours by a person in authority.

2. *Hostile environment* is sexual harassment that occurs without any coercion or extortion, but the occurrence of sexual harassment creates a hostile, intimidating, and discriminating environment. Sexually harassing behaviours of this nature can range from insulting, misplaced comments, through pervasive sex-related verbal or physical conduct, to life threats or physical attacks. According to most research on the incidence of sexual harassment, it is the "hostile environment" type of sexual harassment that is most prevalent.

RPC 6.2

RPC 6.9

RPC 6.10

Sexual Harassment as a Health and Safety Issue

Sexual harassment becomes a health and safety issue for two primary reasons. First, studies show that being the victim of sexual harassment is a stressful experience that is associated with several organizational strains, including increased job dissatisfaction, decreased loyalty to the organization, and increased intent to leave the organization. Some women who have reported being a victim of sexual harassment to their organization experienced the formal process as unjust—in fact, some report that they have been fired after making a sexual harassment claim. There are also personal consequences of sexual harassment, with victims significantly more likely to experience dissatisfaction with life in general and to experience psychosomatic disorders (e.g., respiratory, stomach, and sleep problems; headaches and migraines; weight loss or gain). Thus, exposure to sexual harassment is associated with impaired employee well-being and becomes a health and safety issue.

Second, the courts have increasingly viewed workplace sexual harassment as the responsibility of the employer. Before 1981, sexual harassment on the job was not prohibited by any human rights statute in Canada. A groundbreaking step occurred in 1989, when the Supreme Court of Canada concluded that sexual harassment is a form of sex discrimination and is therefore prohibited in employment. Sex discrimination had been prohibited by human rights statutes for some time in Canada, but sexual harassment was not initially recognized in those statutes.[35] This was an important progression from simply acknowledging that sexual harassment was a serious problem to taking steps to prevent it from occurring.

Occupational Health and Safety Today 6.3

Internet Access and Sexual Harassment

The proliferation of Internet-capable computers in the workplace has lead to a new twist on a long-established health and safety issue. Displays of pornography in the workplace have long been deemed to constitute the creation of a hostile environment. Employees who use office equipment to download, display, or print pornographic images may be creating a hostile environment and employers may be liable for these actions. In response, organizations are increasingly establishing guidelines for what constitutes proper and improper use of office computers. The existence and enforcement of such a policy is the best way to eliminate this form of sexual harassment from the workplace

Another major change occurred when the Supreme Court of Canada stated that an employer is liable for the discriminatory acts of its employees. This decision had great implications, as employers now had a legal motive to prohibit sexual harassment in their companies. Legal liability translates into a strong financial incentive to prevent an illegal act from occurring. For example, in one of the largest lawsuits of its type, Mitsubishi Motors in the United States paid $34 million dollars to settle allegations of sexual harassment filed by the Equal Employment Opportunities Commission on behalf of 300 female employees. Essentially, the allegations were that the women were subjected to sexual comments, innuendo, and unwanted groping, and that plant managers knew of, but did nothing to correct, these problems.

The ruling that employers are liable for discriminatory acts including harassment has several implications for organizations:[36]

1. Employers are responsible for the due care and protection of their employees' human rights in the workplace.
2. Employers are liable for the discriminatory conduct of and sexual harassment by their agents and supervisory personnel.
3. Sexual harassment by a supervisor is automatically attributed to the employer when such harassment results in a tangible job-related disadvantage to the employee.
4. Explicit company policy forbidding sexual harassment and the presence of procedures for reporting misconduct may or may not be sufficient to offset liability.
5. Employers will be pressured to take a more active role in maintaining a harassment-free work environment.
6. Employers will feel a greater discomfort with intimate relationships that develop between supervisors and their subordinates because of the legal implications, and this may motivate employers to discourage such office relationships.
7. Employers' intentions to have effective sexual harassment policies are insufficient. To avoid liability, the policies must be functional and must work as well in practice as they do in theory.

As you can see, the Supreme Court has made employers responsible for any sexual harassment that occurs in the organization. As a result, employers are more likely to initiate interventions to eliminate or at least reduce the occurrence of sexual harassment in their workplace.

Emerging Stressor: Injustice at Work

Recent studies show that employees who experience unfairness in their workplace report higher levels of strain.[37] Researchers have long known that unfairness negatively affects employee attitudes including their intentions to leave their workplace and their commitment to the organization. However, investigations of the relationship between the experience of unfairness at work and employee health are relatively new.

In organizational justice research, "fairness" is not treated as a one-dimensional construct. Researchers in this area focus on three separate categories of fairness judgments that a person can make: (1) the fairness of outcomes, or **distributive justice**, (2) the fairness of processes, or **procedural justice**, and (3) the fairness of interpersonal treatment, or **interactional justice**.[38] All three types of injustice have been associated with increased work stress.

Employees are likely to judge an outcome as unfair when they do not receive a reward or recognition they feel they deserve. For example, Joe, an employee who has recently put in many extra hours on a project at work, may feel that he deserves a bonus in recognition of his extra effort. If he does not receive a bonus, he may feel that he has been the victim of a distributive injustice.

With respect to procedural injustice, people arrive at perceptions regarding the fairness of a procedure by examining several aspects of the process. Procedures that allow employee input and are consistently implemented across conditions, unbiased, accurate, ethical, subject to appeals on the part of those involved, and representative of all relevant parties are viewed as more fair than those that are not.[39] For instance, Ellen may judge the decision to change her work hours from 8 a.m. to 4 p.m. to 9 a.m. to 5 p.m. as more fair if she was consulted about the reason for the decision and permitted to give her opinion about the potential change.

In terms of interactional fairness, individuals judge the fairness of the interpersonal treatment they receive on several levels. For instance, they examine the extent to which their supervisors treat them with kindness and consideration, provide adequate explanations for decisions, and give useful and timely feedback. As an example, Tom is likely to have a better reaction to a negative performance review if his boss delivers that information in a sensitive manner and gives helpful tips on how he can improve his performance before the next performance appraisal.

distributive justice
the perceived fairness of outcomes

procedural justice
the perceived fairness of decision-making processes

interactional justice
the perceived fairness of interpersonal treatment

Creating a Fair Workplace

Organizations can engage in primary stress interventions by working to reduce the occurrence of injustice at work. Organizational leaders should be given training on the importance of fairness at work. Leadership training programs that include a discussion of the value of fair treatment are likely to help leaders see the value of fairness and the damage associated with injustice. The provision of appropriate feedback in a kind and sincere manner can go a long way toward improving an employee's perceptions of interactional justice at work and may have a positive impact on that individual's health.

Organizations can also make an effort to use decision-making processes that are procedurally fair. In that case, organizations may want to consider allowing employee representation on committees or decision-making bodies for important organizational procedures. For instance, if an HR manager is considering changing the employee review process, striking a committee that includes representatives from the various stakeholder groups may increase the perceived fairness of the new evaluation process and ultimately the well-being of the employees who undergo the performance review.

Emerging Stressor: Technology

Innovations in both computer hardware and software have largely changed the workplace, including the way that people do their work and interact with other people on the job.[40] Researchers in occupational health and safety recognize the health risks involved with the increasing presence of technology in the workplace. For instance, increased reliance on computers in the modern work environment is associated with increased risk for physical health problems. The repetitive movements involved with computer use, such as keyboarding and mouse control, place people at risk for musculoskeletal injuries—that is, injuries of the soft tissue such as muscles, tendons, and joints. Carpal tunnel syndrome is an example of a common work-related musculoskeletal disorder that may stem from computer usage. In carpal tunnel syndrome, the median nerve of the arm and hand is compressed.[41]

Musculoskeletal injuries are a prevalent and costly problem for both individuals and organizations. Individuals with these disorders are sometimes in such chronic pain that they are forced to seek disability leave or early retirement.[42] Workers' Compensation claims surrounding musculoskeletal disorders can place large financial demands on companies and government compensation systems. Preventive solutions are available to employers. A field of study called ergonomics emphasizes the importance of creating workstation arrangements that fit the needs of the worker. With respect to technology, research in the area of ergonomics considers the design of such instruments as the computer keyboard and mouse, and the positioning of such items as the computer monitor, with the aim of reducing the likelihood of musculoskeletal strain while working at the computer. For example, an ergonomist might recommend the use of wrist support for individuals who spend a considerable amount of time at the keyboard.

Occupational Health and Safety Notebook 6.2

Technology-Related Stressors

The increasing role of technology in the workplace affects the psychological well-being of workers. Several technology-related factors have been implicated as psychosocial stressors:

Control We have all likely experienced the frustration of an ill-timed computer crash. In these types of situations, our increasing reliance on technology to help us complete our work tasks can in fact be associated with reduced control at work. When our control over our work environment is reduced, increased stress and strain can result.

Isolation Our increasing reliance on technology has been associated with increased isolation in the workplace, reducing the incidence of positive social interactions among workers. For instance, employees who rely on computers are often "tied to their desks" to complete their work and therefore are available for fewer social interactions with their coworkers.

Privacy The advanced state of technology in today's workplaces provides new means of employee surveillance and monitoring. Increasingly, organizations are turning to watchdog systems to keep track of such things as the amount of time an employee spends on the phone or email, the number of keystrokes a worker makes at the keyboard in a given amount of time, or the extent to which people use office technology (e.g., the Internet) for non-work-related tasks. In some cases these systems are used for performance monitoring.

Increased Job Demands The increasing role of technology in the workplace can also increase the demands associated with a job. (Recall that workload and work pace can be potent psychosocial stressors.) With respect to work pace, technological advances have increased the pace of many jobs. For example, the prevalence of technology such as email and fax has shortened the expected turnaround time for work-related communication. Plus the need to keep pace with quickly advancing technology increases the workload of some employees.

Source: Based on Coovert, M. D., & Thompson, L. F. (2003). Technology and workplace health. In J. C. Quick & L. E. Tetrick (Eds.), *Handbook of occupational health psychology* (pp. 223–248). Washington, DC: American Psychological Association.

Summary

In this chapter we have distinguished among the concepts of stressors in the work environment, the experience of stress, and the possible strain consequences. In this discussion we have highlighted that perceiving an event as stressful, or as a stressor, resides within the individual. Not everyone will react to the same situation in the same way. People must perceive the event to be demanding in some way (e.g., a threat or a challenge) for it to be deemed stressful. As we've discussed, stress is an adaptive and individualistic response to the demands of the objective environment (i.e., stressors). We have also demonstrated that these demands take a variety of forms (acute, daily, chronic, catastrophic).

Stress can also have serious consequences. Individuals exposed to continued or high levels of stress develop strain reactions that may be psychological, physical, behavioural, or organizational. In turn, these forms of strain reactions can affect the organization and people's lives. Both the human and the monetary costs of occupational stress warrant our attention.

We also noted the importance of organizationally and individually driven interventions to reduce the extent to which stressors exist in the workplace or to minimize the damage caused by unavoidable stressors. These programs involve primary preventive techniques, secondary interventions to help people avoid the negative consequences of stress, and tertiary programs that help people find the appropriate treatment when they are experiencing strain. The most successful stress management initiatives involve both the individual employee and the organization as a whole.

Workplace violence and sexual harassment are critical issues facing employees in many organizations. Recent research and theorizing has supported the suggestion that both violence and harassment are properly viewed as workplace stressors. Although there are certainly other forms of abusive behaviour occurring in organizations, most attention has focused on workplace violence and sexual harassment because of the dramatic nature of these events and their consequences.

Both injustice and technology are introduced as emerging workplace stressors. Recent research suggests that exposure to unfairness at work and the technological demands placed on today's employees are potential sources of workplace stress. In these sections we highlighted the individual nature of stress. Not all employees reach the same conclusions about the fairness of a single situation, nor are all employees bothered by the increasing technological demands of modern workplaces. However, both these issues are starting to be recognized as potential health and safety issues in the workplace.

Key Terms

buffer, p. 138	psychosocial model of health, p. 135
distributive justice, p. 149	risk factor, p. 138
general adaptation syndrome, p. 137	secondary interventions, p. 142
interactional justice, p. 149	sexual harassment, p. 146
moderator, p. 138	strain, p. 139
negative affectivity, p. 139	stress, p. 137
preventive stress management, p. 141	stressor, p. 135
primary interventions, p. 142	tertiary interventions, p. 143
procedural justice, p. 149	Type A behaviour, p. 138

Weblinks

Canadian Centre for Occupational Health and Safety, "OSH Answers: Health Promotion/Wellness/Psychosocial," **http://www.ccohs.ca/oshanswers/psychosocial/** (p. 135)

CBC News, "Job Stress Compounds Risks for Heart Disease," **http://www.cbc.ca/stories/2002/10/17/job_stress021017** (p. 140)

Canadian Fitness and Lifestyle Research Institute, "Lifestyle Tips," **http://www.cflri.ca/cflri/tips/index.html** (p. 143)

Canadian Centre for Occupational Health and Safety, "Violence in the Workplace," **http://www.ccohs.ca/oshanswers/psychosocial/violence.html** (p. 145)

RPC Icons

RPC 6.1 Implements and evaluates practices in the areas of health, safety, security, and Workers' Compensation.

- investigative techniques
- hazard recognition
- disaster recovery techniques
- relevant legislation
- resource information
- common health and safety practices
- company policies and procedures
- worker protection (including health and safety and Workers' Compensation)
- theories and practices for protection of individuals and groups
- Occupational health and safety legislation (e.g., Occupational Health and Safety Act of Ontario, Workplace Safety and Insurance Act—Bill 99, Workplace Hazardous Materials Information System, Transportation of Dangerous Goods legislation, environmental legislation, smoking in the workplace legislation, civil rights legislation)
- Hazard identification and control
- Management techniques for OH&S programs

RPC 6.2 Ensures due diligence and strict liability requirements are met, e.g. records are kept and formal procedures established.

- relevant legislation and common law
- company policies and procedures
- industry best practices
- program and policy development
- training and development techniques
- risk analysis
- common and statutory law (e.g., employment standard, labour relations)
- worker protection (including health and safety and Workers' Compensation)
- theories and practices for protection of individuals and groups

TASK & KNOWLEDGE REQUIREMENTS
- Occupational health and safety legislation (e.g., Occupational Health and Safety Act of Ontario, Workplace Safety & Insurance Act—Bill 99, Workplace Hazardous Materials Information System, Transportation of Dangerous Goods legislation, environmental legislation, smoking in the workplace legislation, civil rights legislation)
- management techniques for OH&S programs

RPC 6.3 Contributes to policy on the workplace environment (e.g., smoking, workplace violence, scent-free, communicable diseases, and addictions).

- relevant legislation
- program and policy development
- the culture of the organization
- conflict resolution
- record keeping and reporting
- technical terminology
- environmental hazards
- common and statutory law (e.g., employment standard, labour relations)
- worker protection (including health and safety and Workers' Compensation)
- theories and practices for protection of individuals and groups
- Occupational health and safety legislation (e.g., Occupational Health and Safety Act of Ontario, Workplace Safety and Insurance Act—Bill 99, Workplace Hazardous Materials Information System, Transportation of Dangerous Goods legislation, environmental legislation, smoking in the workplace legislation, civil rights legislation)
- management techniques for OH&S programs
- trends in occupational health and safety

RPC 6.4 Ensures internal environmental concerns such as quality of air and water is addressed.

- relevant legislation
- record keeping and reporting

TASK & KNOWLEDGE REQUIREMENTS
- investigative techniques
- hazard identification
- available medical services and other outside resources
- policies and procedures
- the organization's culture
- worker protection (including health and safety and Workers' Compensation)
- theories and practices for protection of individuals and groups
- Occupational health and safety legislation (e.g., Occupational Health and Safety Act of Ontario, Workplace Safety and Insurance Act—Bill 99, Workplace Hazardous Materials Information System, Transportation of Dangerous Goods legislation, environmental legislation, smoking in the workplace legislation, civil rights legislation)
- hazard identification and control

RPC 6.5 Develops or provides for wellness and employee assistance programs to support organizational effectiveness.

- policy/procedure development
- collective agreements
- industry best practices
- outside service providers
- the organization's culture
- conflict resolution techniques
- problem-solving techniques

- report writing and record keeping
- the relationship between employee wellness and productivity
- performance goals of the organization and how these are affected by employee wellness
- key components of an EAP such as intake, assessments, counselling, traumatic incident debriefing, and cap on service
- cost/benefit analysis
- types of employee assistance programs
- types of employee assistance and wellness programs
- conceptual definition and implications of occupational stressors (e.g., potential stressors, methods of identifying potential stressors and strain outcomes, response to organizational stressors, and management of employee strain outcomes)
- trends in occupational health and safety

RPC 6.6 Ensures that mechanisms are in place for responding to crises in the workplace, including critical incident stress management.

- oral and written communication
- training and development techniques
- industry best practices
- the workplace environment, including the availability of emergency equipment
- policy and program development and evaluation
- intervention strategies
- relevant legislation (e.g., fire code, Workers' Compensation)
- investigation techniques
- stress management techniques
- types of employee assistance programs
- Occupational health and safety legislation (e.g., Occupational Health and Safety Act of Ontario, Workplace Safety and Insurance Act—Bill 99, Workplace Hazardous Materials Information System, Transportation of Dangerous Goods legislation, environmental legislation, smoking in the workplace legislation, civil rights legislation)
- hazard identification and control
- accident investigation procedures
- emergency preparedness procedures
- management techniques for OH&S programs
- conceptual definition and implications of occupational stressors (e.g., potential stressors, methods of identifying potential stressors and strain outcomes, response to organizational stressors, and management of employee strain outcomes)

RPC 6.7 Analyses risk to the health and safety of employees and determines appropriate preventative measures, including training, provision of required safety equipment, and administrative practices.

- relevant legislation
- nature of the business and physical work environment
- hazard recognition

- workplace inspection techniques
- safety programs, equipment, and emergency procedures
- ergonomics
- functions of the JHSC [Joint Health and Safety Committee]
- training and development/presentation techniques
- industry best practices
- relevant technical terminology
- the collective agreement
- services and equipment available in the community
- worker protection (including health and safety and Workers' Compensation)
- training and development program design and administration

TASK & KNOWLEDGE REQUIREMENTS

- Occupational health and safety legislation (e.g., Occupational Health and Safety Act of Ontario, Workplace Safety and Insurance Act—Bill 99, Workplace Hazardous Materials Information System, Transportation of Dangerous Goods legislation, environmental legislation, smoking in the workplace legislation, civil rights legislation)
- hazard identification and control
- emergency preparedness procedures
- management techniques for OH&S programs
- types of employee assistance and wellness programs

RPC 6.8 Responds to serious injury or fatality in the workplace.

- program and policy development
- investigation procedures

TASK & KNOWLEDGE REQUIREMENTS

- relevant legislative requirements
- first-aid training and emergency response equipment
- relevant legislative bodies
- pension and insurance benefits/policies
- common and statutory law (e.g., employment standard, labour relations
- worker protection (including health and safety and Workers' Compensation)
- Occupational health and safety legislation (e.g., Occupational Health and Safety Act of Ontario, Workplace Safety and Insurance Act—Bill 99, Workplace Hazardous Materials Information System, Transportation of Dangerous Goods legislation, environmental legislation, smoking in the workplace legislation, civil rights legislation)
- hazard identification and control
- accident investigation procedures
- emergency preparedness procedures

RPC 6.9 Ensures that security programs and policies minimize risks while considering the obligation of the employer and the rights of employees, union, and third parties.

- nature of the business and physical work environment
- relevant legislation
- industry best practices

- program and policy development
- safety and security equipment in the workplace
- risk assessment/techniques
- cost/benefit analysis

RPC 6.10 Ensures compliance with legislated reporting requirements.

- relevant legislation
- methods of reporting incidents
- accident investigation
- training and development techniques
- report writing and record keeping

Task & Knowledge Requirements

- worker protection (including health and safety and Workers' Compensation)
- technical, legislative, political, and personal implications of OHS
- the economic, legal, technical, and moral impact of OHS
- occupational health and safety legislation (e.g., Occupational Health and Safety Act of Ontario, Workplace Safety and Insurance Act—Bill 99, Workplace Hazardous Materials Information System, Transportation of Dangerous Goods legislation, environmental legislation, smoking in the workplace legislation, civil rights legislation)
- hazard identification and control
- accident investigation procedures
- emergency preparedness procedures
- management techniques for OH&S programs

Discussion Questions

1. Think of at least 5 stressors that you have experienced in the last 12 months. Using the guidelines presented in this chapter, categorize the stressors as daily, acute, chronic, or catastrophic. Which, if any, were associated with your experience of strain?
2. If only one individual in a workplace is experiencing strain, are the causes of that strain likely to be in the workplace? Why or why not?
3. What are the major sources of stress in modern workplaces?
4. How does stress manifest itself in behaviour? in organizational functioning?
5. What are some actions that individuals can take to help manage stress? What can organizations do to help employees avoid or manage stress?
6. What are some of the ways in which evolving technology contributes to the experience of workplace stress? What are some interventions that employees and employers might attempt in order to avoid or manage the stress associated with technology?

Using the Internet

1. In this chapter we have discussed workplace violence as a very real and growing occupational health and safety issue. Using Internet resources, research recent news stories involving violence in the workplace. Categorize them as Type 1, Type 2, Type 3, or Type 4 (see Table 6.4).

2. Psychological symptoms have been identified as a health-related outcome of stress. Individuals who feel prolonged stress may experience such symptoms as depression and anxiety. Many employees indicate that they would be uncomfortable telling their boss or coworkers that they were experiencing these types of psychological symptoms because of the stigma associated with these types of mental health problems. Using the website resources of the Canadian Mental Health Association (http://www.cmha.ca), the Canadian Psychiatric Association (http://www.cpa-apc.org), the Canadian Psychological Association (http://www.cpa.ca), the Canadian Centre for Occupational Health and Safety (http://www.ccohs.ca), and other websites, design an awareness program that might help reduce the stigma associated with stress-related mental health issues in the workplace.

3. Although worker health has been a concern for many years, one of the new trends in occupational health is the concept of a "healthy organization." Using Internet resources, define what a healthy organization is. How do companies go about achieving this status? Does the concept of health have value when applied to the organization?

4. Research an organization in which employees may experience work-related threats or assaults. Conduct a risk assessment to determine whether there is a risk of violence. Describe the measures that a human resources manager can take to develop and implement a workplace violence-prevention program. There are numerous websites that will be helpful in this exercise. The Workers' Compensation Board of British Columbia's publication entitled "Take Care: How to Develop and Implement a Workplace Violence Prevention Program" may be particularly useful. It can be downloaded from http://www.worksafebc.com/publications/publication_index/s.asp. (Based on an exercise by Catherine Fitzgerald)

Exercises

1. Think about your current or most recent job. What are/were some of the pertinent stressors? What actions do/did you take to cope with them? How does/did the organization help you to deal with the stress? Talk to some of your friends or members of your family about the stressors they encounter at work and the strategies that they and their employers use to manage workplace stress.

2. Returning to work after a stress-related leave can be difficult for both the individuals coming back to work and their coworkers. Create and enact two role-plays in which you and your classmates are employees at an organization. In one of the scenarios, one of the employees is returning to work after a leave due to a stress-related mental health problem. In the second scenario, one of the coworkers is returning to work following a leave due to a car accident. Following the role-plays discuss each scenario. How did the returning employee feel? What were the responses of the coworkers? Was there a greater sense of discomfort in discussing the well-being of the person who had been on stress leave, relative to the person who was in the car accident? Do you think there are taboos about discussing mental health problems in the workplace? In your follow-up discussion, generate ways that organizations and individual employees might make the transition easier for the person returning to work from a stress-related leave.

3. Imagine you are currently the human resource director for a large organization. You have been given the job of designing and implementing a new performance review system. You know that the employees may find the shift to a new system stressful and that employees often think that performance review instruments are unfair. You are also aware that perceived injustice in the workplace is a stressor and you would like to minimize the extent to which your employees are exposed to work stress. What might you do to maximize the perceived distributive, procedural, and interactional fairness of the performance review process?

4. Contact the human resources department of an organization. Interview the HR manager about psychosocial hazards in the workplace. Some of the things you should ask about are

a. The extent to which he or she considers workplace stress to be a problem in that organization

b. The types of stressors experienced by the employees in that organization

c. The types of strain reported by employees

d. The organizational outcomes of employee stress that the company experiences (e.g. turnover, absenteeism)

e. The types of interventions the company has to help employees reduce or manage stress

Case 1: A Stressful Job

Joan is an emergency room nurse at a busy city hospital. She has always enjoyed the hustle of working emergency and the challenges of dealing with the unexpected. Lately, Joan has been worried about her own well-being. She has been very abrupt with her coworkers on several occasions and has had difficulty concentrating on her job. Although there have been no problems to date, Joan is worried that her deteriorating performance might cause a problem given the critical nature of her work. Her doctor suggested that she take an extended leave because of her "nerves." As the HR representative, what do you think is going on here? Are Joan's concerns likely to be a result of stress? What stressors are present in the environment? If there are 20 employees in emergency and Joan is the only one complaining, does this mean that her complaints are not real?

Case 2: Violence on the Job

Vic Wagar is the new HR manager at Brandon Financial Services. BFS is a mid-sized company with many branches that provides personal and business banking services. Less than one month into his new job, Vic was faced with a novel and unexpected situation. During an attempted robbery at one of the smaller branches, one of BFS's employees was shot. Despite prompt first aid and evacuation, the employee died in hospital the next day. Vic has been asked by senior management to take charge of the situation. In particular, they have asked Vic to make sure that the eight other branch employees are "all right" and are dealing with the tragic event. Vic has been assured that BFS will place all required resources at his disposal to ensure that the remaining employees receive whatever care they need. Knowing of your expertise in these areas, Vic has contacted you for advice. He needs to know what types of reaction to expect from the eight remaining employees. Most important, he wants to know what action, if any, he should be taking. What do you tell him?

Case 3: Technology at Work

SmithCorp is a quickly growing organization specializing in pharmaceuticals. The management of SmithCorp prides itself on being on the cutting edge. Accordingly, it ensures that all its employees are provided with the latest advances in technology. Employees have laptops, wireless Internet access, PDAs, and cell phones. SmithCorp also frequently upgrades its software and network systems. Many of the employees rely heavily on this technology and these programs in their daily work. A large portion of SmithCorp's staff works in sales and product management. They are frequently on the road visiting client sites and making sales calls. As such, much of the communication among coworkers and between coworkers and their managers is technologically mediated. What are some of the potential psychosocial hazards that employees at SmithCorp might face? As an HR manager at SmithCorp's head office, what types of programs could you implement to help employees manage the stress and strain that may result from exposure to these psychosocial hazards?

Endnotes

1. Sauter, S. L., Murphy, L. R., & Hurrell, J. J. (1990). Prevention of work-related psychological disorders: A national strategy proposed by the National Institute for Occupational Safety and Health (NIOSH). *American Psychologist, 45,* 1146–1158.

2. Karasek, R., & Theorell, T. (1990). *Healthy work: Stress, productivity, and the reconstruction of working life.* New York: Basic Books; and Quillian-Wolever, R. E., & Wolever, M. E. (2003). Stress management at work. In J. C. Quick & L. E. Tetrick (Eds.), *Handbook of occupational health psychology* (pp. 355–375). Washington, DC: American Psychological Association.

3. Pratt, L. I., & Barling, J. (1988). Differentiating between daily events, acute and chronic stressors: A framework and its implications. In J. J. Hurrell, L. R. Murphy, S. L. Sauter, & C. L. Cooper (Eds.), *Occupational stress: Issues and development in research* (pp. 41–53). London: Taylor & Francis.

4. Pratt, L. I., & Barling, J. (1988). Differentiating between daily events, acute and chronic stressors: A framework and its implications. In J. J. Hurrell, L. R. Murphy, S. L. Sauter, & C. L. Cooper (Eds.), *Occupational stress: Issues and development in research* (pp. 41–53). London: Taylor & Francis.

5. Sauter, S. L., Murphy, L. R., & Hurrell, J. J. (1990). Prevention of work-related psychological disorders: A national strategy proposed by the National Institute for Occupational Safety and Health (NIOSH). *American Psychologist, 45,* 1146–1158.

6. Selye, H. (1946). The general adaptation syndrome and diseases of adaptation. *Journal of Clinical Endocrinology, 6,* 117; and Theorell, T. (2003). To be able to exert control over one's situation: A necessary condition for coping with stressors. In J. C. Quick & L. E. Tetrick (Eds.), *Handbook of occupational health psychology* (pp. 201–220). Washington, DC: American Psychological Association.

7. Lazarus, R. S., & Folkman, S. (1984). *Stress, appraisal, and coping.* New York: Springer.

8. Gazzaniga, M. S., & Heatherton, T. F. (2003). *Psychological science.* New York: W. W. Norton.

9. Friedman, M., & Rosenman, R. (1974). *Type A behavior and your heart.* New York: Knopf.

10. Helmreich, R. L., Spence, J. T., & Pred, R. S. (1988). Making it without losing it: Type A, achievement motivation and scientific attainment revisited. *Personality and Social Psychology Bulletin, 14,* 495–504.

11. Landsbergis, P. A., Schnall, P. L., Belkic, K. L., Baker, D., Schwartz, J. E., & Pickering, T. G. (2003). The workplace and cardiovascular disease: The relevance and potential role for occupational health psychology. In J. C. Quick & L. E. Tetrick (Eds.), *Handbook of occupational health psychology* (pp. 265–287). Washington, DC: American Psychological Association; and Bluen, S. D., Barling, J., & Burns, W. (1990). Predicting sales performance, job satisfaction, and depression using the achievement striving and impatience-irritability dimensions of Type A behavior. *Journal of Applied Psychology, 75,* 212–216.

12. Speilberger, C. D., Vagg, P. R., & Wasala, C. F. (2003). Occupational stress: Job pressures and lack of support. In J. C. Quick & L. E. Tetrick (Eds.), *Handbook of occupational health psychology* (pp. 185–200). Washington, DC: American Psychological Association.

13. Mohren, C. L., Swaen, G. M. H., Borm, P. J. A., Bast, A., & Galama, J. M. D. (2001). Psychological job demands as a risk factor for common cold in a Dutch working population. *Journal of Psychosomatic Research, 50,* 21–27.

14. Frone, M. R., Cooper, M. L., & Russell, M. (1994). Stressful life events, gender and substance use: An application of Tobit regression. *Psychology of Addictive Behaviors, 8,* 59–69.

15. Quick, J. C., Quick, J. D., Nelson, D. L., & Hurrell, Jr., J. J. (1997). *Preventive stress management in organizations.* Washington, DC: APA Books.

16. Burke, R. J. (1993). Organizational-level interventions to reduce occupational stressors. *Work and Stress, 7,* 77–87; and Hepburn, C. G., Loughlin, C. A, & Barling, J. (1997). Coping with chronic work stress. In B. H. Gottleib (Ed.), *Coping with chronic work stress.* New York: Plenum Press.

17. Hepburn, C. G., Loughlin, C. A, & Barling, J. (1997). Coping with chronic work stress. In B. H. Gottleib (Ed.), *Coping with chronic work stress.* New York: Plenum Press.

18. Hepburn, C. G., Loughlin, C. A, & Barling, J. (1997). Coping with chronic work stress. In B. H. Gottleib (Ed.), *Coping with chronic work stress.* New York: Plenum Press.

19. Hepburn, C. G., Loughlin, C. A, & Barling, J. (1997). Coping with chronic work stress. In B. H. Gottleib (Ed.), *Coping with chronic work stress.* New York: Plenum Press.

20. Quick, J. C., Quick, J. D., Nelson, D. L., & Hurrell, Jr., J. J. (1997). *Preventive stress management in organizations.* Washington, DC: APA Books.

21. Jenkins, E. L. (1996). Workplace homicide: Industries and occupations at high risk. *Occupational Medicine State of Art Reviews, 11*(2), 219–225.

22. National Institute for Occupational Safety and Health. (1996). *Violence in the workplace.* Retrieved from http://www.cdc.gov/niosh/violphs.html, January 7, 2005.

23. International Labour Organization (1998). *Violence on the job—A global problem.* Retrieved from http://www.ilo.org/public/english/bureau/inf/pr/1998/30.htm, January 7, 2005.

24. LeBlanc, M. M., & Barling, J. (2005). Understanding the many faces of workplace violence. In S. Fox & P. E. Spector (Eds.), *Counterproductive workplace behavior: An integration of both*

actor and recipient perspective on causes and consequences (pp. 41–64). Washington, DC: American Psychological Association Press.

25. National Institute for Occupational Safety and Health. (1996). *Violence in the workplace.* Retrieved from http://www.cdc.gov/niosh/violphs.html, January 7, 2005.

26. Braverman, M. (1999). *Preventing workplace violence: A guide for employers and practitioners* (1st ed.). California: Sage.

27. LeBlanc, M. M., & Kelloway, E. K. (2002). Predictors and outcomes of workplace violence. *Journal of Applied Psychology, 87,* 444–453.

28. Schat, A. C., & Kelloway, E. K. (2000). The effects of perceived control on the outcomes of workplace aggression and violence. *Journal of Occupational Health Psychology, 4,* 386–402.

29. Rogers, K., & Kelloway, E. K. (1997). Violence at work: Personal and organizational outcomes. *Journal of Occupational Health Psychology, 2,* 63–71; and Schat, A. C., & Kelloway, E. K. (2000). The effects of perceived control on the outcomes of workplace aggression and violence. *Journal of Occupational Health Psychology, 4,* 386–402.

30. Ilies, R., Hauserman, N., Schwaohau, S., & Stibal, J. (2003). Reported incidence rates of work-related sexual harassment in the United States: Using meta-analysis to explain reported rate disparities. *Personnel Psychology, 56,* 607–631.

31. Crocker, D. & Kalemba, V. (1999). The incidence and impact of women's experiences of sexual harassment in Canadian workplaces. *Canadian Review of Sociology and Anthropology, 46,* 541–558.

32. Fitzgerald, L. F. (1993). Sexual harassment: Violence against women in the workplace. *American Psychologist, 48,* 1070–1076.

33. Aggarwal, A. P. (1992). *Sexual harassment in the workplace.* Toronto: Butterworths Canada Ltd.

34. Aggarwal, A. P. (1992). *Sexual harassment in the workplace.* Toronto: Butterworths Canada Ltd.; and Hesson-McInnis, M. S., & Fitzgerald, L. F. (1997). Sexual harassment: A preliminary test of an integrative model. *Journal of Applied Social Psychology, 27,* 877–901.

35. Aggarwal, A. P. (1992). *Sexual harassment in the workplace.* Toronto: Butterworths Canada Ltd.

36. Aggarwal, A. P. (1992). *Sexual harassment in the workplace.* Toronto: Butterworths Canada Ltd.

37. Elovainio, M., Kivimaki, M., & Helkama, K. (2001). Organizational justice evaluations, job control, and occupational strain. *Journal of Applied Psychology, 86,* 418–424; Francis, L., Kelloway, E. K., Barling, J., & Keeley, C. (2003). *The impact of organizational injustice on the experience of stress.* Paper presented at the Work, Stress and Health Conference, Toronto, ON; and Tepper, B. J. (2001). Health consequences of organizational injustice: Tests of main and interactive effects. *Organizational Behavior and Human Decision Processes, 86,* 197–215.

38. Cropanzano, R., & Greenberg, J. (1997). Progress in organizational justice: Tunneling through the maze. In C. L. Cooper & I. T. Robertson (Eds.), *International review of industrial and organizational psychology,* vol. 12 (pp. 317–372). London: John Wiley & Sons.

39. Leventhal, G. S., Karuza, J., & Fry, W. R. (1980). Beyond fairness: A theory of allocation preferences. In G. Mikula (Ed.), *Justice and social interaction* (pp. 167–218). New York: Springer-Verlag; and Thibaut, J., & Walker, L. (1975). *Procedural justice: A psychological analysis.* Hillsdale, NJ: Erlbaum.

40. Coovert, M. D., & Thompson, L. F. (2003). Technology and workplace health. In J. C. Quick & L. E. Tetrick (Eds.), *Handbook of occupational health psychology* (pp. 221–241). Washington, DC: American Psychological Association.

41. Coovert, M. D., & Thompson, L. F. (2003). Technology and workplace health. In J. C. Quick & L. E. Tetrick (Eds.), *Handbook of occupational health psychology* (pp. 221–241). Washington, DC: American Psychological Association.

42. Brenner, H., & Ahern, W. (2000). Sickness absence and early retirement on health grounds in the construction industry in Ireland. *Occupational and Environmental Medicine, 57,* 615–620.

Hazard Recognition and Assessment

Chapter Learning Objectives

After reading this chapter, you should be able to

- identify the sources of workplace hazards
- describe methods to systematically examine these hazards
- list ways to assess the probability, exposure, and consequences of the hazards
- describe the concept of risk assessment
- recognize and define the terminology associated with hazard recognition
- employ the various techniques available to determine risk
- outline the effects of and necessity for task analysis
- be able to discuss various types of trauma, based on human activity
- describe the nature and etiology of repetitive-strain injuries
- describe the techniques of manual lifting
- recognize the ergonomic factors associated with hazard recognition and assessment
- describe the components of a hazard identification program

CAUGHT IN, UNDER, OR BETWEEN

Occupational health and safety statistics classify some injuries as "caught in, under, or between (CIUB) machinery." For Matthew Underdown, this technical classification is also a tragic reality.

Nineteen-year-old Matthew was working at a Downey Timber Ltd. sawmill in Revelstoke, British Columbia. On March 4, 2004, Matthew was working around a conveyer belt. He reached between the belt and the tail spool to remove a stick. His arm got caught in the machinery. The operation of the machinery tore Matthew's arm off.

We need to classify and analyze workplace hazards to make safer workplaces. Terminology and classification are often "dry" and "boring," but we should never forget that the hazards are real and the consequences immense for both individuals and organizations.

Prompt action by coworkers (packing the severed arm in ice and rushing Matthew to the hospital) and 12 hours of surgery resulted in the successful reattachment of Matthew's arm.

Source: Adapted from "Drs reattach young worker's arm following sawmill accident," *Canadian Occupational Health and Safety News*. Retrieved from http://www.esourcecanada .com/bnn/search.asp on March 30, 2004.

 7.1

Virtually every workplace has recognizable hazards to which people are exposed. A hazard is classically defined as any existing or potential condition in the workplace that, by itself or interacting with other factors, can result in deaths, injuries, property damage, or other losses.[1] Hazard recognition and evaluation refer to the process of determining those factors likely to cause incidents and accidents. The complete process of recognition, assessment, and control is commonly referred to as RAC.

Terminology

The process of hazard identification and evaluation involves some very specific terms, some of which are incorrectly used interchangeably. Although some terms seem similar, they each have a distinctive use within the OH&S field.

1. *Hazard.* A **hazard** is any condition or changing set of circumstances that has the potential to cause an injury. A hazardous condition would include a damaged ladder, an icy porch and steps, or a frayed electrical wire. A changing set of circumstances would include the substitution of a toxic solvent for a nontoxic solvent.
2. *Event.* An **event** is any activity that may occur on a day-to-day basis as a direct or indirect result of some human or human-related undertaking; operating a forklift or word processor is an event.

hazard

any condition or changing set of circumstances that has the potential to cause an injury

event

any activity that may occur on a day-to-day basis as a direct or indirect result of some human or human-related undertaking

3. *Incident.* An **incident** is any observable human activity that is an unwanted event or occurrence that *might have* had a negative impact on the people, property, or process involved. Thus, an incident includes both accidents and close calls. Examples of close calls include not wearing safety glasses when operating a power saw, wearing loose clothing when operating machinery with moving parts, and brushing against hot objects with unprotected hands without getting burned. Incidents involve the presence of a hazard but may or may not result in an accident.

4. *Accident.* An **accident** is any unwanted event that *causes* harm to people, property, or processes. Accidents usually result from direct contact with some form of energy that is greater than the strength of the body or structure to resist. These energies may be
   - electrical, such as a shock from an electrical fixture or static source
   - mechanical, such as being caught in a machine or slipping while walking
   - thermal, causing burns from extreme heat or cold
   - radiative, from any radiation source including the sun and some artificial lighting
   - gravitational, causing unstable objects to fall
   - kinetic, having to do with a body or device that is moving or stopping suddenly
   - chemical, resulting from contact with any chemical substance causing burns

   In most accidents, several types of energies are involved. For example, when a worker falls off a ladder and breaks an arm, the energies involved are gravity (the fast trip to the ground), mechanical (not enough grip between the worker's feet and the ladder rung), and kinetic (the sudden stop).

5. *Injury.* An **injury** is any trauma, physical or mental, direct or indirect, acute or chronic, experienced by a human being. *Physical injury* includes any damage to tissue (resulting from cutting, abrasion, burning, etc.), and can include the inhalation of a toxic substance. A physical injury is very easy to identify. *Mental injury*, which includes such conditions as anxiety or depression, is more difficult to identify and prove. Both types of injuries can be debilitating and both are compensable under most Workers' Compensation programs. There are several classes of injury.
   (a) **Direct injury** is an injury that is the immediate or primary result of an action, such as leaning against a hot stove and being burned.
   (b) **Indirect injury** is a serious complication, such as an infection resulting from being burned by a stove.
   (c) *Acute* trauma is an injury that occurs quickly (e.g., a burn from a stove).
   (d) *Chronic* trauma is a condition or injury that takes many years to develop and manifest itself, such as the development of a malignant tumour 25 years after exposure to a toxic material such as asbestos.

6. **Repetitive-strain injury**. A repetitive-strain injury results from ongoing, continuous, and repetitive actions that cause muscle or skeletal strain (e.g., tennis elbow).

incident

any observable human activity that is an unwanted event or occurrence that *might have* had a negative impact on the people, property, or process involved

accident

any unwanted event that *causes* harm to people, property, or processes

injury

any trauma, physical or mental, direct or indirect, acute or chronic, experienced by a human being

direct injury

an injury that is the immediate or primary result of an action

indirect injury

a serious complication incurred as a result of an injury

repetitive-strain injury

results from ongoing, continuous, and repetitive actions that cause muscle or skeletal strain

An Iceberg Model of Health and Safety Costs

As you might know, the visible part of an iceberg is its smallest part. The bulk of the iceberg is below the surface of the water. This is an apt image for health and safety costs. The visible part of the iceberg, which is the smallest part, represents insured costs (sometimes called direct costs), including fire insurance and compensation. The part below the surface—the major portion—represents uninsured costs (or indirect costs), including time for accident investigation, loss of customers, and loss of employees from a resultant layoff. Practice shows that for every dollar of insured costs, there can be 5 to 10 dollars of uninsured costs, making the latter a serious—though often ignored—cost factor. Hazard analysis is directed at preventing these costs from accumulating.

Types of Injuries

overt traumatic injuries

injuries resulting from coming into contact with an energy source

overexertion injuries

injuries resulting from excessive physical effort, repetitive motions, and, possibly, awkward working positions

Considering the nature of workplace injuries will assist us in identifying what type of hazards we are concerned with in the workplace. There are at least two broad classes of injuries that we see occurring in workplaces. **Overt traumatic injuries** (e.g., cuts, fractures, burns) typically result from coming into contact with an energy source (e.g., falling, being struck by material). In contrast, **overexertion injuries** (e.g., sprains, back pain, tendonitis, carpal tunnel syndrome) typically are caused by excessive physical effort, repetitive motions, and, possibly, awkward working positions. From this observation, it follows that hazard identification and control should focus on identifying and controlling sources of energy that can result in injury and conditions of work that may lead to overexertion.

Overt Injuries

One of the most common causes of workplace accidents is individuals coming into contact with objects and equipment in the workplace (see Table 7.1). For example, individuals may be struck by objects that are falling from overhead or may drop materials on themselves, resulting in crush injuries. Material may be flying through the air because of grinding or cutting operations. The use of compressed air in many industrial settings is a particular hazard, as the stream of compressed air may cause small particles of material to accelerate rapidly through the work environment. Individuals may be struck by moving equipment (e.g., vehicles, forklifts).

Another form of contact with equipment occurs when individuals become caught in, under, or between (CIUB) machinery. The use of industrial presses, for example, frequently is associated with crush injuries when individuals who are feeding the machine stock get their hands caught in the machinery as it presses. Conveyer belts and other power transmission systems (e.g., belts, pulleys) may have "pinch points" in which individuals become entangled.

TABLE 7.1

Most Common Injuries among Young Workers

INDUSTRY	MOST COMMON	SECOND MOST COMMON
Hospitality/food service	Struck by object	Contact with hot object
Retail	Overexertion	Struck by object
Transportation	Overexertion	Struck by object
Construction	Struck by object	Overexertion
Forestry	Struck by object	Falls
Manufacturing: wood paper	Overexertion	Struck by object
Manufacturing: metal	Struck by object	Overexertion
Manufacturing: food processing	Overexertion	Struck by object
Wholesale	Overexertion	Struck by object

Source: Workers' Compensation Board of Yukon, "Yukon employers' guide to young workers' safety." Retrieved from http://www.wcb.yk.ca/fileadmin/user_upload/PDF_files/reports_and_publications/handbook.pdf, March 30, 2004.

Falls also represent a significant source of injury in the workplace. This category includes both falling from a height (e.g., off a ladder, or down a set of stairs) as well as falls on the same level (e.g., slipping on the floor). As we might expect, falls from a height are common in construction, where ladders and other temporary structures (e.g., scaffolding) are frequently used. Falls on the same level frequently result from spilled material (e.g., oil) or by tripping over poorly placed material, uneven surfaces, and so on.

Although frequently overlooked as a type of workplace accident, motor vehicle accidents are a significant health and safety concern. Individuals who drive for a living are exposed to hazardous driving conditions to a much greater extent than are most drivers. Moreover, professional drivers may also deal with shift work and demanding delivery schedules. The equipment they drive is also subject to more rigorous use than the traditional passenger vehicle and requires exceptional ongoing maintenance to ensure safety.

Overt traumatic injuries also result from coming into contact with sources of energy such as electricity, chemicals (e.g., chemical burns), and heat (e.g., touching hot surfaces results in a burn). Using abrasives or prolonged kneeling can result in abrasive injuries in which the skin is torn or rubbed raw.

In each case of overt injury, prevention focuses on (1) recognizing the source of the hazard (i.e., the potential energy source), (2) eliminating the hazard, and (3) protecting workers from exposure to the energy source (i.e., through personal protective equipment).

Overexertion Injuries

Although there are numerous types of overexertion or repetitive strain injuries, most result from one of three basic causes: lifting, working in awkward positions, and repetition.

Materials handling, which involves lifting, carrying, and lowering, is a frequently performed operation in many organizations that can result in high-risk injuries through overexertion and poor posture, both of which are the primary cause of lower back pain. The appendix to this chapter contains a method for estimating lifting tolerances recommended by the National Institute for Occupational Safety and Health (NIOSH) in the United States.[2] Back injuries—from stabbing pain to total disability—can have far-reaching effects for the worker, the worker's family, and the company. Low back pain, frequently associated with materials handling, accounts for more than 50% of all musculoskelatal complaints and is the fastest-growing category of disability.[3]

When lifting activities are identified as a workplace hazard, materials handling should be mechanized through the use of conveyors and forklift trucks or other lifting devices, or it can be automated through the use of automated guided vehicles (AGV), which follow sensor lines on the floor, stopping as required to transfer their product, or computer-controlled inventory systems that allow computer-controlled machines to pick up or stock inventory. Thus,

---

Occupational Health and Safety Notebook 7.2

Twelve Rules for Proper Lifting

1. Size up the load and check the overall conditions. Is the load being picked up in the open, or is it surrounded by other boxes? Is it too large to grasp? How far does it have to be carried? How high does it have to be lifted? Is the floor dry or slippery?

2. Choose the lifting position that feels the best. There are several "correct" ways to lift a load. Figure 7.1 illustrates two of the more common ones: the straight back leg lift and the stoop lift.

3. Check for slivers, nails, sharp edges, and so on. Sustaining a penetration injury while lifting is both painful and awkward.

4. Lift by gripping the load with both the fingers and the palms of the hand. The more the hand is in contact with the object, the better the control and the more positive the application of the lifting force.

5. Keep the back straight. A straight back (not a vertical back) will reduce stress on the spine and make the load distribution on each vertebral disc uniform.

6. Maintain good balance. If you are not steady on your feet, then an off-balance motion can impose significant stress on the discs.

7. Avoid any unnecessary bending. Do not place loads on the floor but on a platform or rack if they have to be picked up again later. Bend the knees, and do not stoop.

8. Avoid unnecessary twisting. No twisting is acceptable. Turn the feet, not the hips or shoulders.

9. Avoid reaching out. Keep all loads as close to the body as possible. The farther away from the body centre, the greater the disc load and hence stress (see Figure 7.2).

10. Avoid excessive weight. If the load is too heavy or too awkward, get help. The definition of "excessive" will depend on the individual and his or her physical condition and training.

11. Lift slowly and smoothly. Use your body weight to start the load moving and then lift using your legs and arms.

12. Keep in good physical shape. The better your physical condition, the easier lifting will be and the lower the risk of sustaining a lower back injury.

Sources: WorkSafe Alberta, "Back/Lifting." Retrieved from http://www3.gov.ab.ca/hre/whs/network/hstopics/ergonomics/backcare.asp, October 10, 2004; North American Occupational Safety and Health, "Preventing back injury in manual materials handling." Retrieved from http://www.naosh.org/english/documents/mmh.html, October 10, 2004; WorkSafe BC, "Top seven dangers for young workers." Retrieved from http://youngworker.healthandsafetycentre.org/s/Top-Seven-Dangers.asp?ReportID=33144, October 10, 2004.

many of the risks associated with lifting can be greatly reduced. Supports that force the back to remain straight but do not prevent the worker from lifting or handling heavier loads are used by some workers. Although the logic of using back supports is appealing, agencies such as NIOSH in the U.S. have suggested that there is no scientific support for the use of such devices. The Canadian Task Force on Preventative Health Care found that randomized control trials did not support the use of back supports.[4] Of the five trials reviewed, three found no effect and the remaining two found marginal effects.

Figure 7.1

Lift Positions

FIGURE 7.2

Relationship between Load Position and Lower Back Stress

LOWER BACK STRESS = (A + B) × C

where A = distance from front of body to rotation point of spine, approximately 20 cm

B = distance in front of body to load centre of mass

C = load weight

$$(20 + 15) \times 10$$
$$= 350 \text{ kg/cm}$$

$$(20 + 22.5) \times 10$$
$$= 425 \text{ kg/cm}$$

$$(20 + 30) \times 10$$
$$= 500 \text{ kg/cm}$$

Repetitive-Strain Injuries

Repetitive-strain injury (RSI), cumulative trauma disorder (CTD), musculo-skeletal injury (MSI), and overuse syndrome (OS) are injuries whose origins can be traced to continuous and repetitive actions that produce muscle or skeletal strain. Because the terms are basically interchangeable, the term RSI will refer to all these conditions in this chapter.

Any strain-producing body action that involves use of the fingers, wrists, arms, elbows, shoulders, neck, back, and, to a lesser extent, the lower body and legs, and is repeated over a long period, can cause damage to joints and tissues. Tennis elbow, golfer's elbow, telephone operator's elbow, writer's cramp, and postal worker's shoulder are well-known examples of RSI. More recently named conditions include carpal tunnel syndrome, thoracic outlet syndrome, and white fingers disease or Raynaud's syndrome. The latter, as previously mentioned, is also caused by vibration.

RSI is fast becoming the most common occupational injury. Data from the Canadian Community Health Survey suggest that 1 in 20 Canadians over the age of 20 have experienced RSI.[5] This translates into 2.3 million cases, the majority of which result from work activities.

Recognizing RSI: Risk Factors and Symptoms

Recognizing the risk factors for and symptoms of RSI is the first step toward taking preventative and remedial action. Your job puts you at risk for RSI if

- you spend a large amount of time in continuous computer use or other repetitive action;
- you do not take frequent breaks to stretch;
- your workstation is poorly designed from an ergonomic standpoint;
- you use the computer but have poor typing skills (i.e., poor hand position, excessive force in striking the keys).

The symptoms of RSI can include

- weakness in a limb or limbs
- tingling or numbness in a limb
- pain
- lack of endurance (e.g., hand tires rapidly)
- clumsiness (e.g., difficulty picking things up, buttoning clothing)

Sources: Engineering Electronics, "Computer related repetitive stress injury." Retrieved from http://eeshop.unl.edu/rsi.html, October 10, 2004; and Canadian Auto Workers, "What is RSI?" Retrieved from http://www.caw.ca/whatwedo/health&safety/pdf/03-RSIDayPamphletGeneric1.pdf, October 10, 2004.

The origins of RSI can be traced to the following four general conditions:

1. *Unnatural joint position or posture.* Whenever a joint is forced to work in a position that is unnatural or stressed, the risk of RSI is increased. For instance, during keyboarding the wrists are forced out of axial alignment with the arm. The use of a hand tool such as a pair of pliers can force the wrist–arm axes out of line, creating a stress condition that could eventually cause joint irritation

2. *Force application to hinge joints.* When these joints are forced to carry applied loading, particularly when flexed, the joint load distribution of the cartilage is uneven, causing excessive stress in a small area of the joint. The wrist is a good example of a hinge joint. When performing a task such as lifting while bent, this joint can begin to ache. Repetition of the activity can result in a loss of strength.

3. *Activity repetition.* Tasks such as keyboarding (computer operator) or using a hammer (carpenter) involve a repetitive flexing of the fingers and wrists. The action of typing applies low-load repetition to the fingers (touching the keys) and medium loading to the wrist (supporting the hand). The action of hammering applies a high-impact loading to the wrist, which is flexed into a nonaligned axis on impact. The shock effect increases the potential risk of tissue damage.

4. *Preexisting conditions.* Ailments such as arthritis or circulation disorders can have a synergistic effect on RSI conditions. For example, arthritis is an inflammation condition of the joints that can be aggravated by the stress associated with hammering or keyboarding activity.

Artistic Occupations at Risk

If you search for RSI on the web, you will mostly find articles focused on the hazards of computer work and industrial jobs that involve repetitive motions. It may surprise you to know that people in other occupations—such as dancers and musicians—are also at risk for RSI. These occupations involve considerable repetition (practice, practice, practice) and often involve awkward hand or body positions. Intense preparation for a performance, learning new pieces (requiring extensive practice and repetition), changes in techniques or instruments, and prolonged performances are all risk factors for performing artists. Dancers are at risk because of these factors but also because forceful exertions can lead to stress factors and similar injuries.

Source: Safety and Health in Arts, Production and Entertainment, "Preventing musculoskeletal injury (MSI) for musicians and dancers." Retrieved from http://www.shape.bc.ca/resources/pdf/msi.pdf, October 10, 2004.

Awkward Working Positions

Strains and sprains can also result from bending, twisting, and working in a variety of awkward positions. Frequently, the work position may compound or interact with other factors. For example, an individual may be lifting a load that normally would present no problem but is working in a confined space that prohibits following safe lifting procedures, resulting in an injury.

Perhaps the most common types of injury result from bending or twisting the torso, extending the reach beyond the body, and working overhead with the hands and arms. As a general guideline, individuals should not have to reach below the knees or raise their arms above the shoulder for any length of time. The design of workstations and work procedures should ensure that individuals work in a comfortable position. Moreover, equipment and machinery should be adjustable to accommodate differences in body size.

RPC 7.2

RPC 7.3

RPC 7.4

Hazard Identification

The identification of hazards includes four areas of analysis: ergonomic factors, human factors, situational factors, and environmental factors. This section is not to be confused with the categories of information to be collected in Chapter 12, which uses the latter three classifications of human, situational, and environmental factors to determine the areas of investigation.

Ergonomic Factors

Ergonomics-related issues are becoming increasingly prominent and important. Over a five-year-period, one-third of compensation claims in British Columbia resulted from ergonomics-related injuries, costing $400 million for more than 100,000 claims.[6] British Columbia was the first province to pass ergonomics legislation.

Studies have indicated that workplaces designed along ergonomic principles not only decrease the risk of physical injury but also increase productivity and efficiency. One airline that introduced ergonomic equipment such as adjustable work surfaces, footrests, and document holders reported a 93% reduction in errors, a 50% decrease in musculoskeletal problems, a 33% drop in visual fatigue, with a 33% increase in efficiency.[7] The redesign of computer workstations has been associated with increases in both productivity[8,9] and user satisfaction.[10]

The goal of an ergonomics program is to design a work system in which the work methods, machines, equipment, layout, and environment (noise, heat, light, and air quality) are matched or are compatible with the physical and behavioural characteristics of the worker to reduce risk.[11] Workplace design has traditionally focused on standardization—one size fits all—despite the wide variations in the physical characteristics of employees. **Anthropometric** factors such as height, weight, reach, and strength influence how the work is done and the likelihood of achieving efficiency and safety. Inexperience and idiosyncratic ways of doing work increase the probability of injuries. Tasks have to be matched to human capabilities to ensure optimal performance and reduction of risk.

anthropometry

study of the measurements of the human body to determine differences in individuals or groups of individuals

Human Factors

Incidents involving humans (often referred to as unsafe acts) fall into two main categories, *predictable* and *random*. An incident that is a result of a predictable action is something that the perpetrator did knowingly. For example, a worker who locks out a machine before making some adjustments is performing a correct, voluntary action, thereby avoiding any possible injury from the operating machine. In most cases, sources of potential accidents are predictable (e.g., a worker knows that it is possible for a ladder rung to break, but uses the ladder anyway). A random event, in contrast, is by its very nature difficult to predict. For example, the worker climbing the ladder could have fallen because another worker walked into the ladder. No one could have predicted this event. However, at times, the same action could also be predictable, depending on circumstances. If the same worker had placed the ladder in a crowded corridor, the event could be considered predictable. A change in conditions can thus transform a random event into a predictable one.

Occupational Health and Safety Today 7.2

Safety Policy at Simplot Canada

Simplot Canada Limited is a major producer of fertilizer products and potato products in Western Canada. Based in the United States, Simplot operates a fertilizer complex in Brandon, Manitoba. Simplot Canada believes that all injuries, safety incidents, and occupational illnesses are preventable. Their safety policy includes recognition that all employees should look for potential hazards and unsafe behaviours and intervene to prevent unsafe behaviours.

Source: Simplot Canada, "Our safety philosophy, policies, services, goals and objectives." Retrieved from http://www.simplotcanada.ca/page.cfm?bv=3&docid=79&catid=3, October 10, 2004.

human factor

when a person causes an accident by commission, poor judgment, or omission (failing to do something)

When a worker or another person causes an accident by commission, poor judgment, or omission (failing to do something), the cause is labelled a **human factor**. However, analysts distinguish between fact finding and fault finding. A human action may have been directly or indirectly involved in the event, but "human error" or blame will neither be used nor implied. In a similar vein, no one would willingly or intentionally injure himself or herself, which tends to support the idea that a human action should not be considered "human error" and have blame assigned. No matter how many backup systems are in place, some shortcut or personal foible can cause the system to fail. The intent of hazard recognition, assessment, and control is not to find a scapegoat, but to correct procedures and behaviours so that the likelihood of the accident occurring again is reduced. Similarly there are techniques—see the fault tree analysis in the appendix—that can permit a professional to identify hazardous conditions or activities and implement correct procedures before hazardous events occur.

unsafe act

generally refers to a deviation from standard job procedures or practices that increases a worker's exposure to a hazard

An **unsafe act** generally refers to a deviation from standard job procedures or practices that increases a worker's exposure to a hazard. Unsafe acts may be direct and indirect. A human action that may cause an immediate event of any type, and over which the person has control, is considered a direct, unsafe act (sometimes referred to as a *substandard practice*). An example would be the improper modifications to a respirator used in a paint booth to allow a cigarette to be smoked through the filter cassette. An indirect, unsafe act is one in which the human action is only indirectly involved. Consider the following example. A designer of a machine alters a braking system on a punch press that allows the machine to complete its operating cycle after the emergency stop is activated instead of immediately stopping. In this instance, there is overlap between an indirect unsafe act and an unsafe condition. The machine defect started as an indirect unsafe act but resulted in an unsafe condition for the operators using the machine.

Some safety professionals differentiate between the terms "unsafe act" and "substandard practice" by suggesting that the latter implies a much broader application. In this text, the term unsafe act will be used to indicate acts or practices that are unsafe or potentially unsafe. Following are some examples of unsafe acts:

- Unauthorized operation of equipment—using after hours or without training
- Improper use of equipment—using a forklift truck to lift a load beyond its weight limit
- Use of defective equipment—using a broken ladder
- Failure to lock out power when servicing equipment
- Removal or disabling of safety devices—removing the guard from a table saw
- Failure to warn or secure—leaving a forklift truck running unattended
- Improper lifting, loading, or positioning—lifting a package that is too long or too heavy
- Failure to use personal protective equipment—not wearing safety glasses when using a table saw

Interaction of Factors

The four factors discussed in this chapter (ergonomic, human, situational, and environmental) do not happen in isolation–rather they may interact to result in accidents or injury. Consider the case of the Ocean Ranger.

In February 1982, a giant oil rig, the Ocean Ranger, capsized and sank off the coast of Newfoundland, resulting in the loss of the entire crew of 84 men. A subsequent investigation revealed errors on the part of the crew in charge of ballast control. Part of their job was to assess the draft of the rig by looking out a porthole in one of the legs of the rig, which was more than 8 metres above mean water level. To save time and energy, they left the porthole open. During a storm, water entered through the porthole and damaged the ballast control system. The problem was compounded when the crew misread the control manual and opened instead of closed the ballast tanks. This case illustrates the importance of presenting display information in a way that will allow for error-free interpretation.

Although the focus here is on display design, what other factors were at play?

Sources: CBC Archives, "The Ocean Ranger disaster." Retrieved from http://archives.cbc.ca/IDD-1-70-349/disasters_tragedies/ocean_ranger/, October 10, 2004; CBC News, "How the Ocean Ranger disaster changed oil exploration." Retrieved from http://www.cbc.ca/news/features/oil_rigs.html; October 10, 2004; and Atlantic Oil & Gas Works Online, "Future offshore safety was a prime concern." Retrieved from http://www.oilworks.com/February2002/NewMag/safety.html, October 10, 2004.

- Improper use of personal protective equipment—using a respirator that is unsuitable for the aerosols involved
- Alcohol or drug abuse—being under the influence at work
- Horseplay—throwing snowballs in a factory

Situational Factors

Situational factors, also known as *unsafe conditions*, exist when a company does not provide proper equipment, tools, or facilities, or when its operations are unsafe. The following are examples of unsafe conditions:

- Improper illumination—too dark or too much glare
- Poor exhaust or ventilation systems—the toxic vapours from a process hang in the air rather than being removed
- Defective equipment and materials—not to the required specifications
- Airborne toxic chemical agents—aerosols that are generated by poor control of the process
- Physical agents—machinery noise
- Fire and explosion conditions—improper use or handling of flammable materials
- Poor housekeeping—oil spills and trash allowed to remain
- Adverse temperature conditions—working around a furnace on a hot summer day
- Poor indoor air quality—odours and stuffiness

situational factors

also known as unsafe conditions, exist when a company does not provide proper equipment, tools, or facilities, or when its operations are unsafe

- Ineffective personal protective equipment—not the correct type of protection for the specific conditions, such as providing dust masks where vapour masks should be used
- Continuance of improper procedures or practices—continuing to allow machine adjustment while the machine is operating

The above situational factors can be grouped into four categories:[12]

1. Defects in design
2. Substandard construction
3. Improper storage of hazardous materials
4. Inadequate planning, layout, and design

Environmental Factors

Environmental factors, including physical factors, chemical factors, biological factors, and ergonomic factors, can play either a direct or indirect role in accidents. For example, physical factors such as noise, vibration, illumination, and temperature extremes have an obvious relation to safety. A noisy work environment may prevent a worker from hearing approaching vehicles or may damage hearing over time. Similarly, chemical factors such as airborne toxic gases may not only cause illness, but may also impair a worker's reaction, judgment, or concentration. Contact with biological agents such as viruses or parasites may cause either minor illness—a cold—or something more serious—hepatitis B. Ergonomic factors such as poor desk-chair design or improper lifting techniques can cause discomfort and muscle strain.

Choosing a Hazard Identification Program

Safety and HR professionals have several choices to make when determining the type of hazard identification program they will undertake. The factors influencing this decision include the source of the request for information, the nature of the hazards to be identified, and the costs associated with the program.

Source of Request

The identification of workplace hazards may be prompted by a request from a Ministry of Labour or a Workers' Compensation Board (resulting from the presence of specific substances or conditions in the workplace) or from the joint health and safety committee (resulting from a complaint or inspection). Alternatively, the program may be initiated as part of an organization's safety program. The person responsible for OH&S may decide to survey one procedure, one area, or the entire plant, depending on the request.

Nature of Hazards

Some tests can be performed on a single employee, while others require samples from many workers. Similarly, some hazards (such as a broken tool) can be identified within minutes; other hazards, such as chemical agents, may require months of testing. All have an injury potential.

Cost

Cost will also determine the extent of the program. For example, to obtain an air sample for benzene contamination, sampling may have to be done in several locations over an eight-hour shift. Several air samples, including blanks, may have to be taken at each location. (A **blank** is an unopened cassette or other sampling device, such as a charcoal tube, that is used as a baseline or zero point for comparison in chemical testing.) The cost of obtaining three samples, plus a blank, in five locations (including the eight hours of the safety professional's time) would be more than $3,000. Unless it is a required legal assessment or a due diligence requirement, then a cost-benefit analysis would have to be done—comparing test costs to a reduction in cost for lost-time injuries.

blank

an unopened cassette or other sampling device, such as a charcoal tube, that is used as a baseline or zero point for comparison in chemical testing

Use of Safety Experts

Most organizations have a network of associations with people who have a great deal of knowledge about OH&S in the workplace. These experts include occupational health and safety inspectors, the suppliers who manufacture the tools and equipment used at the worksite, insurance company loss control specialists, safety personnel in the same occupational sector, labour representatives specializing in safety issues, and agencies such as the Industrial Accident Prevention Association (IAPA) or the Construction Safety Association of Ontario (CSAO).

Components of the Hazard Identification Program

A safety professional can enter a worksite and, by walking through, be able to note hazards. The utility of a **walk-through survey** is increased by arranging to have the supervisor and a worker member of the joint health and safety committee accompany the safety expert. **Safety sampling**, often referred to as *behaviour* or *activity sampling*, is a systematic survey procedure undertaken by safety personnel who record their observations of unsafe practices on a sampling document. They might observe, for example, workers without hardhats where they are required.

Actual and observable exposures to hazards are the focus of the survey. Examples of exposure include chemical substances such as solvents and physical agents such as noise. Safety personnel might observe escaping smoke, or open containers, or the wrong type of personal protective equipment worn by employees. However, potential and inferred exposures would not be ignored. The former includes any substance for which an intended control procedure is being considered. The latter includes any observable accumulation of material such as dust, which might become an airborne hazard.

Following the walk-through survey, the safety personnel encode and count their observations. A report is then submitted to management to provide an objective evaluation of the type and number of unsafe acts and conditions.

walk-through survey

a survey in which a safety professional walks through a worksite and notes hazards

safety sampling

a systematic survey procedure undertaken by safety personnel who record their observations of unsafe practices on a sampling document

RPC 7.3

Management can ask workers who represent a variety of tasks and jobs to identify hazards and unsafe conditions. Employees might report that they are required to adapt tools (thus rendering them potentially hazardous) in order to meet production quotas, or that a machine is dripping oil, rendering a corridor slippery and treacherous. Discussions with both the experts and the employees should be supplemented by an analysis of the job site and the work performed.

Analysis of the Plant, Tasks, and Jobs

Geographical Information

The company should have a detailed layout of the plant or premises, showing the location of processes, machinery, materials storage, shipping, and so forth. A drawing showing the location of any toxic materials and storage arrangement must be available under WHMIS requirements.

Task and Job Inventory

A description of the job and its associated tasks should be obtained and organized by department, operation, or product. The human resources department can assist by providing the **job description** and **job specifications**. Flow process charts that incorporate standard industrial engineering symbols can clarify the relationships among tasks, jobs, and procedures (see Figure 7.3).

job description

the content and hierarchy specific to a particular job

job specifications

the requirements necessary to perform the various functions of a job (e.g., ability to lift weight, education level)

Task Analysis

Task analysis refers to the systematic examination of a job's many components. It consists of a list of tasks and the job of which they are a part, the number of workers who perform the same or similar tasks, the time spent on each task, the importance of the task to the job, the complexity and criticality of the job, the learning curve if complicated and repetitive, and the effort required. The analysis identifies the various demands on the worker, the tasks that are susceptible to worker error and stress, and potentially hazardous conditions. Industrial engineering methods are best for performing this kind of analysis.

Reports and Audits

A review of the reports filed after an incident, accident, injury, or as part of a safety inspection will provide valuable information on hazards. Occupational health and safety departments and safety associations can also provide written information about the type of accidents in similar industries. Accident and injury rates published by governments are another source of information. Most Workers' Compensation Boards (for a complete list, see Chapter 3), for example, publish regular reports on accident statistics. Audit information, which is obtained by reviewing records of all injuries, accidents, incidents, workplace design changes, and environmental sampling, is an extremely useful source for cataloguing hazards. Most large

FIGURE 7.3

Flow Chart for Table Tennis Paddle Assembly

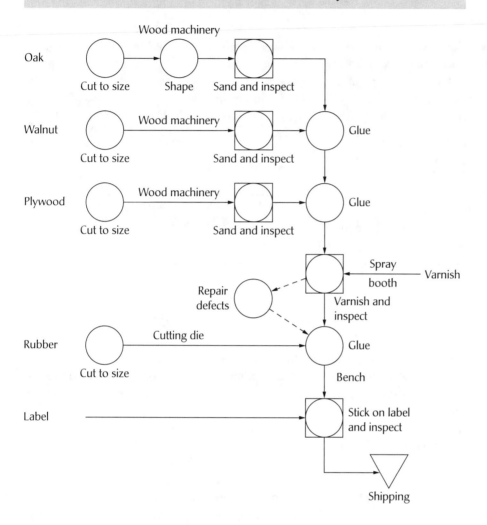

organizations are using computers to store, analyze, and report on hazards and incidents, thus facilitating the identification of hazards by type or department.[13]

Hazard Analysis

Hazard analysis is used to acquire specific hazard and failure information about a given system.[14] Hazard analysis is an orderly, analytical technique that examines a system for the most probable hazards having the severest consequences, for the purpose of establishing corrective or control mechanisms. The most common form of hazard analysis is the analytical tree of which there are two types. The **positive tree** shows, graphically, how a job should be done. The more frequently used tree is the **fault tree**, which provides an illustration of things that can go wrong. A typical fault tree structure is shown in Figure 7.6 in the appendix at the end of this chapter.

hazard analysis

an orderly, analytical technique that examines a system for the most probable hazards having the severest consequences, for the purpose of establishing corrective or control mechanisms

positive tree

shows, graphically, how a job should be done

fault tree

an illustration of things that can go wrong

Job Safety Analysis

One particularly useful means of identifying potential hazards in a job is to conduct a job safety analysis. Typically, this analysis is conducted by a team of subject matter experts, including the workers who do the job, supervisors, and health and safety specialists. The job safety analysis consists of

1. Breaking down the job into its constituent elements (e.g., tasks and sequences of tasks).
2. Analyzing each element to identify potential hazards. This may (and should) include the worker "walking through" each element of the job and explaining the details of each element to the team.
3. Considering "critical incidents" in which accidents or near misses occurred to inform the team's analysis.
4. Making recommendations to change the workstation, process, or method in order to control all the identified hazards.

Source: Canadian Centre for Occupational Health and Safety, "What is a job hazard analysis?" Retrieved from http://www.ccohs.ca/oshanswers/hsprograms/job–haz.html, October 10, 2004.

Risk Assessment

Once hazards have been identified, the risk of an incident, accident, or injury must be determined. Insurance companies have long used risk evaluation to determine the susceptibility of humans to having accidents and even to dying. The rates that subscribers pay are predicated on this type of evaluation. For example, younger drivers pay higher insurance rates because they are involved in a disproportionate number of accidents. Insurers similarly measure the relative risk of such events as theft, fire, flood, and vandalism. The same concept can be applied to health and safety.

R P C 7.2

R P C 7.4

Risk is the probability of an injury expressed as a percentage. The assessment of risk is calculated by determining the probability of an occurrence, the consequences of that occurrence, and the exposure to the cause of the occurrence expressed as

$$\text{Risk} = \text{Probability} \times \text{Consequences} \times \text{Exposure}$$

probability

the chance or likelihood that an event will occur

Probability refers to the chance or likelihood that an event will happen. The range of probabilities for risk runs from about 5% to about 95%. For management purposes, probability can also be measured in the following terms:[15]

- Likely will occur immediately or shortly after exposure to the hazard
- Probably will occur in time
- Possibly will occur in time
- Unlikely will occur

exposure

how regularly, or the number of times, a contact is made with the event

Any measurement of the risk of an accident occurring will have to take into account the degree of worker **exposure** to the hazard. This estimate includes not only the number of people who are regularly exposed, but also the frequency of the exposure. The more contact one has with a known hazard, the greater the risk. A worker who operates a lathe continuously throughout an eight-hour shift has more exposure than does the worker who uses the lathe only once or twice. However, consideration must also be given to the worker's level of experience. Generally, the more experience a worker has in dealing with a potentially dangerous work situation, the lower the possibility of injury. A professional race-car driver should be at a lower risk of injury when driving on a busy highway than is a regular commuter. Even a driver who has done skid-school training should be at a lower risk on the same roadway. A distracter such as an automobile accident can increase the probability of an accident. The number of workers exposed to a hazard could be used in a ranking or weighting system as part of the risk formula. Thus, probability can be affected by

- experience
- exposure
- proximity
- external stimuli or distraction
- illumination

Factors such as noise and light can increase the probability of an accident. The machine-generated noises in an assembly plant may mask the sound of an approaching vehicle like a forklift truck. Dimly lit workstations and pathways may increase the risks associated with potential hazards such as protruding sharp material and steps. The loud talking of a coworker may distract a worker who is engaged in a potentially hazardous task.

Consequences correspond to the severity of the injury, and can range from dust in the eye, to amputation of a finger, to death. Below is a subjective ranking system that can be used to classify the degree of hazard consequence:[16]

consequences
the results or severity of the injury

1. *Catastrophic:* may cause death or loss of a facility
2. *Critical:* may cause severe injury, occupational illness, or major property damage
3. *Marginal:* may cause minor injury or minor occupational illness resulting in lost workday(s), or minor property damage
4. *Negligible:* probably would not affect personnel safety or health but still in violation of specific criteria

By estimating probability, consequence, and exposure, safety personnel can determine the risk involved in any given job or task. Table 7.2 is a sample layout that can be used for hazard inventory and risk evaluation. The first column includes a brief description of the job or task being inventoried (a weld assembly operation in our example). The second column shows the hazard or hazards associated with the task (flash burns, skin burns, toxic fumes, lifting sprains, etc.). The third column shows an estimate of the percent probability for each hazard, and the fourth column lists the corresponding consequences of each hazard (e.g., "vision loss" for flash burns). Under each heading (probability, consequence, and exposure), the hazards can be rated using a scale of 1 to 10.

Chapter 7: Hazard Recognition and Assessment

TABLE 7.2

Sample Hazard Inventory and Risk Evaluation

Job/Task	Hazard(s)	Probability	Risk Consequence		Risk Exposure	
Weld assembly	Flash burns	6	Temporary or partial blindness, lost time	4	Daily while welding	8
	Skin burns	2	Discomfort	3	Rarely	3
	Lifting strains	5	Back injury if heavy material lifted, lost time	4	Occasionally	6
	Toxic fumes	6	Respiratory difficulty without personal protective equipment	4	Daily while welding	8

The factors in Table 7.3 correspond to the numbers shown in Table 7.2. Thus if the worker's risk of coming in contact with toxic fumes as a result of welding is calculated from the values assigned out of a maximum of 1000 as a percent then

Risk = $6 \times 4 \times 8 = 192/1000 = 0.192$ or 19.2%

In this example, the worker would have a 19.2% risk of contact with toxic fumes while welding. To determine whether this value is too high, the chemical content and toxicity of the fumes would have to be known. This information appears on the labels of hazardous products.

TABLE 7.3

Factors for Evaluating Risk

	Probability		Consequence		Exposure
10	Predicted or expected	10	Catastrophic	10	Continuous daily
9		9		9	
8	Almost certain	8	Fatality	8	Frequently, daily
7		7		7	
6	Possible	6	Serious injury	6	Occasional (1/wk–1/mo)
5	50/50 chance	5		5	
4	Coincidence	4	Disabling injury	4	Unusual (1/mo–1/yr)
3	Never occurred before	3	Minor	3	Rare
2	Almost impossible	2	Nerves ("close call")	2	Remotely possible

Follow-Up

The information obtained through hazard identification and assessment should be communicated to the plant manager, the immediate supervisor, and the health and safety committee. Some reports may be forwarded to the Ministry of Labour (if the substance is under assessment), or the Ministry of Environment, or to the corporation's lawyers. Safety professionals and supervisors who do not pass on information about unsafe conditions to a responsible manager could be charged under the Occupational Health and Safety Act.

When presented with information about hazards, management may decide to (1) take no action, (2) take corrective action, or (3) consider a cost-benefit analysis to determine whether the anticipated losses are worth the cost of correcting the problem.

Summary

The primary goal of hazard recognition and assessment is to reduce incidents, accidents, injuries, and property damage. A variety of methods are used to identify hazards: safety experts; plant, task, and job analysis; reports and audits; and use of monitoring instruments. Hazard analysis is then used to acquire specific information about the hazards in a given system. The hazards are rated according to their degree of risk, and calculations that take probabilities, consequences, and exposures into consideration are formulated. Although accidents and injuries cannot be eliminated, risk assessment can greatly reduce these undesirable events.

The increase in nontraumatic injuries such as back strain and RSI is costing employers in terms of lost production and compensation. Ergonomics, the design of the workplace to accommodate human characteristics and work methods, offers some solutions. The application of ergonomic principles to lifting, sitting, tool, and worksite design reduces the number of injuries and increases productivity.

Key Terms

accident, p. 165
anthropometry, p. 173
blank, p. 177
consequences, p. 181
direct injury, p. 165
event, p. 164
exposure, p. 180
fault tree, p. 179
hazard, p. 164
hazard analysis, p. 179
human factor, p. 174
incident, p. 165
indirect injury, p. 165

injury, p. 165
job description, p. 178
job specifications, p. 178
overexertion injuries, p. 166
overt traumatic injuries, p. 166
positive tree, p. 179
probability, p. 180
repetitive-strain injury, p. 165
safety sampling, p. 177
situational factors, p. 175
top event, p. 189
unsafe act, p. 174
walk-through survey, p. 177

Weblinks

Workplace Health, Safety and Compensation Commission of Newfoundland and Labrador, "Workplace hazard analysis form," **http://www.whscc.nf.ca/resource/SafetyHandouts/hazardanalysis.pdf** (p. 164)

Industrial Accident Prevention Association, "Determining significant hazards at work: A guide for Employers and JHSCs," **http://www.iapa.ca/pdf/SIGHAZWEB.pdf** (p. 166)

Constructions Safety Magazine, "Crushed/Hit," **http://66.203.200.8/UploadFiles/Magazine/VOL11NO3/fatals.htm** (p. 166)

Constructions Safety Magazine, "Falls: The number one cause of construction deaths," **http://66.203.200.8/UploadFiles/Magazine/VOL10NO3/falls.htm** (p. 167)

WorkSafe Saskatchewan, "Important safety tips on using portable ladders," **http://www.worksafesask.ca/files/naosh_week/w24-13en.htm?noframe** (p. 167)

National Institute for Occupational Safety and Health, "Back belts: Do they prevent injury?" **http://www.cdc.gov/niosh/backbelt.html** (p. 169)

Shelter Online, "Online RSI resources," **http://www.shelterpub.com/_fitness/_office_fitness_clinic/OFC_resources .html** (p. 170)

WorkSafe BC, "Injury prevention resources for performing arts & film—Music," **http://artsandfilm.healthandsafetycentre.org/s/Music.asp** (p. 171)

Manitoba Ministry of Labour and Immigration, "Guidelines—Ergonomics," **http://www.gov.mb.ca/labour/safety/ergoguide.html** (p. 173)

Health Care Health and Safety Association, "Workplace inspection report," **http://www.hchsa.on.ca/products/forms/lap_005.pdf** (p. 174)

Association of Workers' Compensation Boards of Canada, "National work injuries statistics program," **http://www.awcbc.org/english/NWISP_Stats.htm** (p. 178)

RPC Icons

RPC 7.1 Implements and evaluates practices in the areas of health, safety, security, and Workers' Compensation.

- investigative techniques
- hazard recognition
- disaster recovery techniques
- relevant legislation
- resource information

- common health and safety practices
- company policies and procedures
- Worker Protection (including health and safety and Workers' Compensation)
- theories and practices for protection of individuals and groups
- Occupational health and safety legislation (e.g., Occupational Health and Safety Act of Ontario, Workplace Safety & Insurance Act—Bill 99, Workplace Hazardous Materials Information System, Transportation of Dangerous Goods legislation, environmental legislation, smoking in the workplace legislation, civil rights legislation)
- hazard identification and control
- management techniques for OH&S Programs

RPC 7.2 Analyses risk to the health and safety of employees and determines appropriate preventative measures, including training, provision of required safety equipment, and administrative practices.

- relevant legislation
- nature of the business and physical work environment
- hazard recognition
- workplace inspection techniques
- safety programs, equipment, and emergency procedures
- ergonomics
- functions of the JHSC
- training and development/presentation techniques
- industry best practices
- relevant technical terminology
- the collective agreement
- services and equipment available in the community
- Worker Protection (including health and safety and Workers' Compensation)
- training and development program design and administration

TASK & KNOWLEDGE REQUIREMENTS
- Occupational health and safety legislation (e.g., Occupational Health and Safety Act of Ontario, Workplace Safety & Insurance Act—Bill 99, Workplace Hazardous Materials Information System, Transportation of Dangerous Goods legislation, environmental legislation, smoking in the workplace legislation, civil rights legislation)
- hazard identification and control
- emergency preparedness procedures
- management techniques for OH&S Programs
- types of employee assistance and wellness programs

RPC 7.3 Establishes effective programs for accident prevention, incident investigation, inspections, fire and emergency response, and required training.

- relevant legislation
- workplace inspection and accident investigation techniques
- nature of the business and physical work environment
- potential risks and hazards in the workplace
- emergency response planning

- community emergency response services
- training and development
- industry best practices
- Worker Protection (including health and safety and Workers' Compensation)
- training and development program design and administration
- hazard identification and control
- accident investigation procedures
- emergency preparedness procedures
- management techniques for OH&S Programs

RPC 7.4 Ensures that security programs and policies minimize risks while considering the obligation of the employer and the rights of employees, union, and third parties.

- nature of the business and physical work environment
- relevant legislation
- industry best practices
- program and policy development
- safety and security equipment in the workplace
- risk assessment/techniques
- cost/benefit analysis

Task & Knowledge Requirements
- available community resources
- Worker Protection (including health and safety and Workers' Compensation)
- unions' role in health and safety and in employee involvement
- Occupational health and safety legislation (e.g., Occupational Health and Safety Act of Ontario, Workplace Safety & Insurance Act—Bill 99, Workplace Hazardous Materials Information System, Transportation of Dangerous Goods legislation, environmental legislation, smoking in the workplace legislation, civil rights legislation)
- emergency preparedness procedures
- management techniques for OH&S Programs
- types of employee assistance and wellness programs

Discussion Questions

1. Select any lifting task at your workplace or simulate one at home. Using the NIOSH lifting equations (provided in the appendix), calculate the acceptability of the lift and recommend ways to make it less risky and more efficient.

2. A worker has to lift a package weighing approximately 16 kg onto a shelf that is 60 cm from where he or she is standing. The worker picks up the load from a point 30 cm from the floor; the final position on the shelf is 170 cm from the floor. The lift is repeated once each minute. Calculate the AL and the MPL, and determine the acceptability of the operation (see appendix).

3. Determine the administrative controls available at your workplace for dealing with potential back problems or RSI.

4. Examine available literature and catalogues to determine how many methods and accessories are available to prevent keyboard-related RSI. How many of these devices do you have in your own workstation?

5. Outline all the methods that a manager of a small plant could use to identify hazards. What could a safety professional add to this manager's hazard-identification program?

6. Choose any operation in your workplace or at school and identify the hazards associated with it. Perform a risk analysis to determine whether or not these hazards are dangerous. Outline the changes that could be made to reduce the level of risk associated with the hazards.

Using the Internet

1. Human resource managers are responsible for ensuring that workplace safety inspections take place regularly. Using your text and online resources, describe how you would conduct an effective safety inspection program. (Hint: go to http://www.worksafebc.com/publications/publication_index/s.asp and scroll down to a publication called *Safety Inspections*.) (Based on an exercise by Catherine Fitzgerald)

Exercise

1. In law, the "thin skull argument" refers to a perfectly healthy person whose minor trauma caused serious injury. Were it not for the trauma, the individual would not have been hurt. However, other individuals who experience the trauma are not hurt. Imagine, for example, four workers who are struck in the head by flying objects. Three workers suffer no injury whatsoever; the other (perhaps because of an abnormally thin skull) suffers serious brain damage. Is the damage a result of the hazard or the individual's preexisting condition? How should health and safety programs account for individual variability like this?

Case 1: Industrial Hazard Assessment

The plant is experiencing some difficulties with a clamping device on a holding fixture that keeps a metal part in position while it is fed into an automatic stamping machine. The clamp does not always allow the metal part to be fed into the machine properly aligned. The worker who was operating the machine had 32 years' experience with this type of equipment. While attempting to make the necessary adjustments for smooth operation without shutting off the power, she had to reach into the machine. She placed her left hand between the feed-in mechanism levers while her right hand was positioning the misaligned part between the open clamps of the fixture.

Unfortunately, the one-button actuating control was located immediately to the left of the worker's body, about hip level. The worker inadvertently depressed the button with her leg while reaching into the machine. The machine cycled—the feed mechanism slid forward while the fixture clamps closed. The worker had a portion of her left middle finger amputated.

List the following:

a. the unsafe acts
b. the unsafe conditions
c. the energies involved
d. the steps to be taken to prevent this situation from recurring

Case 2: Danger in the Grocery Store

Tadao works as a butcher in a large chain grocery store. His primary responsibility is cutting up meat using large (and very sharp) knives. He's been on the job now for four years and never had a health and safety complaint. Lately, though, he's been experiencing some difficulties. Actually, it started a couple of years ago when Tadao noticed that his right hand was painful at the end of the day and that he was unable to use the hand for several hours after work. The pain and fatigue didn't last long, and Tadao assumed that he was just overworking the hand (Tadao is right-handed). In the past month or so, the pain has escalated—it frequently lasts all night and makes sleep difficult. Tadao also experiences numbness and tingling in the hand. Tadao has begun to avoid activities that require using his right hand, including shaking hands with people.

Last Tuesday, Tadao came to work and could not pick up the knife in his right hand—he had to pick up the knife with his left hand and place it in his right hand to begin work. Watching him go through this procedure a coworker observed, "Well, it looks like you've developed butcher's claw—it comes from doing the same motion over and over again. It happens to us all and there's not much you can do about it." As an HR professional responsible for health and safety, do you have a better answer for Tadao?

Appendix

The material covered in this appendix incorporates two major techniques for workplace analysis. The first is a system known as "fault tree analysis," simplified, which allows an analyst to determine the human factor effect of any job or potential hazard condition. The second is a simplified method of measuring the lifting requirements or conditions of any task or job. Either technique may be required in the specific course outline of the academic institution involved.

RPC 7.1

RPC 7.3

Fault Tree Analysis

Fault tree analysis is a useful technique for evaluating hazards and risk.[17] The process, developed from decision tree theory[18] is unique in that it reasons backward from a series of conditions to some predetermined, undesired result called a **top event**. The key to its success is the determination of the origin of the top event (undesired result) and inclusion of the human element.

The following are some examples of top events:

1. *Injury to a person*. A worker is injured while performing a task.
2. *Equipment activated*. Some piece of machinery that was shut down is accidentally turned on while work is being done.
3. *Equipment failure*. A piece of equipment fails to start or else operates improperly.
4. *Worker exposure*. Airborne toxic chemicals or harmful physical agents contaminate the worker.
5. *Explosion or sudden release of energy*. High concentrations of solvents or dust may explode, or a source of high pressure may be released into the atmosphere.

Fault tree analysis uses a series of symbols (see Figure 7.4) to illustrate the various conditions, situations, or event sequences that could result in the undesired or top event. The events or conditions that lead into the top event

top event

a predetermined, undesired result, the origin of which is determined through fault tree analysis

FIGURE 7.4

Fault Tree Analysis Symbols

A condition or event requiring further development or examination (e.g., an injury)

A basic event not needing further analysis—failure data assigned (e.g., a bulb burns out)

"AND" gate: All inputs must act together for the event to occur

"OR" gate: Any of the inputs individually will cause the event

A secondary event with assumed risk, with insufficient data to develop (e.g., a break in a telephone connection)

A human factor; a special secondary event situation (e.g., power not locked out)

A constraint that further explains or qualifies an event at the gate

An event normally expected to occur (e.g., fire creates heat)

filter through a gate (see Figure 7.5) that specifies the sequences for the lower conditions and their effect on the top event.

To set up the initial fault tree, follow six steps:

1. Identify the top event (e.g., foreign particle in eye).
2. Identify the possible causes or conditions that could result in the chosen top event, and list them horizontally.
3. Determine whether the gate should be "and" or "or." This will depend on whether the noted conditions will act independently ("or") or in concert ("and").
4. Determine whether the causes or conditions identified in step 2 require further investigation or consideration. A rectangle indicates further information is required.
5. For each rectangle, repeat steps 2 through 4.
6. Once the tree has been constructed (see Figure 7.6 for an example), estimate and note at each event or condition the probabilities of occurrence for each element.

FIGURE 7.5

Gate Arrangements

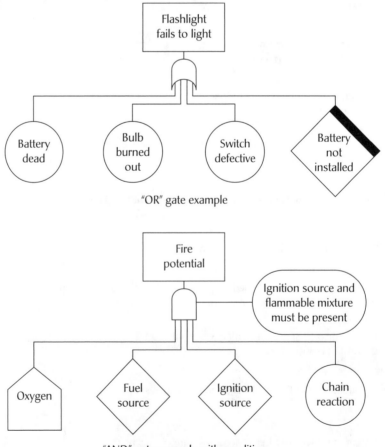

"OR" gate example

"AND" gate example with condition

FIGURE 7.6

Example of a Fault Tree

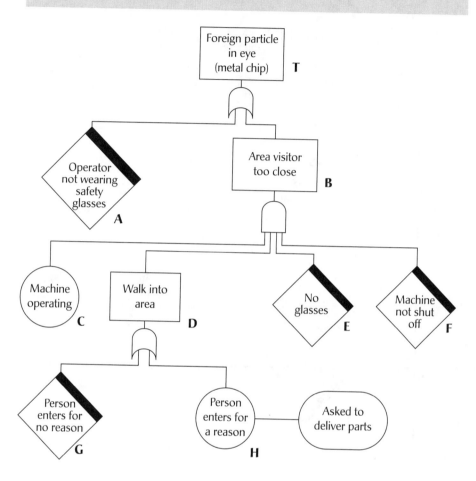

There are two methods of dealing with these probabilities of occurrence. The first (Figure 7.7) considers each row leading into a gate as a separate set of conditions. The probability of occurrence is estimated for each element in the row. The sum of the probabilities must equal 1.00. The critical path can now be highlighted by starting at the lowest element with the highest probability and tracing the path back to the top event. Thus, in this example, the condition at H—the person entering the area for a reason—will be the probable initiating source of the top event.

In the second technique (see Figure 7.8), a probability is assigned to each element randomly. Using the mathematical relationships noted, the probability at each rectangle can then be calculated. The advantage of method is its flexibility without bias. Once an identification and estimation of the hazard and the associated risk has been made, prevention strategies can be developed.

Obviously, a technical expert is needed to do a fault tree analysis. When should management use such expertise? Any job, operation, or task that has a history of accidents or injuries should receive top priority. Fault tree analysis

FIGURE 7.7

Fault Tree with Simplified Probabilities Added

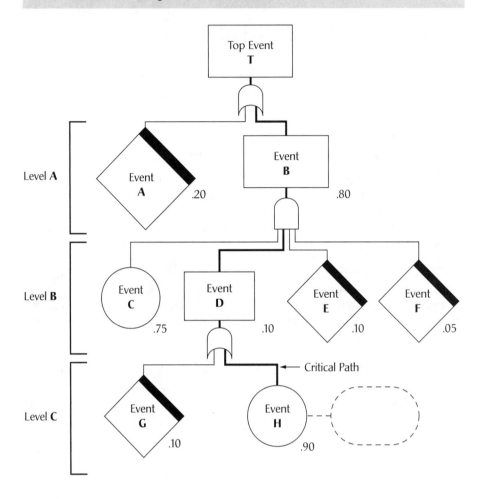

might also be used in situations in which the severity of the accident is great or where there is a high potential for accidents. When new equipment or operations are introduced, fault tree analysis can be used as a preventative tool.

Lifting Calculations Using the NIOSH Method

The NIOSH method examines the weight of the object to be lifted, the height it is to be lifted, the distance from the body, and the location of the load at the start of the lift or pick. Two factors are calculated and compared with the weight of the lifted object. These factors are the action limit (AL) and the maximum permissible limit (MPL).

The action limit is based on the following:

a. Epidemiological data indicating that some workers would be at increased risk of injury on jobs exceeding the AL.

b. Biomechanical studies indicating that lower back, disc-compression forces created at the AL can be tolerated by most (not all) people.

FIGURE 7.8

Fault Tree Example with Probabilities Added

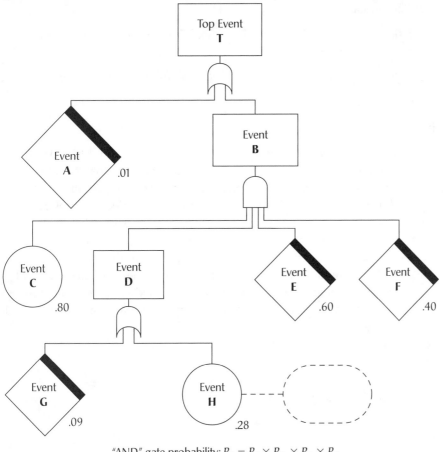

"AND" gate probability: $P_B = P_C \times P_D \times P_E \times P_F$
"OR" gate probability: $P_D = 1 - (1 - P_G \times P_H)$

c. Physiological studies showing that the average metabolic requirement for the AL would be 3.5 kcal/min.
d. Psychophysical studies showing that more than 75% of women and 99% of men could lift loads at the AL.

The maximum permissible limit is based on the following:

a. Epidemiological data indicating that musculoskeletal injury and severity rates are significantly higher for most workers placed on jobs exceeding the MPL.
b. Biomechanical studies indicating that lower back, disc-compression forces created at the MPL cannot be tolerated by most workers.
c. Physiological studies showing that the metabolic expenditure would be excessive for most workers frequently lifting loads at the MPL.

The equations for calculating the AL and the MPL are simple and straight-forward and can be easily used on the job. Simply examine a specific lifting task and take a series of measurements (see Figure 7.9). Then enter the data into the two equations and compare the results to the weight of the item being lifted. The equations are

$$AL \text{ (kg)} = 40(15/H)(1 - 0.004 \, |V - 75|)(0.7 + 7.5/D)(1 - F/F_{max}) \text{ for centimetres}$$

$$AL \text{ (lb.)} = 90(6/H)(1 - 0.01 \, |V - 30|)(0.7 + 3/D)(1 - F/F_{max}) \text{ for inches}$$

$$MPL = 3(AL)$$

where

> H is the horizontal distance (cm or in.) or reach, measured from the load centre of mass (usually where the hands grasp the load) to the mid-point between the ankles (the ankle bone) at the origin of the lift. H is between 15 cm (6 in.) and 80 cm (32 in.). Objects cannot be closer than 15 cm without interfering with the body; objects farther than 80 cm cannot be reached by most people.
>
> V is the vertical distance (cm or in.) measured from the load origin or centre of mass (or to the hands if the object does not have handles) to floor level at the origin of lift. V is assumed to be between 0 cm and 175 cm (70 in.), representing the upward-reach envelope of most people.

FIGURE 7.9

NIOSH Lifting Calculation Data

D is the vertical travel distance (cm or in.) of the object measured between the origin location and the destination location. D is assumed a minimum value of 25 cm (10 in.) and a maximum of 200-V cm (80-V in.). If the distance is less than 25 cm, then set $D = 25$ cm.

F is the average frequency of lifting (lifts/min.) with a minimum of 0.2 lifts/min., or once every 5 minutes as occasional lifting.

F_{max} is a factor based on duration and operator posture as shown in Table 7.4.

When the AL and the MPL have been calculated, the results are compared with the three lifting regions to determine the acceptability of the lifting task and whether controls will be necessary. Lifting tasks with the weight smaller in value than the AL are considered acceptable. Lifting tasks between the AL and the MPL require administrative controls (e.g., training, employee selection, and placement) or engineering controls. Lifting tasks above the MPL represent an unacceptable condition and require engineering controls (e.g., redesign) for worker protection.

To illustrate the analysis, assume a worker is lifting a 27 kg load from a skid onto a conveyor. The task is performed once each minute. The worker lifts for 8 hours and is required to bend over. The job and lift dimensions, measured using a tape measure, are as follows:

$W = 27$ kg—the weight of the item to be lifted
$D = 56$ cm—the vertical distance the item is lifted from rest
$H = 53$ cm—the reach
$V = 30$ cm—the vertical distance from the item at rest to the floor
$F = 1$ lift/min.—lift frequency
$F_{max} = 12$ from Table 7.4—for 8-hour shift in stooped position

Solving the AL and MPL equations with these values:

$$AL = 40(15/53)(1 - 0.004 |30 - 75|)(0.7 + 7.5/56)(1 - 1/12)$$

$$= 40(0.28)(0.82)(0.83)(0.92)$$

$$= 7.0 \text{ kg (The term } |V - 75| \text{ indicates an absolute value or a value that is always positive even if the arithmetic shows negative.)}$$

$$MPL = 3 \text{ AL} = 3(7.0) = 21.0 \text{ kg}$$

The load weight of 27 kg is greater than the AL and the MPL; therefore, the task as noted is unacceptable and engineering controls will be necessary.

TABLE 7.4

F_{max} Table Average Vertical Location of Lift

DURATION	V > 75 CM (30") (STANDING)	V ≤ 75 CM (30") (STOOPED)
1 hour	18	15
8 hours	15	12

If the task is to be redesigned, an analysis of the lifting conditions shows the order of factors, from most to least effective, to be: H—reach, V—distance to the floor, D—vertical lift distance, and F—lift frequency. To improve the lifting task in the above example, the workstation can be redesigned by moving the worker closer to the load position (H); by presenting the load at a higher level (V) standing; and by lifting the load a shorter distance (D).

If these revised values are

$W = 27$ kg
$D = 25$ cm
$H = 30$ cm
$V = 80$ cm
$F = 1$ lift/min.
$F_{max} = 15$ from Table 7.4

then substituting these values into the lifting equations for AL and MPL shows

$$AL = 40(15/30)(1 - 0.004\,|80 - 75|)(0.7 + 7.5/25)\,(1 - 1/15)$$

$$= 40(0.50)(0.98)(1.0)(0.94)$$

$$= 18.4 \text{ kg}$$

$$MPL = 3(18.4) = 55.2 \text{ kg}$$

Even with the redesign, the load weight is still greater than the AL but is now lower than the MPL. Some additional engineering controls may still be necessary (e.g., mechanical assists or reducing the load size). Administrative controls are also necessary (e.g., two-person lifting, work rotation, or weight training).

Previous studies have shown that RSI frequency rates (injuries per hours on the job) and severity rates (hours lost per hours on the job) increase significantly when

- heavy objects are lifted (W is large)
- the object is bulky—increased reach (H is large)
- distances moved are large (D is large)
- objects are lifted frequently (F is large)[19]

Any control strategy should consider the variability and the effects of these factors. Lower back discomfort and trauma are the usual results of improper lifting.

Endnotes

1. Firenze, R. J. (1978). *The process of hazard control*. Dubuque, Iowa: Kendall/Hunt Publishing.
2. National Institute of Occupational Safety and Health. (1983). *A work practices guide for manual lifting: Technical report 81–122*. Cincinnati, Ohio: U.S. Department of Health and Human Services.
3. Kim, P., Hayden, J. A., & Mior, S. A. (2004). The cost-effectiveness of a back education program for firefighters: A case study. *Journal of the Canadian Chiropractic Association, 48*(1), 13–19.
4. Ammendolia, C., Kerr, M. S., & Bombardier, C. (2002). *The use of back belts for prevention of occupational low back*

pain: *systematic review and recommendations*. CTFPHC Technical Rep no 02-1. London, Ont.: Canadian Task Force.

5. Statistics Canada. (2001). *Canadian community health survey*. Ottawa, ON.

6. McDonald, H. (1995, January/February). To regulate or not to regulate. *Accident Prevention*, 9–11.

7. Dolan, S. L., & Schuler, R. S. (1994). *Human resources management*: *A Canadian perspective*. Scarborough, Ont.: Nelson Canada.

8. Purdie, J. (1990, November 26). Better offices means greater productivity. *The Financial Post*, p. 35.

9. Smith, M. J., & Bayehi, A. D. (2003). Do ergonomic improvements increase computer workers' productivity? An intervention study in a call center. *Ergonomics*, *46*, 3–18.

10. May, D. R., Reed, K., Schwoerer, C. E., & Potter, P. (2004). Ergonomic office design and aging: A quasi-experimental field study of employee reactions to an ergonomics intervention program. *Journal of Occupational Health Psychology*, *9*(2), 123–135.

11. Laing, P. M. (Ed.). (1992). *Accident prevention manual for business and industry*: *Administration and programs* (10th ed.). Washington, D.C.: National Safety Council.

12. Laing, P. M. (Ed.). (1992). *Accident prevention manual for business and industry*: *Administration and programs* (10th ed.). Washington, D.C.: National Safety Council.

13. Rampton, G., Turnbull, I., & Doran, G. (1996). *Human resources management systems*. Scarborough, Ont.: Nelson Canada.

14. Firenze, R. J. (1978). *The process of hazard control*. Dubuque, Iowa: Kendall/Hunt Publishing.

15. Laing, P. M. (Ed.). (1992). *Accident prevention manual for business and industry*: *Administration and programs* (10th ed.). Washington, D.C.: National Safety Council.

16. Laing, P. M. (Ed.). (1992). *Accident prevention manual for business and industry*: *Administration and programs* (10th ed.). Washington, D.C.: National Safety Council.

17. Fabrycky, W. J., & Mize, J. H. (Eds.). (1976). *System analysis and design for safety*. Englewood Cliffs, N.J.: Prentice Hall.

18. Raiffa, H. (1968). *Decision analysis*. Reading, Mass.: Addison-Wesley.

19. National Institute of Occupational Safety and Health. (1983). *A work practices guide for manual lifting*: *Technical report 81–122*. Cincinnati, Ohio: U.S. Department of Health and Human Services.

Interventions

Chapter 8

Hazard Control

Chapter Learning Objectives

After reading this chapter, you should be able to

- define the many terms used in hazard control
- distinguish between events and actions that constitute precontact, contact, and postcontact control
- describe the requirements for machine guarding
- explain the requirements for lockout procedures and confined space entry
- discuss the necessity of work permits
- explain the concept of source–path–human control
- explain the concept of safety awareness and give examples of awareness campaigns

CAUGHT IN THE ICE

It was one of the worst tragedies in Canadian occupational health and safety. In March 2004, a 25-km stretch of metre-thick pack ice drifted toward two natural gas rigs located offshore from Nova Scotia. The Venture gas production rig and the exploration rig Rowan Gorilla V stood in imminent danger of having their supporting legs swept out from under them. More than 100 workers on the rigs would be dumped into the North Atlantic almost 300 km offshore.

If you are not familiar with the tragedy, that's because it never happened. Having recognized the hazard and assessed the danger, both ExxonMobil Canada (owners of the Venture platform) and Canadian Superior (owners of the Rowan Gorilla V), implemented precontact control measures designed to minimize the potential impact of the hazard.

As a first priority, they evacuated the rigs, removing some 100 workers to safety ashore. Rigs were secured against possible damage and both tugboats and Coast Guard icebreakers were on site to try to divert the ice from the rigs. As a result of these actions, nobody was injured and the rigs were not harmed. The companies involved controlled the hazard—hazard control is the focus of this chapter.

Source: "Ice forces evacuation of two offshore rigs near Nova Scotia's Sable Island," *Brockville Recorder and Times*. Retrieved from http://www.recorder.ca/cp/National/040308/n0308137A.html, March 30, 2004.

---

hazard control

the program or process used to establish preventative and corrective measures

precontact control

addressing issues before an incident or accident occurs

contact control

identifying ways in which a hazardous situation can be prevented from becoming worse and harming workers

postcontact control

putting in place medical and cleanup operations and ensuring that the event cannot be repeated

 8.1

administrative control

management involvement, training of employees, rotation of employees, environmental sampling, and medical surveillance to protect individuals

Hazard control refers to the program or process used to establish preventative and corrective measures as the final stage of hazard recognition, assessment, and control (RAC). The goal is to eliminate, reduce, or control hazards so as to minimize injuries and losses, including accidents, property damage, time lost, and so on. The first step in hazard control is hazard recognition and assessment, the subject of the previous chapter. This chapter will examine the next three steps in the hazard-control process: (1) **precontact control** (addressing issues before an incident or accident occurs), (2) **contact control** (identifying ways in which a hazardous situation can be prevented from becoming worse and harming workers), and (3) **postcontact control** (putting in place medical and cleanup operations and ensuring that the event cannot be repeated).

Administrative Control

Administrative control is the use of management involvement, training of employees, rotation of employees, environmental sampling, and medical surveillance to protect individuals.[1] Administrative control is the second level of priority for worker protection after engineering controls and before personal protective equipment. Against some negative attitudes, administrative controls can have some effect in minimizing hazardous conditions. The most serious failure of this method is the company's reluctance or lack of appreciation. Using administrative controls, the HR practitioner can be effective by (1) introducing preplacement examinations that can help find an employee with suitable characteristics for the job (e.g., the ability to lift materials), (2) scheduling job rotation that allows a worker to spend time in less hazardous jobs, thereby reducing exposures (e.g., working with toxic materials in the morning and nontoxic materials in the afternoon), (3) moving the worker to another permanent job after exposure to toxic materials, and (4) performing periodic monitoring.

RPC 8.2

RPC 8.3

Some common examples of administrative control include safety awareness programs, the use of incentives, housekeeping programs, preventative maintenance, and the development of policies and training for unique situations such as confined space entry.

Safety Awareness

Safety awareness refers to programs that attempt to inform workers about health and safety issues and to remind them of the importance of health and safety.

Visible Reminders

Posters and signs at worker entrances and other points of entry are one way to promote safety awareness. A company-designed booklet dealing with health and safety issues can be issued to employees. Safety message inserts can be added to paycheques. Placemats and napkins in the dining area can be imprinted with safety messages. Decals (self-adhesive or magnetic labels) can be applied to specific objects as a safety reminder. In addition, safety displays can be set up at entrances and in cafeterias. These displays can feature photographs of the Safe Employee of the Month or brief statements by workers who were saved from injury by, for example, correct use of personal protective

Occupational Health and Safety Today 8.1

Young Worker Awareness Program

In response to the high rate of injuries among young workers, virtually every jurisdiction has begun to address the issue of young workers' health and safety. The Young Worker Awareness Program in Ontario is funded by the Workplace Safety and Insurance Board and is delivered through various agencies. The intent of the program is to increase young people's awareness of health and safety issues, the importance of health and safety, and their rights under the law.

Source: Workplace Safety and Insurance Board of Ontario, "Young worker awareness program." Retrieved from http://www.youngworker.ca/english/, October 11, 2004.

equipment (e.g., safety glasses). Newsletters, bulletin boards, and billboards are other vehicles for promoting safety awareness. Finally, safety campaigns can be used to target a specific hazard or unsafe practice. All these efforts and presentations will not be effective unless the senior managers are fully behind the programs.

Special Events

Numerous special events have been developed to promote safety awareness in the workplace. Table 8.1 presents some of the events in Canada. In general, the intent of these special events is to increase awareness of safety issues in the workplace by focusing on safety or a specific element of safety in the workplace.

Awards and Incentives

Safety awards are another vehicle used to increase awareness of safety. By establishing an award, the sponsoring agency or company creates an "event" comprising a presentation and a media announcement. The resulting publicity can be used to raise safety awareness. Safety award programs have been created by industrial associations, governments, and agencies to recognize achievements in safety (see the Weblinks section at the end of the chapter).

TABLE 8.1

Awareness Events

Event	Date	Purpose
RSI Day	Usually the last day of February	Promote awareness of RSI and related disorders
National Farm Safety Week	March 14–20	Promote awareness of various farm safety issues
National Day of Mourning	April 28	Remember those who have been killed at work; promote safety awareness
North American Occupational Safety and Health Week (NAOSH Week)	First full week of May	Focus the attention of employers, employees, the general public, and all partners in occupational health and safety on the importance of preventing illness and injury in the workplace
National Road Safety Week	May 21–27	Increase awareness of road safety
Healthy Workplace Week	October 25–31	Promote a comprehensive and integrated approach to workplace health in order to improve and sustain the health of Canadian organizations, their work environments, and their employees
National Safe Driving Week	December 1–7	Promote safe driving

Within organizations, individual employees can be given incentives to maintain a good safety performance. These incentives can range from individual payoffs to team rewards. For example, DuPont Canada employees were given special scratch-and-win lottery tickets.[2] Other organizations recognize good safety performance through such incentives as private parking spaces or dinners (see Chapter 10 for a discussion of behaviour-based safety programs, which frequently involve the use of incentives of some form). In addition, supervisors may receive a reward based on the number of employees who attend safety talks or on the number of safety deficiencies that are corrected in an expeditious fashion. Contests may be held in which employees compete to produce the best safety slogan. Finally, safety records can be used as one factor in the evaluation of supervisory and managerial performance. Care must be taken with this approach, since some supervisors may be tempted to hide problems and serious hazards.

Housekeeping

Ensuring that the worksite is clean and that workers have access to cleaning facilities will contribute to the control of hazards. A clean, orderly workplace can reduce hazards and at the same time increase efficiency. Every worksite contains potentially hazardous tools and equipment. For example, a plant site may have containers of chemicals such as solvents, tools such as drills, and processes that generate dust or scrap material. Maintaining a clean and orderly job site reduces the risk of injury due to falls, fires, and so forth. Furthermore, it is easier to locate first-aid equipment or exits in an environment in which all tools and equipment are in their assigned places.

 8.4

RPC 8.5

Housekeeping is not just a good practice—it is a legal requirement under most health and safety legislation. Although legislation varies across jurisdictions, the Canadian Health and Safety Regulations under the Canada Labour Code (see the Weblink) are typical:

1. Every exterior stairway, walkway, ramp and passageway that may be used by employees shall be kept free of accumulations of ice and snow or other slipping or tripping hazards.

2. All dust, dirt, waste and scrap material in every work place in a building shall be removed as often as is necessary to protect the health and safety of employees and shall be disposed of in such a manner that the health and safety of employees is not endangered.

3. Every travelled surface in a work place shall be

(a) slip resistant; and

(b) kept free of splinters, holes, loose boards and tiles and similar defects. (SOR/2000-374, s. 2; SOR/2002-208, s. 6).

The cleaning process itself should be evaluated. Besides the obvious hazards posed by solvents used for cleaning, other hazards may be involved in operations such as dust removal. Workers using compressed air may be

Occupational Health and Safety Notebook 8.1

Preventing Slips and Falls through Housekeeping

Good housekeeping practices are perhaps the simplest and most effective way to prevent slips and falls in the workplace. These include the following:

- Keeping walkways and stairwells clear of clutter
- Closing drawers, doors, and storage bins after use
- Keeping floors free of debris or spills

- Marking hazards (e.g., spills, debris) until they can be cleaned up
- Ensuring adequate lighting

Source: Canadian Centre for Occupational Health and Safety, "Why should we pay attention to housekeeping at work?" Retrieved from http://www.ccohs.ca/oshanswers/hsprograms/house.html, October 10, 2004.

---

tempted to blow dust off work surfaces and even clothing; however, compressed air can be forced through the skin, enter the bloodstream, and cause death.

Organizations that employ workers who handle toxic materials should ensure that washing facilities are located close to the work area. Workers should wash before drinking or eating to prevent the ingestion of toxic materials. No food or drinks should be permitted at the worksite. Workers exposed to chemicals should have showers and change clothes before leaving the worksite. Where appropriate, hazardous materials (hazmat) suits should be available and workers should be trained in their use.

preventative maintenance
the orderly, continuous, and scheduled protection and repair of equipment and buildings

Preventative Maintenance

Preventative maintenance refers to the orderly, continuous, and scheduled protection and repair of equipment and buildings. The primary goals of preventative maintenance are the determination of potential problems and the

Occupational Health and Safety Notebook 8.2

Administrative Controls for Struck-by-Object Injuries

To reduce injuries attributable to falling objects:

- Provide and require the use of safety helmets.
- Provide safety signage and warning where overhead hazards are present.
- Train and ensure the use of safe-rigging and safe-storage procedures.
- Provide and require the use of safety shoes.

To reduce CIUB injuries:

- Lockout procedures require the operator or maintenance provider to turn the power off and to lock the switch in the off position using a personal padlock. Because each worker is the only one with the key to his or her lock, it is impossible to inadvertently start the machine during maintenance.

Source: Canadian Centre for Occupational Health and Safety. Retrieved from http://www.ccohs.ca, October 10, 2004.

implementation of corrective action. The primary benefits of this process are uninterrupted production and the reduction of potential hazards caused by equipment failure.

®℗© 8.4

®℗© 8.5

Generally speaking, equipment failures do not happen without warning. We are all familiar with the atypical noises our cars or air conditioners produce as a signal that something needs to be fixed. However, maintenance should enter the picture before the emergence of warning signs. It is more cost effective to perform maintenance routinely while the equipment or machines are still operating than it is after they have failed, necessitating shutdown of the entire operation. Checking the level of oil in your car at every second fuel stop is preventative maintenance. To let the oil level drop and the engine seize is expensive and unnecessary.

Record keeping is an essential part of any preventative maintenance program. Maintenance information should be recorded at the time the maintenance work is done. Pertinent data would include part replacement and frequency, lubrication, bearings and drive repairs, electrical failures, and cleanliness. Once the historical information is available, failure trends—commonly referred to as failure mode analysis or maintenance hazard analysis—can be anticipated and addressed.

Work Permits

Before any high-risk work is undertaken, a series of work permits must be in place, one for each type of activity. These permits are, in effect, in-house licences to perform dangerous work. Permits are required for confined space entry, electrical work, excavation work, safety-valve work, scaffolding work, radiation work, and equipment disconnecting work (lockout procedures). "Hot work" permits may be required for activities such as cutting, welding, and soldering wherein the heat involved may trigger the fire alarm system or present a fire hazard. A sample work permit for scaffolding is shown in Figure 8.1.

Lockout Procedures

When maintenance or adjustment is performed on any machine, the machine must be shut off and locked out. For example, replacing the signal light on a residential stove involves accessing the interior of the appliance. Shutting off the stove entails turning off the switches; locking it out entails turning off the power at the main fuse box or circuit breaker and removing the appropriate fuses in either the power panel or the stove. With these precautions, no one can turn the stove on and cause an electrical shock or burn injury. Figure 8.2 shows an example of a clamp used for multiple padlocks in a lockout procedure. A more complicated appliance like a furnace necessitates not only the removal of fuses, but also the shutting off of fuel lines and disassembly of a supply flange joint.

The following are some of the precautions that must be taken during the lockout process:

1. Only one person should be in charge of the lockout procedure.
2. The worker must ensure that the machine is shut off completely, that all internal pressure sources (hydraulic, air, and steam) are bled off

FIGURE 8.1

Example of Scaffold Use Permit

SIRTE OIL COMPANY	**SCAFFOLDING PERMIT**

SIDE 1

SIRTE OIL COMPANY — **SCAFFOLDING PERMIT**

DATE | TIME FROM: | TO:

PLANT:

EQUIPMENT & LOCATION:

DESCRIPTION OF WORK TO BE DONE: ☐ ERECTION   ☐ REMOVAL

SCAFFOLD DUTY: ☐ LIGHT   ☐ GENERAL   ☐ HEAVY

HEIGHT = ___ M   WIDTH = ___ M   ☐ CONSULT CIVIL ENG. GROUP

ANSWER WITH (X) WHERE APPLICABLE: YES
1. FAMILIAR WITH AREA HAZARDS/SAF. RULES?   ☐
2. SCAFFOLD TYPE/MATERIAL AGREED TO?   ☐
3. SCAFFOLD ANCHORING POINTS APPROVED?   ☐
4. FOUNDATION/FOOTING PREPARED?   ☐
5. HAZARD CREATED TO/FROM TRAFFIC?   ☐
6. AREA FREE OF COMB./TOXIC GAS?   ☐
7. ACCEPTANCE APPROVAL NEEDED?   ☐

SPECIAL PROTECTION REQUIRED
☐ MONITOR FOR _____   ☐ SAFETY BELTS/LINE
☐ LIFTING DEVICE APPROVAL   ☐ STANDBYS
☐ BARRIERS/ROPING OFF   ☐ (SPECIFY)

THE EQUIPMENT AND/OR LOCATION WHERE THE WORK IS TO BE DONE HAS BEEN INSPECTED & POINTS 1-7 ABOVE HAVE BEEN INVESTIGATED TO MY SATISFACTION.

_____
SIGNATURE OF PERSON AUTHORIZING THIS PERMIT

I UNDERSTAND THE HAZARDS INVOLVED IN THE ABOVE PERMITTED WORK AND THE LIMITATIONS REQUIRED HAVE BEEN EXPLAINED TO ME.

7-3 SHIFT | 3-11 SHIFT | 11-7 SHIFT

SIGNATURE OF AUTHORIZED CRAFTSMAN

PERMIT CLOSED OUT | WORK COMPLETED
DATE   TIME | YES ☐   NO ☐
AUTHORIZED CRAFTSMAN | OPERATING SUPERVISOR
APPROVAL FOR USE OF COMPLETED SCAFFOLD | NAME | SIGNATURE | DATE

SIDE 1

CHECKLIST FOR THE AUTHORIZED CRAFTSMAN
PREPARATIONS
☐ SPECIFICATIONS/DRAWING PROVIDED?
☐ FOUNDATIONS/FOOTING PREPARED?
☐ LIFTING DEVICES NEEDED?
☐ ERECTION PERSONNEL EXPERIENCED?
☐ SUPERVISION APPOINTED? COMPETENT?
☐ AREA HAZARDS/SAF. RULES KNOWN?
☐ ADDITIONAL JOB DEMONSTRATION NEEDED?
☐ STRUCTURE INSPECTION/APPROVAL BY A COMPETENT PERSON NEEDED?

STABILITY & CONSTRUCTION
☐ ANCHORING POINTS SELECTED? APPROVED? SUFFICIENT?
☐ SCAFF. MATERIAL INSPECTED? SELECTED? IN GOOD CONDITION?
☐ FOOTING FIRM?
☐ STANDARDS SPACING ADEQUATE?
☐ BRACING USED? SUFFICIENT?
☐ PLATFORMS FULL? TRIPPING? OPENINGS?
☐ GUARDRAILS? TOE BOARDS?
☐ ACCESS ADEQUATE? LADDERS FIXED?

IN USE
☐ STRUCTURE INSPECTED DAILY?
☐ TRAFFIC HAZARDS?
☐ OVERLOADING?
☐ USE OF PERSONAL PROTECTION?
☐ RESPONSE TO EMERGENCY KNOWN?

DISMANTLING
☐ METHOD AGREED TO?
☐ HAZARD CREATED TO SURROUNDING?
☐ FINAL SITE CLEARING ENSURED?

SPECIAL INSTRUCTIONS

SIDE 2

to atmospheric level and the valves are locked open, and that any movable parts, such as flywheels or rams, are immobilized.

3. After the machine has been shut down, all the disconnect points, such as the electrical panel, must be left open.

4. Before work begins, complete testing must be undertaken to ensure that all energy sources are inoperative.

5. The worker must use an approved lockout tag and single key padlock (not keyed alike) to secure the equipment.

6. Only the workers who installed each lock are permitted to remove the lock in the reverse order to the lock installation, beginning and ending with the project manager.

7. Each worker must sign off the work permit as his or her lock is removed.

FIGURE 8.2

Clamp Used for Multiple Padlocks

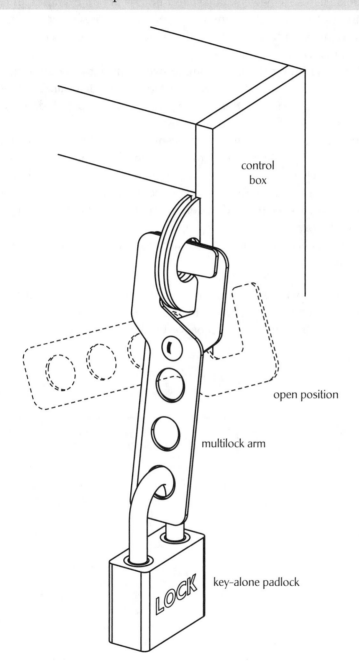

control
box

open position

multilock arm

key-alone padlock

LOCK

When the project is finished, the equipment will be activated in the reverse sequence to the shutdown. Checks must be made to ensure that guards are in place, isolation devices have been removed, all tools are accounted for, energy controls have been closed and put back into operating condition, and tags and locks have been removed. The last lock removed is that of the manager of the project from the shift on which the lock was applied.

Confined Space Entry

confined space

a space that is potentially deficient in oxygen and could contain toxic aerosols

Confined space refers to a space that is potentially deficient in oxygen and could contain toxic aerosols. Sewers, tanks, and boilers are all examples of confined spaces. Examples also include any long, small tunnel, a shower stall, and some specialty rooms such as computer equipment rooms that are completely independent from any adjacent spaces.

At home, cleaning the bathroom shower stall with the door closed and using a tile cleaner will trap the vapours from the cleanser. These vapours may accumulate near the floor where the work is being done, displace oxygen, and cause drowsiness or fainting.

Entry into industrial confined spaces is addressed in various OH&S regulations. One of the first things to determine is whether the space to be entered is, in fact, a confined space. The flow diagram shown in Figure 8.3 can be used to determine if confined-space procedures are necessary. The diagram shown in Figure 8.4 can be used to determine the extent of the testing that will be required before actual entry.

Once it has been established that a confined space exists, the following steps should be taken:

1. Issue a proper work permit and follow all the lockout procedures.
2. Determine the ease of access to and from the space and develop appropriate contingency plans for worker emergencies.

FIGURE 8.3

Hazard Rating of Confined Space before Entry

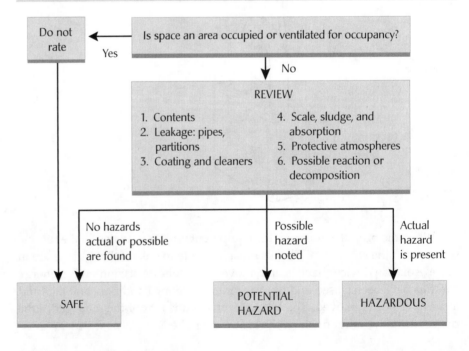

Part Three: Interventions

FIGURE 8.4

Review of Confined Space before Entry

Occupational Health and Safety Today 8.2

Tragedy on the Farm

A grain bin is similar to a silo and is used to store grain. The bin has a large opening in the bottom, and an auger (similar to a large drill bit) is used to extract the grain. Robert Héroux of Louisville, Quebec, entered his grain silo on July 25, 2003, to break up the grain and get it flowing through the auger again. The bridge he was walking on collapsed, and Mr. Héroux sank into the grain and suffocated. Experts suggest that you can be trapped in the grain within 2 to 3 seconds and completely submerged within 10 seconds. The lack of confined-space procedures and proper fall protection meant that Mr. Héroux never had a chance once the bridge collapsed.

Source: Dumyn, L. (2003). Worker buried alive when grain releases. *OHS Canada* (July/August).

3. Make sure that all the proper tools and equipment are on hand to do the job.
4. Communicate to workers that no smoking or open flames are to be permitted at or near the worksite.
5. Purge the space of all contaminants and test the air quality several times to ensure that all impurities have been removed.
6. Ensure that a constant forced airflow into the space is provided.
7. Clean the interior of the space to ensure that no hazardous scale or deposits are present.
8. Post a trained safety lookout outside the space. (The inside workers should be kept in full view at all times.)
9. Attach a lifeline to each worker in the space. (The free end should be controlled by the safety lookout.)

On completion of the confined-space work, equipment startup can be undertaken in the reverse order to the shutdown. The permit and lockout systems should be followed without deviation.

Engineering Control

engineering control

modification of work processes, equipment, and materials to reduce exposure to hazards

Engineering control refers to the modification of work processes, equipment, and materials in order to reduce exposure to hazards.[3] Hazard control should be built into the design of the work itself. Before equipment and materials are purchased, specifications for efficient and safe operations should be determined. For example, noise-emission limits for noisy equipment can be specified before the equipment is purchased, thus reducing possible worker exposure. Engineering control also refers to the installation of auxiliary equipment, such as physical barriers and ventilation systems, in order to reduce hazards, dealing with the source and path. Various methods of controlling hazards through engineering are discussed below.

Design of Hand Tools

Virtually every activity we undertake that requires the use of our hands involves a tool of some sort. Although a computer-controlled machining centre is not considered a hand tool in the same sense as a screwdriver or toothbrush, each individual piece of production equipment poses its own RSI problems. Nevertheless, these items are rarely designed to fit the human hand. The common in-line screwdriver configuration, for example, requires that the hand and wrist be forced out of line. However, the T-bar handle in the ergonomic screwdriver allows the hand and arm to be kept in alignment by producing a lower wrist–arm angle (see Figure 8.5). The key to effective hand tool design is to maintain natural joint alignment such as that illustrated by the ergonomic hammer in Figure 8.6.

Ergonomically designed keyboards, which are available in some computer stores, are constructed to match the natural position of the hands at rest.

FIGURE 8.5

Screwdriver Configurations

a) conventional screwdriver

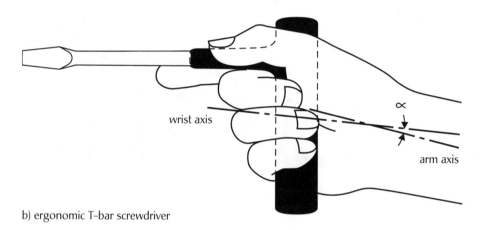

b) ergonomic T-bar screwdriver

Hand-operated tools and devices must allow the hand–wrist–arm group to function in a neutral position (i.e., axes in line). Tools that are used in an assembly operation should be vertically suspended over the workstation on a balancer so that the worker can reach for and grasp the tool without twisting the arm–wrist axis. The tool should be cycled with a handgrip, not a single finger trigger.

Tools should be designed so that excessive holding force to maintain proper control is not required. A vibrating tool can be hard to control without maintaining a very tight and stressful handhold or grip. Workers should move their arms more than their wrists and hands. Greater force can be exerted by the thumb and the middle finger than by the other fingers.

Substitution

Safety professionals can sometimes replace hazardous equipment or materials with those that are less hazardous. For example, replacing a light, fluffy powder with the same material in granular form will result in a reduction of airborne

FIGURE 8.6

Hammer Configurations

a) conventional hammer

b) ergonomic hammer

Occupational Health and Safety Notebook 8.3

Controlling RSI through Workspace Design

The application of ergonomic design principles to the design of workspaces, and more specifically to the prevention of RSI, is an example of engineering control of workplace hazards. The predominant method of control involves keeping joints in their natural position or aligned with the connecting limb. To illustrate the joint alignment argument, place your right hand flat on a table, thumb extended to the left. In the natural position, the hand and arm axes will be in line. Now, without moving your arm, flex your wrist to the left in the direction of the thumb. This position is known as "radial deviation." Flex your wrist in the opposite direction. This position is called "ulnar deviation." Raising your fingers off the table, while keeping your arm on the table, will create a position known as "dorsiflexion." If the hand and fingers are flexed downward, the resulting position is "palmar flexion." Each of these positions, if held for any length of time, will become uncomfortable. The radial deviation position and possibly the dorsiflexion position are associated with keyboarding.

Sources: Occupational Health Clinics for Ontario Workers, "Repetitive strain injury day." Retrieved from http://www.ohcow.on.ca/press_release/rsiday.html, October 10, 2004; and "The hidden costs of occupation repetitive stress injuries," *Canadian Occupational Safety Magazine* (June 2004). Retrieved from http://www.industrialsourcebook.com/cgi-bin/archivef.pl?id=726, October 10, 2004.

dust levels. Lead paints can be replaced with less toxic material such as water-based coatings. Similarly, electric trucks can be substituted for gasoline-powered ones with a resultant decrease in exposure to carbon monoxide. The substitute should, of course, be checked for other types of hazards. The introduction of electric trucks will reduce the serious risk of carbon monoxide exposure but increase less serious exposure to flammable hydrogen or electric shock from batteries.

Workstation Design

The four major components of workstation design are layout, control and display panels, seating, and lighting.

LAYOUT   Design the workstation so that the arm is not used in an extended or reaching position. The farther the hand is from the body, the less power it can exert and the smaller load it can handle. The arm can push and pull greater loads at a worktable if the action is to or from the body than it can if pushing or pulling transversely.

Tasks should be designed so that the preferred hand (left or right) can do the most critical tasks. Foot motions can be used for minor operations, thereby relieving the hands from some repetitive actions. Avoid simultaneous hand-and-foot motions when the task requires close attention. Arm motions are faster and more accurate than foot motions. The hand and arm can be used for fine control or operation; the foot can be used to stop or start a cycle that involves no accuracy of placement.

Tasks that require frequent arm movements should be carried out with the elbows bent and close to the body. Arm movements should be smooth rather than jerky. The hand and arm can pull down with more strength than they can push up. The push power of the arm is greater when the hand is 50 cm in front of the body; the pull power of the arm is greater when the hand is 70 cm in front of the body.[4] The greatest push power for the legs occurs when the angle at the knee is 140–165 degrees—close to standing. The greatest bending strength occurs when the angle of the elbow is 80–120 degrees—close to a right angle.[5] Pushing power is greater than pulling power.

CONTROL AND DISPLAY PANELS   Controls and displays such as an automobile instrument panel or a machine operating panel must exhibit the following four characteristics:

1. *Visibility*. The display must be within the worker's field of vision, with no obstructions. Characters should be of a readable size, with high contrast.
2. *Legibility*. Characters must be adequately spaced as well as distinguishable (a "3" should not look like an "8"). No more than one line or pointer should appear on each display.
3. *Interpretability*. The displays must be interpreted in the same way by all observers. Universal symbols help but can lead to misunderstandings. For example, the red exit symbols may be confused with the red glow that means "stop." In Europe, exit symbols are green.

4. *User-friendliness.* Each control must be a different shape and have a different operating direction in order to be easily distinguished from adjacent controls. Picture the controls in your car: the radio volume rotates, while the station-change button is pushed; the most important controls—the fuel gauge and the speedometer—are displayed most prominently.

SEATING Employees can spend long periods seated at their workstations. Poor sitting positions or posture can restrict blood circulation, increase blood pooling in the legs and feet, and add to the compressive load on the spine. Correct chair design will minimize the concentration of pressures under the thigh and the back of the knee. The most commonly recommended sitting posture is illustrated in Figure 8.7.

FIGURE 8.7

Side View of Chair Dimensions

Work seating must be completely adjustable in all directions and planes. A forward-tilting seat may be preferred by employees who must lean over a workstation. (Interestingly, a study by Ontario Hydro revealed that only 5% of users adjust their furniture.[6]) Seat cushions should have about a 2.5 cm compression, with minimal contouring to allow ease of position shift. Permeable fabrics allow ventilation and absorption of perspiration.

The backrest should be curved in the vertical and horizontal planes. It should also be vertically adjustable (so that the point of contact fits the small of the back in the lumbar region) as well as horizontally adjustable. Armrests are recommended unless a wide variety of arm movements are required. The chair base should provide stability and mobility. Five casters with a wide spread will prevent tipping.[7]

LIGHTING Lighting has two main purposes: to illuminate the tasks and to increase the safety and comfort of the worker. Bright overhead lighting can produce glare and annoying reflections on a computer screen, resulting in eyestrain and headaches. Choosing the correct lighting for a workplace will involve consideration of the following factors:

- *Intensity:* the amount of light given off by a source
- *Luminance:* the amount of light uniformly reflected or emitted from a surface and the background
- *Reflectance:* the amount of light reflected from a surface (luminance) and the amount of light falling on the surface (illuminance) as in Figure 8.8. A dull black surface has 9% reflectance, while a shiny white surface has closer to 100% reflectance.

FIGURE 8.8

Reflectance Schematic

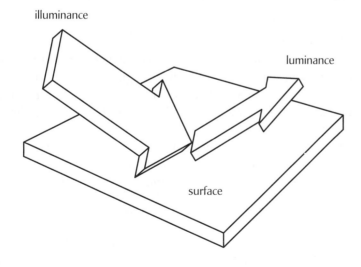

illuminance

luminance

surface

$$\% \text{ Reflectance} = \frac{\text{Luminance}}{\text{Illuminance}}$$

- *Luminaire:* a complete lighting device
- *Contrast:* the relationship between the amount of light from a surface and the background
- *Glare:* the reduction of visibility caused by brightness differences between an object and its background

Both the quantity and quality of light must be considered. In the context of workstation design, quantity refers to the correct amount of light needed to perform a task. Quality is more complex and includes measures of distribution (or spread), glare, diffusion, shadows, contrast, and colour.

Process Modification

Sometimes changing the manner in which the work is done can increase safety. Moving from a manual operation to an automated one, or from batch processes to continuous processes, may result in fewer hazards.

Effective job design is key to worker safety and efficiency. Frederick Taylor (1856–1915), the founder of industrial engineering, tried to increase both by breaking a job into its basic components and then assigning to each task specific times and methods (motions). Taylor's ideas were applied to the shovelling of coal at the Bethlehem Steel Company in what was to become a classic motion study. This application demonstrated that a stoker could shovel more coal into the blast furnace by using a larger shovel and engaging in fewer work cycles. Decreasing the repetition of the task served to reduce fatigue and back strains.

Subsequent efficiency experts addressed the tedium associated with simple task repetition. Inspired by the Hawthorne studies of the 1920s, the sociotechnological approach to work design was concerned with enhancing worker involvement and satisfaction. What has this to do with health and safety? The more interested and motivated the worker, the lower the probability of a serious accident or injury.

Isolation or Segregation

In this approach, the hazardous job or task is isolated from the employees in order to reduce their exposure. Isolation strategies may be as simple as putting a physical barrier around a chemical or noise source, or removing a hazardous operation to a separate facility. Robots can handle tasks that are too dangerous for humans.

Segregating the hazardous operation in time as well as space is also advisable. Cleanups, maintenance, and particularly hazardous tasks such as spray painting can be done on weekends or at night, when fewer workers are present.

Purchasing

Purchasing agents have an important role to play in the control of hazards. In addition to price, quality, and efficiency, the purchasing agent must consider safety. At a minimum, the equipment must meet the regulatory requirements of the Canadian Standards Association and Ministry regulations.

Purchasing machinery without proper or minimal safety specifications or compatibility can result in equipment failure or injury. Workers can have their toes crushed if they wear safety shoes with inadequate metal caps, or they can suffer from headaches because their safety goggles have imperfections in the lenses. The idea that one size of personal protection equipment fits all is a major fallacy. The best time to eliminate hazards is at the design stage, with input from the company OH&S function.

Once specifications have been met, the safety features of competing brands can be compared. The purchasing agent should consult the company safety specialist and safety records for accidents and incidents that resulted from defects in equipment, machinery, or materials. He or she can use the information contained in these records to defend certain purchasing decisions on a cost-benefit basis.

Machine Guarding

Machine guarding is necessary to protect a worker from the hazards and energies created by moving machinery. According to Ontario's Ministry of Labour, more orders citing problems are written for nonexistent or improper guarding than for any other.[8] The problem is serious enough to have prompted the Canadian Standards Association to issue standard Z432–94, *Safeguarding of Machinery*,[9] which covers the topic of machine guarding thoroughly.

machine guarding
protection for workers from the hazards and energies created by moving machinery

The following basic guidelines for machine guarding apply, regardless of the type or operation of the equipment:

1. The guard must be sturdy enough to resist external source damage that will interfere with the operation of the machine, such as being struck by a forklift truck.
2. The guard must permit required maintenance tasks without excessive dismantling or reassembly labour.
3. The guard must be properly and securely mounted to prevent rattling, which is a distraction, or part interference, which can cause snags and force the operator to attempt to free them, possibly without proper precautions.
4. There should be no parts that, if removed, will compromise the protection provided by the guard—there should always be some guarding left.
5. Construction should be relatively simple so that problems can be immediately identified and corrected during an inspection.

Thoroughness in guard design is essential. An incomplete guard may be as much of a hazard as no guard at all. The guard must not create a false sense of security that may cause accidents and possible injuries. When the guard is in operation, all parts of the body must be excluded, and no access is permitted. The barrier or guard will prevent a worker from being caught in, on, or between moving equipment (kinetic energy), or from being struck by flying, sliding, or falling objects (gravity energy).

Floor barriers installed around pumps and other hazardous equipment must be strong enough to resist damage by, for example, forklift truck impact (mechanical energy), and high enough so that a worker will not trip or fall over them. Expanded metal should fill the open spaces to prevent parts from rolling into the hazard area and fingers from being poked through.

Several devices can be used to control point-of-operation hazards. *Barrier* or *enclosure guards* prevent workers from entering a hazardous area. The barrier may be mechanical (a cage that covers the work action) or electrical (a photocell that will not permit the machine to cycle while the beam is broken). The emergency stop button is another form of guard; for it to be effective, the machine must be equipped with a braking system that will stop the machine in mid-cycle.

Guarding by distance involves keeping workers physically removed from the machine hazard. One of the most common methods is the two-handed trip guard or control, which is located near but not in the midst of the hazard site. Both hands are required to press each button simultaneously for the machine to cycle.

Hand-removal devices are designed to physically remove the worker's hands and arms from the activated machine. The "hand pullout" is a harness-like system fastened to the worker's wrists at one end and to the machine at the other end. When the machine (say a punch press) is activated, the harness mechanism physically pulls the worker's hands out of the way. Short of removing the harness, the worker cannot win the ensuing tug of war.

The "sweep away" is a device with one or two arms (single sweep or double sweep) that, when activated by the machine cycle, will swing across in front of the worker, forcibly removing his or her hands from the danger area. A small panel attached to each arm screens the swept area to keep the worker's hands from reentering the danger zone after the sweep arm passes. The sweep away device is not a recommended guard.

Occupational Health and Safety Today 8.3

Death in a Bakery

David Ellis was 18 years old when he reported to work for his second day at New Sun Cookies in Oakville, Ontario, on February 11, 1999. His job assignment was to run the industrial-sized cookie dough mixer (imagine a 2-metre high version of a mixer used in a home kitchen that can process 90 kg of dough at a time). The mixer had no lockout features and no machine guards to protect people from the blades while the mixer was in action. These issues had been pointed out to the employer by a provincial health and safety inspector 18 months before the accident. However, the inspector did not issue a written order and nothing was done. About halfway through the shift on February 11, David was removing dough from the mixer bowl when somehow the mixer was turned on, and he was caught in the blades, suffering severe injuries to his head and hands. As a result of the head injuries, David died on February 17, 1999. The company and the company owner received fines; the supervisor was sentenced to 20 days in jail to be served on weekends.

Seven months later, 16-year-old Ivan Golyashov was in almost exactly the same type of accident while working at the Fiera Food Bakery in Toronto. He too died of his injuries.

Sources: Beharie, N. (2001). Young workers: profile of an accident victim. *OHS Canada* (October/ November); and CBC News, "Second dough mixer death." Retrieved from http://www.toronto.cbc.ca/cgi-bin/templates/view cgi?/ news/1999/09/27/dough270999, October 10, 2004.

The *photoelectric eye* is a light beam that, when broken, will not allow the machine to cycle. This type of device has the advantage of not adding to the machine any obstructions that can make maintenance difficult. It is generally expensive to install and maintain but very effective.

Feeding tools include hand-held tongs, push sticks, or clamps that allow the operator access to the machine while keeping his or her hands out of the way. Metal tools are usually made of aluminum or magnesium, which will crush easily if caught in the machine, thereby saving the die sets and not allowing the type of **kickback** that could direct the worker's hands into the machine. A press forge operator will use a set of special tongs to hold a red-hot piece of metal in place in the dies while the machine forms the part. In a similar manner, a set of handles secured to sheet glass or metal by vacuum will permit a worker to handle the material without being cut by sharp edges.

kickback
action of having a work piece suddenly thrown backward into the operator

Contact Control

If the machine, equipment, or plant becomes damaged from accidental causes or emergencies then control of the hazard site is necessary so the worker can be protected. The main purpose of contact control is to ensure that the workers and emergency crews—fire fighters—are not added to the possible injury list. Steps to be taken can be grouped into the five following categories:

1. *Suppression.* Reduce or eliminate the ongoing hazard condition by using standard fire-fighting techniques: install fans to help clear the contaminants from the surrounding air and turn off the power and utilities to the area. For example, dust from an explosion in a mining operation can be controlled by spraying water at the rock surface.
2. *Barriers.* Barriers installed between workers and sources of the emergency keep unauthorized personnel out of the area.
3. *Modifications.* Identify and modify equipment or structures that need to be strengthened to prevent further damage from occurring, such as adding shoring to weakened walls to prevent collapse.
4. *Substitution.* Eliminate potentially harmful energies that have been unleashed by the event and replace with safer, independent devices— use portable flood lighting to replace the existing plant lighting if there is a possibility that damaged electrical equipment could cause a fire.
5. *Isolation.* Isolate energy sources from the emergency personnel and plant workers. Shut off all energy sources in the plant to prevent additional problems and replace with outside equipment if possible, such as a portable air compressor to replace the one in the damage area. Shut down any expensive equipment that could be damaged by energy surges.

Postcontact Control

The following are some steps that should be taken in the aftermath of an event:

1. Ensure that any injured worker receives immediate and thorough emergency care. The injury could be anything from a blow to the head to exposure to a hazardous chemical. Provisions for first aid and

emergency care should be made during the precontact control process. The extent of these provisions will depend on the number of workers in an organization and the types of hazards they face.

2. Lock out the machinery involved until the accident investigation is complete and the damage repaired.
3. Keep unauthorized people out of the area.
4. Determine what can be salvaged and what waste must be disposed of. Environmental regulations may prohibit the easy removal of certain hazardous waste (e.g., PCB-contaminated oils from a damaged power transformer).
5. Apprise the joint health and safety committee, affected managers, and government agencies of the event—fire, police, and paramedics will probably already know.
6. Complete all accident reports to determine what happened. Use report recommendations to ensure the accident will not be repeated.
7. Review all company procedures and revise where appropriate.
8. Communicate with workers about the event. If necessary, implement safety retraining and possibly trauma counselling depending on the seriousness of the event.

Points 2 to 5 are requirements of the Ministry of Labour in most provinces and territories, and the Workers' Compensation Board in B.C.

Source-Path-Human

Hazards can be controlled or eliminated by identifying and attacking the source of the hazard, the path it travels, and the employee or recipient of the hazard. The strategies discussed in this chapter can be regrouped along these lines, as shown in Figure 8.9. This schematic provides a useful summary of the information on hazard control. Placing control strategies in categories is less important than having a thorough understanding that hazard control is necessary and possible.

FIGURE 8.9

Source-Path-Human Controls

| Source | Path | Receiver |

Monitoring/Auditing

Monitoring is an important part of the hazard-control process. Audits are done to ensure that hazard controls are functioning effectively, as well as to identify new hazards. Monitoring can be done daily by supervisors and maintenance personnel, weekly by department heads, monthly by health and safety committees, and as needed by compliance officers.[10] The auditing process itself affects safety. A 50% decrease in accidents in one organization over a 2-year period was attributed to the fact that managers began to audit.[11]

An audit program can be used to evaluate health and safety performance in the workplace. A number of audit methods are available. One very effective technique, which involves the application of total quality control methodologies and trend analysis, relates the number of incidents to some predetermined goal. If it seems from the number of events in a particular time frame that a safety goal failure is imminent, then steps can be taken to prevent the occurrence.

The audit program should do the following:

1. Ensure that safety programs are being carried out without restrictions
2. Ensure that safety programs are up to date and that deficiencies are documented
3. Be carried out by people with some understanding of both the audit methods and the material being examined (the various members of the joint health and safety committee should be able to carry out this inspection)
4. Stimulate discussion among all managers and workers, and ultimately produce conclusions and recommendations
5. Be conducted at least annually by companies with high-risk hazards
6. Include all documentation (WSIB/WCB statements, Ministry of Labour citations, air-sampling results, first-aid and incident reports, hazard analyses, discipline records, cost-benefit studies, etc.).

Record Keeping

Information obtained at all stages of the hazard-control process should be stored in a database. These records are used to identify frequency of events as well as trends in hazards. They are also a source of information on worker training and equipment maintenance. The provision of monthly updates to managers will assist them in their efforts at ongoing hazard control. The length of time records should be kept varies with the nature of the record. Records on individual employees should be kept for as long as that individual is with the company. In some cases (for example, individual records of exposure to radiation) records may have to be kept for the length of employment plus an additional period (e.g., 10 years).

RPC 8.4

RPC 8.5

RPC 8.2

Summary

The control of hazards has multiple payoffs for organizations. Planning for, eliminating, or controlling hazards can be done at the precontact stage through training, safety awareness, administrative controls, engineering controls, purchasing, housekeeping, preventative maintenance, and machine guarding. Strategies at the contact stage include how easily and quickly the event can be stabilized. Postcontact control is intended to minimize the damaging effects of hazards by instituting actions that greatly reduce the possibility of recurrence.

Key Terms

administrative control, p. 202

confined space, p. 210

contact control, p. 202

engineering control, p. 212

hazard control, p. 202

kickback, p. 221

machine guarding, p. 219

postcontact control, p. 202

precontact control, p. 202

preventative maintenance, p. 206

Weblinks

Safe Communities Foundation,
http://www.safecommunities.ca/home.htm (p. 204)

Industrial Accident Prevention Association, "IAPA's health and safety awards: Start the journey towards health & safety excellence,"
http://www.iapa.ca/awards/awards_intro.asp (p. 204)

Nova Scotia Ministry of Labour, "Health and safety awards,"
http://www.gov.ns.ca/enla/ohs/Awardapp.pdf (p. 205)

National Quality Institute, "Canada awards for excellence,"
http://www.nqi.ca/caeawards/default.aspx (p. 205)

Canadian Legal Information Institute, "Canada Occupational Health and Safety Regulations, [SOR/86–304],"
http://www.canlii.org/ca/regu/sor86–304/ (p. 205)

RPC Icons

RPC 8.1 Implements and evaluates practices in the areas of health, safety, security, and Workers' Compensation.

- investigative techniques
- hazard recognition
- disaster recovery techniques
- relevant legislation

- resource information
- common health and safety practices
- company policies and procedures
- Worker Protection (including health and safety and Workers' Compensation)
- theories and practices for protection of individuals and groups
- Occupational health and safety legislation (e.g., Occupational Health and Safety Act of Ontario, Workplace Safety & Insurance Act—Bill 99, Workplace Hazardous Materials Information System, Transportation of Dangerous Goods legislation, environmental legislation, smoking in the workplace legislation, civil rights legislation)
- hazard identification and control
- management techniques for OH&S Programs

RPC 8.2 Ensures due diligence and strict liability requirements are met, e.g. records are kept and formal procedures established.

- relevant legislation and common law
- company policies and procedures
- industry best practices
- program and policy development
- training and development techniques
- risk analysis
- common and statutory law (e.g., employment standard: labour relations)
- Worker Protection (including health and safety and Workers' Compensation)
- theories and practices for protection of individuals and groups

TASK & KNOWLEDGE REQUIREMENTS
- Occupational health and safety legislation (e.g., Occupational Health and Safety Act of Ontario, Workplace Safety & Insurance Act—Bill 99, Workplace Hazardous Materials Information System, Transportation of Dangerous Goods legislation, environmental legislation, smoking in the workplace legislation, civil rights legislation)
- management techniques for OH&S Programs

RPC 8.3 Ensures that mechanisms are in place for responding to crises in the workplace, including critical incident stress management.

- oral and written communication
- training and development techniques
- industry best practices
- the workplace environment including the availability of emergency equipment
- policy and program development and evaluation
- intervention strategies
- relevant legislation (e.g., fire code, Workers' Compensation)
- investigation techniques
- stress management techniques
- types of employee assistance programs
- Occupational health and safety legislation (e.g., Occupational Health and Safety Act of Ontario, Workplace Safety & Insurance Act—Bill 99, Workplace Hazardous Materials Information System, Transportation

of Dangerous Goods legislation, environmental legislation, smoking in the workplace legislation, civil rights legislation)
- hazard identification and control
- accident investigation procedures
- emergency preparedness procedures
- management techniques for OH&S Programs
- conceptual definition and implications of occupational stressors (e.g., potential stressors, methods of identifying potential stressors and strain outcomes, response to organizational stressors, and management of employee strain outcomes)

RPC 8.4 Analyses risk to the health and safety of employees and determines appropriate preventative measures, including training, provision of required safety equipment, and administrative practices.

- relevant legislation
- nature of the business and physical work environment
- hazard recognition
- workplace inspection techniques
- safety programs, equipment, and emergency procedures
- ergonomics
- functions of the JHSC
- training and development/presentation techniques
- industry best practices
- relevant technical terminology
- the collective agreement
- services and equipment available in the community
- Worker Protection (including health and safety and Workers' Compensation)
- training and development program design and administration

Task & Knowledge Requirements
- Occupational health and safety legislation (e.g., Occupational Health and Safety Act of Ontario, Workplace Safety & Insurance Act—Bill 99, Workplace Hazardous Materials Information System, Transportation of Dangerous Goods legislation, environmental legislation, smoking in the workplace legislation, civil rights legislation)
- hazard identification and control
- emergency preparedness procedures
- management techniques for OH&S Programs
- types of employee assistance and wellness programs

RPC 8.5 Establishes effective programs for accident prevention, incident investigation, inspections, fire and emergency response, and required training.

- relevant legislation
- workplace inspection and accident investigation techniques
- nature of the business and physical work environment
- potential risks and hazards in the workplace
- emergency response planning
- community emergency response services

- training and development
- industry best practices
- Worker Protection (including health and safety and Workers' Compensation)
- training and development program design and administration
- hazard identification and control
- accident investigation procedures
- emergency preparedness procedures
- management techniques for OH&S Programs

Discussion Questions

1. Explain why hazard control at the precontact stage is better than hazard control at the other stages.
2. In recent years there has been a move to make ergonomic design and ergonomic standards mandatory in workplaces. Should your jurisdiction implement legislation requiring ergonomic analysis and design of work processes? Why or why not?
3. A maintenance crew has been hired to enter an underground sewer line to do some minor repair work. They call and ask you for advice about necessary equipment and procedures. Briefly outline your response.

Using the Internet

1. Table 8.1 presented a series of special awareness events. Use the web to determine (a) how these events are celebrated or implemented in your local area and (b) what other safety awareness events are held in your area.

Exercise

1. Identify a hazard at your workplace (or a workplace with which you are familiar). List all the approaches you could undertake to control or minimize the hazards.

Case: Hazard Control

A new plating machine had been installed and was being checked for proper operation. During this check it was discovered that the bearings on the caustic-solution circulating pump were defective and had to be replaced. The pump was removed, repaired, and was being reinstalled. An electrician was assigned to make the electrical connections, while a plumber performed the necessary pipe connections on the same pump.

The electrician finished the assignment except for checking the direction of shaft rotation. Since the plumber was out of the area, the electrician asked the company representative supplying the equipment if the pump was ready to be tried out. The representative stated that it was. The electrician walked to the end of the plater to start the motor, just as the plumber appeared. The plumber's shouts to the electrician not to start the pump were too late because the pump had already been turned on. At that moment, hot caustic solution showered out of the pipe flange, which had not been tightened after reassembly. The solution splashed onto the plumber, two engineers in the area, another plant engineering employee, and the vendor representative. The plumber received burns requiring immediate hospitalization and was off work for about two months. One engineer required subsequent hospitalization for eye burns and was off work for more than a week. The other three involved received minor burns. The accident occurred at 10:45 a.m. on a Wednesday.

What would you recommend for contact and postcontact control?

Endnotes

1. DiNardi, S. (Ed.). (1997). *The occupational environment—Its evaluation and control* (2nd ed.). Fairfax, VA: American Industrial Hygiene Association.

2. Schuler, R., & Dolan, S. (1994). *Human resources management: A Canadian perspective*. Scarborough, Ont.: Nelson Canada.

3. Pilger, C. W. (1994). Hazard control procedures. Presentation at the 23rd Intensive Workshop in Industrial Hygiene, September 27.

4. Grandjean, E. (1988). *Fitting the task to the man* (4th ed.). London, England: Taylor & Francis.

5. Astrand, P. O., & Rodahl, K. (1986). *Textbook of work physiology* (3rd ed.). New York: McGraw-Hill.

6. McDonald, H. (1995, March/April). Know thy users. *Accident Prevention*, 11–12.

7. Canadian Standards Association. (1995). *Office ergonomics*. CSA Standard, CAN/CSA Z412-M89, section 5.

8. Somasunder, S. (1993, September/October). Machine safeguarding. *OH&S Canada*, 9(5), 30–31.

9. Canadian Standards Association. (1994). *Safeguarding of machinery*. Standard Z432–94.

10. Laing, P. (Ed.). (1992). *Accident prevention manual for business and industry: Administration and programs* (10th ed.). Washington, D.C.: National Safety Council.

11. Taylor, J. (1991). Guide to health and safety management: 20 proven programs. *Safety Auditing*. Don Mills, Ont.: Southam Business Communications Inc.

Chapter 9

Training

Chapter Learning Objectives

After reading this chapter, you should be able to

- discuss the importance of occupational health and safety training
- identify the components of a training program
- explain the role of a needs assessment when designing a training program
- discuss issues that arise in training design and delivery
- describe various options for the delivery of health and safety training programs
- discuss the role of evaluation in any training program
- evaluate the measurement concerns surrounding organizational measures of occupational safety training effectiveness
- describe some common health and safety training initiatives including safety orientation, first-aid training, and WHMIS

THE LIFEQUILT

The Canadian LifeQuilt is a memorial created by artist Laurie Swim and a large number of volunteers that honours the lives of the many young Canadian workers between the ages of 15 and 24 who have been injured or killed on the job. The tapestry itself, dedicated to all young workers who have sustained injuries or died in work-related incidents, contains 100 quilted squares, each one recognizing a particular young worker's experience. *Shawna Michele Vezina*, 19, was hit and killed by an oncoming vehicle while working as a traffic controller at a road construction site. *David Ellis* was only 18 years old when he was pulled into an industrial mixer on the second day of his temporary job at a bakery. Nineteen-year-old *Sean Kells* died in 1994 in an explosion that occurred while he was pouring a highly flammable chemical. This event occurred on Sean's third day on the job. He had not been advised that the activity was dangerous. *Kelly Newton*, aged 22, was crushed by logs moving on a skidder. Kelly had been on the job less than three weeks when this tragedy occurred. At the time of his death, he was working without supervision and had not received training.

The image in the centre of the LifeQuilt is that of a young person. Organza ribbons overlaid on this part of the quilt honour young people injured in the workplace. Consider the case of *Candace Carnahan*, who at age 21 lost a leg below the knee when her leg was caught in a moving conveyor belt. *Stephen Nicholson* was also injured in the workplace. At age 19, he suffered third-degree burns to 85% of his body as a result of an explosion in the workplace.

The Canadian LifeQuilt represents a sad reality. Estimates suggest that one in seven young workers is injured on the job. In fact, work-related incidents involving machinery and electrocution are the second-leading cause of death among youths in Canada—second only to car accidents. Programs like the LifeQuilt raise awareness among parents, youths, and employers about young workers' safety. As part of the awareness campaign, the Young Worker Zone on the CCOHS website includes resources and recommendations for young workers, their parents, and their employers. A major recommendation for employers is for the provision of health and safety training for new employees, particularly young workers. Young workers are encouraged to know their rights and ask questions about safety at work.

Such recommendations are certainly timely and appropriate. Many youths who are injured at work report that they were not aware of the life-threatening hazards in the workplace. In fact, reports from many accidents involving young workers indicate that injuries could easily have been avoided if basic safety rules had been followed. Trusting young workers, eager to please their new employers, often believe that someone is looking out for their safety while at work. However, many companies do not provide adequate safety training regarding the hazards in the workplace. In fact, studies reveal that 80% of young workers report that they did not receive occupational health and safety training or a workplace orientation. In this chapter we will consider the issue of occupational health and safety training.

Sources: Young Workers Memorial Life Quilt. Retrieved from http://www.youngworkerquilt.ca, October 6, 2004; Canadian Centre for Occupational Health and Safety, "Young Workers Zone." Retrieved from http://www.ccohs.ca/youngworkers/, October 6, 2004; Chapeskie, K. K., & Breslin, C. F. (2003). Securing a safe and healthy future: The road to injury prevention of Ontario's young workers. *In Focus*, 34a. Retrieved from the Institute for Work and Health, http://www.iwh.on.ca, March 15, 2004.

The tragedy of workplace injury and fatality among young workers as commemorated by the LifeQuilt project illustrates the disastrous events that can happen when the appropriate health and safety training is not delivered in workplaces. Although young workers appear to experience injuries at a higher rate than do other groups of workers, the dangers of the workplace are a reality for all workers. Workers of all ages and experience levels can and do experience accidents at work. Recent Canadian statistics show that many workers in this country have not been adequately trained. A recent survey of Canadian workers by Ipsos-Reid revealed that less than half the workers polled had received any safety training for their current job duties.[1] When we consider the statistics for individuals starting new jobs, the numbers are even more pressing. A 1999 survey of Canadian workers who had started with a new employer within six months of answering the survey found that only 19.8% had received health and safety training or a safety orientation.[2] This figure is especially disturbing since the risk of injury is highest when a person enters a new job. In this chapter we explore the topic of health and safety training. We apply a basic model of training in organizations to the specific concerns of training workers in the area of occupational health and safety. In particular we consider the processes of designing, implementing, and evaluating a health and safety training program in an organization.

The Role of Occupational Health and Safety Training

All workers have several rights pertaining to their health and safety while at work. Three basic rights apply to all Canadian employees:

1. *The right to know.* Workers have a right to be informed about dangerous or unsafe materials and machinery in the workplace.
2. *The right to participate.* Workers have a right to actively take part in the protection of their own health and safety. This participation generally involves reporting unsafe work practices and conditions.

RPC 9.2

RPC 9.3

3. *The right to refuse unsafe work.* Workers have a right to withhold their services if they are asked to perform a task that they deem to be unsafe or are asked to use equipment that is not in good repair.

It is easy to see the vital role of training in the fulfillment of these basic rights. First, employees—especially new employees—must be advised of these rights. The communication of these basic rights might take place in a safety orientation when a person starts a new job.

Once employees are aware of their basic rights regarding health and safety at work, safety-related training is needed to help individuals ensure that these rights are being upheld. For instance, with respect to the right to know, employees must receive training on the potential dangers in their workplaces. Similarly, regarding the right to refuse unsafe work, effective health and safety training will help individuals accurately evaluate what tasks are indeed unsafe. As such, health and safety training plays a vital role in the protection of an employee's basics rights, and its provision is mandated in occupational health and safety acts across the country. The importance of health and safety training is recognized internationally as well. For example, in the United States, training is prominently placed as one of five essential elements of occupational health and safety programs, along with employer commitment, hazard surveillance, hazard control and prevention, and program evaluation.[3]

Given the importance of the effective communication of health and safety information in today's workplaces, the question of how to develop and implement effective health and safety training programs is vital. In the remainder of this chapter, we will consider the process of implementing

Occupational Health and Safety Today 9.1

The Vital Role of Health and Safety Training following the "Westray" Legislation

Many Canadians report that they have not received health and safety training in their workplaces. Organizations failing to provide safety training are in fact failing to meet legal requirements. All employees have the right to be fully aware of the hazards associated with their work and receive training that allows them to operate in a safe manner while working. Because employers are responsible for the health and safety of workers, organizations that fail to provide health and safety training or that provide inadequate training can be held responsible for any accidents or other safety-related incidents that occur.

Bill C-45, commonly referred to as the "Westray Bill," became law on March 31, 2004. This law means that the

ramifications for employers failing to provide appropriate health and safety training have become more severe in Canada. This bill amended the Criminal Code of Canada to hold corporations and their stakeholders accountable for work-related acts that are deemed criminally negligent. Employers bear a large responsibility to ensure that Canadian workers know about hazards in the workplace and are able to refuse work deemed unsafe. This new legislation means that failure to provide appropriate health and safety training can be labelled a criminal offence and can ultimately result in criminal charges against organizations.

a health and safety training program. As our starting point we take a basic model of training in organizations and discuss its application to health and safety–related concerns.

Health and Safety Training Programs

As our starting point we take the **instructional systems design (ISD) model of training**.[4] The ISD model of training incorporates a three-part process: (1) needs analysis, (2) training design and delivery, and (3) training evaluation. The model is depicted in Figure 9.1. Each stage of the model, with its applicability to health and safety training, is detailed in the sections that follow.

Needs Analysis

The training and development process begins when some form of need or concern arises. With respect to health and safety training, that concern might be the occurrence of a number of accidents or injuries in the workplace. Following such incidents, company officials may be concerned about the safety of their workers and want to develop a training program to improve workplace safety. A large number of workplace accidents in a particular company may also draw attention from various occupational health and safety governing bodies. These groups may determine that safety training is required and mandate training within a particular organization. Alternatively, the move toward safety training could be prompted by new legislation requiring that a particular type of health and safety training be offered in all workplaces within a certain industry or to deal with identified hazards. Whatever the case, a health and safety training development process begins with a **needs analysis**.

Needs analysis is the recommended starting point in many models of organizational training.[5] A needs analysis helps determine the nature of the problem at hand. Needs analysis is a way to determine the "gap between the

instructional systems design (ISD) model of training

a general model of the training process that incorporates needs analysis, training design and delivery, and training evaluation, and notes the interdependencies among the three major components of the training process

RPC 9.4

RPC 9.5

needs analysis

the initial stage of the training development process, intended to identify employee and organizational deficiencies that can be addressed with training and to recognize potential obstacles to success of a training program

FIGURE 9.1

The Instructional Systems Design Model of Training

Source: Adapted from Saks, A. M., & Haccoun, R. R. (2004). *Managing performance through training and development* (3rd ed.). Toronto: Nelson Canada.

way things are and the way things should be."[6] Needs analysis can also be used to identify potential obstacles to the effectiveness of a training program so that they can be dealt with early in the training and development process. Such an analysis ideally includes an assessment of the organization, the task or job at hand, and the employee(s) in question. The inclusion of all three levels in the initial analysis will help answer questions about what ground-work must be done before training begins, what the content of the training program should be, who should receive training, and how the program should be delivered. Let's consider the pertinent issues when assessing the needs of the organization, the task or job, and the employee.

Organizational Analysis

A needs analysis at the organizational level should be the starting point in any training intervention.[7] The **organizational analysis** should involve a study of the whole organization, considering such areas as the resources and strategy of the organization and the industry in which it operates. The organizational analysis can identify the health and safety areas that need improvement and may be targets for a training program. This analysis should also highlight any constraints that may limit the success of a training program before the design and delivery of the training.

Successful training initiatives tend to be those that are in line with the organization's overall strategy. Similarly, it is important to consider the resources that the organization can dedicate to the training process. The extent of the available resources can influence the nature of the training program. For example, if the organization has training facilities on-site, this may influence decisions about the delivery of the training. The budget available for training should also be considered, as financial constraints will influence decisions later in the training development process. Similarly, it is important to consider the industry and environmental factors that may affect the training program. For instance, if the organization is unionized, consider the role of the union in training program development.

Another major goal of the organizational analysis should be to establish the degree of organizational support for a training intervention. This can be done by developing a relationship with management. Support from the organization is vital to the success of any training program. If an organization truly values training, it will provide the necessary resources to make the training program a success. For instance, an organization that supports a training intervention is more likely to encourage their employees to actively take part in the program than is an organization that is merely going through the motions of implementing some form of training.

With respect to health and safety training, it is important that the individual conducting the organizational needs analysis determine not only the degree of organizational support for training and learning, but also the support for health and safety initiatives in general. A recent review of the research literature on occupational health and safety training noted that the effectiveness of health and safety efforts "will be a function of the organization's

🅡🅟🅒 9.6

organizational analysis

an analysis of the entire organization designed to examine its resources, strategy, and environment in order to assess the organization's support for training overall commitment to providing a safe work environment and the employee's perception and recognition of that commitment."[8] Certainly, studies show that organizational support plays a vital role in the success of health and safety training initiatives. In one examination of the effectiveness of health and safety training among employees at toxic waste sites, trainees reported that attempts to act on what they had learned in training were far more likely to succeed and had a better chance of success when their managers were supportive of the program.[9] In general, investigations of the impact of management attitudes toward health and safety training illustrate the importance of managerial support for sustaining the positive outcomes associated with such training.

One way for the individual(s) conducting the needs analysis to determine the extent of organizational support for a health and safety training program is to examine the **safety climate** of the organization. An organization's safety climate relates to the perceptions regarding safety-related policies, procedures, and practices that are shared by all the stakeholders in the organization.[10] An organization that has explicitly enacted policies on safety, encourages safety-related training, and promotes safety might be said to have a strong safety climate. A company that has a strong safety climate is likely to support and enable initiatives relating to health and safety training. These organizations will invest the necessary money and time to make the training program a success, and employees are likely to be responsive to the effort.

> **safety climate**
> shared perceptions of the importance of safety in the workplace

However, consider an organization that does not place a high value on safety, that is, a company that does not have a strong safety climate. This type of operation may be hesitant to provide the type of support necessary to make health and safety training a successful endeavour. Similarly, employees of such an organization may be suspicious of the training program—wondering why the company suddenly appears to be concerned about their health and well-being. If the organizational analysis reveals that the safety climate of the organization is not currently conducive to safety training, the next logical step may be to emphasize to organizational management the need for increased organizational attention to safety and the necessity of communicating to employees the intended move toward a health and safety focus. These efforts, if launched early in the overall training development process, will lay important groundwork for a health and safety training effort and ultimately contribute to the success of the training program.

One situation that might arise when conducting an organizational analysis regarding health and safety training needs is finding an organization that does not generally focus on employee health and safety and does not have a strong safety climate, but that is mandated to offer safety training because of legislation. There is no easy answer for how to deal with such a situation. However, we suggest that individuals involved in a training needs analysis with such an organization should emphasize the importance of a supportive organizational environment in successful training. Managers in this type of organization may respond to a bottom line approach—an argument based on the return on investment of training dollars. If management can be convinced that their support will result in increased training effectiveness and ultimately tangible organizational benefits, they will be more likely to make an effort to provide a supportive training environment.

Job/Task Analysis

Following the organizational analysis, the second step in the training needs analysis is to conduct a **job/task analysis.** The first critical step is to identify the jobs that are targeted for training. With respect to health and safety training, the scope of the jobs involved in a training program will depend on the nature of the training programs. Some forms of training, like a basic safety orientation or a seminar on the role of a health and safety committee, will apply to employees in many positions within the organization. Other types of training will be far more specific in its target jobs. For example, training on the safe operation of a particular piece of machinery will apply only to those individuals whose jobs bring them into contact with the equipment in question.

Once the target job has been identified, obtain a detailed job description that outlines the tasks, duties, and responsibilities for individuals who hold that position. By working with a group of job incumbents and subject matter experts, we can rate the required tasks on their importance and frequency in the job. With respect to health and safety–related training, incumbents and subject matter experts should also be surveyed on the health and safety risks involved in each task and their perceived competence to perform the task in a safe manner. The person developing the training program might also want to observe several people performing the tasks in question to identify potential health and safety concerns that were not mentioned by the subject matter experts. From here, the information can be analyzed and interpreted.

The evaluation of the job in question and the inclusion of people with experience performing the job can greatly inform the training program that will ultimately be offered. The task analysis can help determine the exact nature and scope of the problem to be solved. To consider a health and safety example, the survey component of the task analysis might reveal that although employees are vigilant about wearing their protective equipment, they tend to use it incorrectly. In that case, the training program should focus more on instruction in the proper use of the equipment rather than on convincing people to wear the equipment. This point might have been missed if it were not for the completion of a task analysis.

Person Analysis

The final assessment to be carried out in the training needs analysis is to investigate the training needs of individual employees. Individual employees' behaviour is considered to see if performance meets desired standards. The ultimate goal in the **person analysis** is to determine who needs training. Such a decision can be made by comparing a person's current performance with a desired standard or level of performance. Which individuals will be included at this stage of the analysis will be largely determined by the needs of the organization. In some cases the consultant or training director may be asked to assess those individuals who have demonstrated poor or unsafe performance in the past. In other organizations, employees included in the person analysis may be chosen randomly.

The next step in the individual assessment is to identify the method of assessment. Common needs assessment techniques include observation, work samples, and tests.[11] From here the relationship between the desired standard for performance and the actual performance can be measured and the potential reason for performance gaps can be determined. The data gathered during this stage of the process inform the next steps in developing a training program. In some cases the person analysis may reveal that training will not be able to address the barriers to effective performance. For instance, it might be discovered that certain safety concerns are the result of worn equipment that is continually in a state of ill repair. In this case, the maintenance or replacement of equipment, rather than a training program, would be the next logical step. In other situations, training will be a viable option to address the problems uncovered in the needs analysis.

The type of training offered will depend on the nature of the problem. For example, if the person analysis reveals that safety concerns stem from the fact that individuals are not well versed in the operation of dangerous equipment, the training program to follow should focus on delivering knowledge about the proper operation of the machinery. Again, consider a case in which the person analysis revealed that although individuals are aware of safety regulations in the operation of equipment and are capable of complying with these protocols, they choose to ignore them. In this situation, the training would best focus on safety-related attitudes in the workplace.

Training Design and Delivery

Following the needs analysis process, an informed decision about the potential effectiveness of training as an option to address health and safety concerns can be made. If training has a role to play in the solution to a health and safety problem, several decisions must now be made. These decisions involve translating what was learned from the needs assessment into the actual training initiative. Some of the pertinent decisions include the following:

1. What are the objectives for training?
2. Will the training program be designed or purchased?
3. What is the appropriate content for the training?
4. Who will receive the training?
5. Who will deliver the training?
6. Where will the training take place?

Let's consider some of these questions as they apply to the case of occupational health and safety training.

The first pressing question involves the objectives for training. In other words, what do you hope the trainees will take away from the training program? In general the **training objectives** will involve the knowledge, skill, and behavioural changes that will be acquired through training. Objectives serve a number

training objectives

statements regarding the knowledge, skill, and behavioural changes that trainees should acquire in the training program

An Example of Training Objectives for a Health and Safety Course

The Workers' Compensation Board of British Columbia offers several WorkSafe health and safety training courses on such vital topics as hazard recognition; control, prevention, and investigation of musculoskeletal injury (MSI); and joint health and safety committees. As an example of training objectives in an occupational health and safety course, consider the objectives laid out for the course in preventing and investigating MSI. According to the WorkSafe website, the course aims to provide both employers and employees with the knowledge and skill to prevent and investigate MSI incidents. The course contains four modules, including ergonomic requirements and the prevention process, risk identification and assessment, risk control and early treatment, and investigation of MSI incidents. The course objectives as listed in the course description are as follows:

Successful completion of this course will enable participants to

1. Identify key components of the ergonomics (MSI) requirements
2. Explain the seven-step musculoskeletal injury prevention (MSIP) process
3. Explain five categories of risk factors associated with MSI
4. Explain three main types of risk control of the risk factors
5. Use a checklist to identify and address risk factors
6. Determine ways to control identified risk factors
7. Apply early treatment and intervention principles
8. Investigate MSI incidents to prevent recurrence

The value of these objectives in designing the content of the training program and deciding appropriate ways to assess what the trainees learned during training is obvious. Every health and safety training program should have a set of clearly stated objectives that provide specific information about what trainees will know and be able to do upon completion of the program.

Source: BC Workers' Compensation Board WorkSafe Education Network. Course descriptions are available online at http://www.worksafebc.com/news/worksafe_courses/default.asp

 9.7

 9.8

of important functions, including setting the groundwork for the needed training content and providing a starting point for tools to evaluate the effectiveness of the training program.

A second question in the development of a training program is whether an existing training package can be purchased or an original program needs to be designed. In many cases the purchase of an existing prepackaged program is more economical and fully meets the needs of the organization. With the case of health and safety concerns, many existing training programs are readily available for purchase. For instance, institutions such as St. John Ambulance specialize in first-aid and CPR training. In fact, St. John Ambulance offers readily available generic and custom first-aid and CPR programs. In the case of an organization wanting to institute a first-aid training program for individuals involved in particular high-risk jobs, it would make sense to choose a proven, prepackaged program from a reputable provider. The time and cost of developing a first-aid course, paying a qualified trainer, and purchasing the necessary tools would be both unnecessary and prohibitive given the quality and accessibility of existing programs.

In other cases the final decision reached by an organization will be to design a custom health and safety training program from scratch, either in-house or via the services of a consultant. In what situations might an organization decide that a customized program is needed? We suggest that in cases in which the content of the program is highly specific to the organization in question, the custom design of a program may be necessary. For instance, a company wanting to offer a health and safety orientation for their new hires would need to incorporate information that is unique to their company; such a program would be difficult to purchase in a prepackaged form. Additionally, training in the safe use of particular equipment or the performance of particular tasks may require a training program that is not readily available for purchase, and as such, a customized program may be the only option.

With respect to training content, it is important that the content of the training program matches the needs identified in the needs analysis and allows trainees to achieve the training objectives. Even if the training program is purchased, there is likely some flexibility in the material that will be presented. One way to ensure that the training content is appropriate is to consult subject matter experts in the area in question. For instance, in a training program on the safe handling of hazardous materials, individuals who have expertise in industrial hygiene may be consulted and asked for their input on the needed components of the training program.

Who will receive the training is also an important question at this phase of the curriculum development. In some cases, the answer will be obvious. If law mandates that all operators of a particular type of machinery must have training in the operation of that equipment, then all operators must be trained. In this situation, the job of selecting who receives training is as simple as identifying the operators. Similarly, if the training program is a health and safety orientation for all new employees, each employee will complete the program on joining the organization. In other cases, the decision of who receives training will not be as obvious. For instance, provincial and territorial legislation requires that organizations have a certain number of trained first-aid providers on site. Only a small number of employees will need to complete this training. The decision of who enters the program is one that will have to be dealt with case by case.

A related issue to who will receive training is that of how many people will be trained at the same time. The accumulated research on training in general and that pertaining to health and safety training in particular shows that smaller groups make for more effective learning environments.[12] Individuals within the training groups should also have similar jobs characterized by common risk exposure.[13] This combination of people will contribute to the maximal success of health and safety training initiatives.

Another issue to consider when designing training programs is who will deliver the training. An effective trainer is a vital aspect of a successful training program. Of course, the trainer should be both knowledgeable about the material and an effective communicator. In some cases the trainer will require certification in a particular area—for instance, the person who delivers first-aid training will need certification as an instructor.

train the trainer

programs designed to offer subject matter experts in various content areas skills in program delivery and communication

Another approach to finding effective trainers who are both subject matter experts and effective educators is to use a **train the trainer** program. In train the trainer initiatives, a subject matter expert with the appropriate content skills is given coaching in such areas as program delivery and communication. An effective train the trainer program can provide organizations with the ability to use in-house individuals to deliver training programs. For example, an individual who is a member of an organization's health and safety committee may be trained to deliver the health and safety orientation for new employees.

The research literature has examined the effectiveness of subject matter experts who have undergone train the trainer programs in the delivery of occupational health and safety training. Generally, it appears that trainees respond well to subject matter experts as trainers and that such an approach to training delivery can result in improved safety performance in the workplace.[14]

Occupational Health and Safety Notebook 9.2

Learning Theory and Training Delivery

How information is presented is a vital decision in the design of any training effort, including occupational health and safety training. The ultimate goal is that the knowledge and skills gained in the training environment are transferred to the workplace. Principles determined from extensive psychological research on learning can help create such a training environment. Two major approaches to the study of learning are the behaviourist perspective and the cognitive perspective. How might these learning theories from the behaviourist and cognitive approaches influence the design of health and safety training programs?

Behaviourist Theory

The behaviourist approach characterizes learning in terms of observable stimuli and responses, without reference to any activity that occurs inside the individual.[1] Behaviourists state that a person's behaviour is a product of the person's past experience in an environment. Certainly, this notion applies to the training context; the experience gained during training should influence later job performance.

Several behaviourist principles have been used to inform the design of training programs. A substantial concern for training designers is transfer of training. Transfer of training refers to the degree to which the knowledge, skills, and abilities gained in the training environment are then applied in the job environment. Four basic learning principles have been used extensively in an attempt to maximize transfer of training.[2] These are reviewed below.

1. *Identical elements:* According to this principle, transfer of training is maximized to the extent that the stimuli in the training environment are identical to those in the transfer environment. Therefore, the training environment should be as similar as possible to the job environment. For instance, in a safety training program on the proper use of protective equipment, the very same brand and type of safety gear that is used on the job site should also be used in the training program.

2. *General principles:* Learning theory suggests that transfer of training is improved when trainees are taught not only applicable skills, but also general rules that underlie the training content. For example, a training program on the safe operation of a piece of heavy equipment should also stress underlying principles regarding the widespread importance of safe behaviour in the workplace and the basic workings of the machinery itself.

Learning Theory and Training Delivery

3. *Stimulus variability:* Multiple examples of a concept should be provided for trainees. Having access to multiple examples allows trainees to see the applicability of the training content in their job environment and thus enhances transfer of training. To apply this notion to safety training, consider an emergency preparedness training program. The trainers should be sure to provide examples from several types of emergency scenarios.

4. *Conditions of practice:* Conditions of practice refers to the manner in which the trainee is exposed to the content of the training program.

   a. *Whole versus part learning* addresses whether the knowledge, skills, and abilities being covered in the training program should be introduced to trainees as the whole task or as separate task elements. Whole learning involves practising an entire duty, whereas part learning asks participants to practise pieces of a larger task separately. The general finding is that for tasks that have highly interdependent parts, whole learning is preferred. However, tasks that have largely independent elements should be trained using part learning.

   b. *Spaced versus massed practice* concerns the dispersion of practice sessions. With spaced trials, a rest period is allowed between practice sessions, whereas with massed practice the trainee practises the task continually until mastery. It is generally accepted that spaced trials are preferable. This conclusion is generally applicable in safety training as well.[3] However, massed practice may be used in a case in which errors are critical and learning from errors is important.

   c. *Overlearning* implies that a task should be practised until it can be performed with few attentional resources (i.e., automatically). Overlearning is invaluable in health and safety–related training programs, specifically those involving safety procedures in an emergency situation, when actions must be performed under pressure and quickly.

Cognitive Learning Theories

The increasingly complex nature of many jobs requires that workers have complex cognitive skills.[4] One popular cognitive approach to learning is social learning theory, which posits that people observe others to learn. Observing others can help us learn various motor skills or styles of behaving. For instance, observing more experienced people can help a new employee learn how to properly use safety equipment at work. The people that we observe during social learning are called models. The psychologist most often associated with social learning theory is Canadian Albert Bandura. Bandura proposed that four mental processes facilitate social learning:[5]

1. Attention: The learner must notice the behavioural models and find them interesting. For instance, new employees who are looking for models will likely look to experienced employees who attract their attention and seem willing to help.

2. *Memory:* The learner must be able to remember the information obtained by observation to use at a later time. New employees who are observing senior employees operate a particular piece of machinery must remember all the actions taken by the senior employees as they complete the task.

3. *Motor control:* Learners must be able to use the information obtained from observation to guide their own actions. With respect to safe behaviour in the workplace, new employees who have been observing others must be able to reproduce their behaviour. If a particular work task involves heavy lifting, the new employees must be capable of lifting that weight.

4. Motivation: The learner must have some reason to perform the modelled actions. In the case of occupational health and safety, the learner must be motivated to perform the job in a safe manner.

It is clear that the four components of Bandura's social learning theory can be useful in the training environment. The trainer assumes the role of the model. The

(continued)

trainer must capture the attention of the trainee and appear interesting. Thus, the trainer should be perceived as an expert in the relevant field and be credible and appealing to the trainees. The information should be presented in such a manner that the trainees store it in memory and draw on this information to guide their performance in the future (i.e., when they are back on the job). Social learning theory also stresses the importance of motivation in training, an issue we will consider extensively in Chapter 10.

Sources:
1. Gazzaniga, M. S., & Heatherton, T. F. (2003). *Psychological science*: *Mind, brain, and behavior*. New York: Norton.

2. Baldwin, T. T., & Ford, J. K. (1988). Transfer of training: A review and directions for future research. *Personnel Psychology*, *41*, 63–105.
3. Colligan, M. J., & Cohen, A. (2004). The role of training in promoting workplace safety and health. In J. Barling & M. Frone (Eds.), *Handbook of workplace safety* (pp. 223–248). Washington, DC: American Psychological Association.
4. Goldstein, I. L. (1993). *Training in organizations*: *Needs assessments, development and evaluation* (3rd ed.). Pacific Grove, CA: Brooks/Cole Publishing.
5. Bandura, A. (1986). *Social functions of thought and action*: *A social cognitive theory*. Englewood Cliffs, NJ: Prentice Hall.

 9.9

WHMIS

Workplace Hazardous Materials Information System; a legislated training program in the handling of potentially hazardous chemicals in the workplace that ensures that Canadian workers recognize hazardous materials and are knowledgeable in emergency procedures following a chemical spill

The final training delivery question that we will consider in the current discussion is where will the training take place. Traditionally, this has been a question of on-the-job or off-the-job training. On-the-job training takes place while individuals are at work performing their regular job tasks. In other words, the training is incorporated while the task is being conducted. For example, on-the-job training in the safe operation of a particular tool may have subject matter experts demonstrate the safe use of the tool while a new hire observes the process. The new hire may then have the opportunity to use the tool under the guidance of the subject matter expert.

Off-the-job training is training that takes place away from the area where the work is conducted. It may be in a room on-site or in a different facility. The nature of the room will depend on the nature of the training. Some forms of training may require little more than a boardroom and PowerPoint slides. Other forms of training may require simulators or particular equipment.

More recently, a third dimension has been added to the question of where health and safety training will occur. Some health and safety training programs are now been offered via the World Wide Web. For example, courses in the **Workplace Hazardous Materials Information System (WHMIS)**, a legislated program in the safe handling of hazardous materials, are now being offered online. For more information on this program, see Occupational Health and Safety Today 9.2. Web-based training in programs such as WHMIS may prove useful to a company that frequently has new hires who are computer savvy. However, it may not be as appealing or effective when the individuals who require training do not have access to or a high degree of comfort using computers and the Internet. Ultimately, the program delivery choice will depend on the unique needs of the organization and employees.

Online WHMIS Courses

A quick Internet search will reveal any number of providers offering online training programs in WHMIS. Most of these websites note the speed, ease, and convenience of using Internet-based training for this often-required health and safety training program. One such provider, WHMIS-in-Minutes, provides training programs in both English and French and promotes its online course as suitable for individuals who are interested in a refresher course and for those who are learning about hazardous materials for the first time. This program features a certificate of completion and does not require that the organization pay startup fees. Rather the fee is on a per-user basis. The cost is about $10 per user. They note a number of well-known clients, including Human Resources Development Canada, Xerox, and several provincial governments. An administrative feature enables the system to track for organizations which employees have completed the training program. Another basis on which the online service is promoted is the possibility of customization. Additional questions, customized to the organization's needs, can be added to the standard WHMIS program.

Source: WHMIS-in-Minutes. Retrieved from http://www.whmis.net, March 27, 2004.

Regardless of the chosen location for training, research on the effectiveness of various health and safety training initiatives emphasizes the importance of active approaches to learning.[15] Training efforts predominantly relying on posters or videos result in initial improvements in safety behaviour, but the results may be short lived. Alternatively, more active forms of training such as hands-on or interactive electronic techniques appear to have a stronger, more durable effect on behaviour.

Even when safety training programs have demonstrated a positive impact on safety-related actions in the workplace, continued upgrading of skills may be important if employees are to maintain the knowledge and skills they gained in training. Consider the case of employees who are designated first-aid providers in their workplaces. It is conceivable that these individuals could experience long periods when they are not called on to use their first-aid skills. However, in the event of an emergency, it is imperative that they correctly recall what they learned in training. Periodic refresher courses that reinforce what employees learned in their initial training program will go a long way in ensuring that first-aid providers correctly and quickly recall their treatment skills when called on to do so.[16] In fact, retraining, upgrading, and refresher courses are valuable in all areas of safety training. The more often employees are reminded of safety-related issues in the workplace, the more likely they are to properly enact safety behaviour.

Training Evaluation

Evaluation efforts following training programs consider the extent to which the training program has added value to the organization and the individual employees. Information gathered during **training evaluation** may be useful for identifying strengths and weaknesses in the training program and thus

training evaluation

a component of the ISD training model designed to assess the value added for individuals and organizations following the implementation of a training program

RPC 9.10

guide further curriculum development. Evaluation results may also be used to estimate the economic value of a training program. In a safety training endeavour, an economic factor that may be evaluated is the number of accidents or injuries. If a training program designed to improve safety in the workplace actually reduces injury, it will save the company money in days lost and compensation claims.

What type of information should be considered in the evaluation of a health and safety training program? Kirkpatrick's hierarchical model, a frequently used training evaluation model, suggests that there are four important levels of training outcomes that provide insight into the effectiveness of a training program.[17] Kirkpatrick suggests that a training evaluation effort should ask the following four questions:

1. Did the trainees have positive *reactions* to the training?
2. Did the trainees *learn* the material covered in the training?
3. Did the trainees apply what they learned in training and realize a change in their work *behaviour*?
4. Did the organization see positive *organizational results* following training?

According to Kirkpatrick, these levels of evaluation outcomes form a hierarchy—with succeeding levels providing increasingly important information regarding the value of the training program. Training programs in which trainees report positive reactions, successfully learn the material, apply that learning to their workplace behaviour, and contribute to positive organizational outcomes (e.g., increased productivity, fewer lost-time injuries) are considered effective.

How might a training evaluator go about gathering information on these four levels of training outcomes? The HR manager or training consultant has several measurement options open to him or her. Individual reactions to the training program might be assessed using such tools as surveys, interviews, or focus groups. Questions should be designed to assess all aspects of the program—including overall reactions and attitudes toward particular aspects of the training schedule. For instance, a training evaluation questionnaire for a workplace safety orientation might ask trainees to share their perceptions of the presentation by the health and safety committee chairperson, to indicate whether they thought the safety walkabout—where the trainees tour various parts of the building to discuss the safety issues at each site—was informative, to report their degree of satisfaction with the overall curriculum, and to rate the effectiveness of the orientation facilitator. From these examples, you can see that both affective reactions and utility-based reactions can be garnered at this stage of the evaluation. Affective reactions involve whether the trainees enjoyed the program, and utility reactions incorporate the trainees' perceptions of the usefulness of the program.[18] Positive affective and utility reactions are important in training programs. If employees do not enjoy the training program or do not feel it is useful, they may be less likely to give it their full attention. As such they are unlikely to take away the important messages delivered in the program.

Efforts to measure learning must assess trainee mastery of the information presented in the training session. Evaluators are generally interested in how well the trainees recall that information and the extent to which they are able to incorporate the information into actions. For instance, in a health and safety training program designed to teach the safe operating procedures for heavy machinery, the evaluator would be interested in the trainee's ability to recall the points on the safety inspection checklist for a particular piece of equipment. There are a number of ways to assess this knowledge. An evaluation may measure a trainee's ability to recognize the material covered in training using multiple-choice tests. The mastery of skills introduced in the training program can also be assessed using longer, written test formats. To continue the example given above, a trainee may be asked to list all the steps included in the safety inspection for a particular piece of equipment. Obviously, a successful training program is one that results in considerable knowledge and skill acquisition on the part of trainees.

Behavioural outcomes following training are assessed in the workplace. On-the-job behaviour may be assessed using self-report inventories in which trainees rate their own behaviour or by having supervisors complete a report on trainees' actions when performing the task in question. Similarly, the training evaluator may observe the employees' on-the-job performance. For example, following the training program on the safe operation of heavy machinery introduced above, a supervisor may observe an employee performing a safety inspection on the piece of equipment in question and rate his or her performance. The evaluator may also be able to use objective indexes of performance to assess behavioural change. For instance, after a training program on the importance and use of safety equipment such as earplugs for loud environments, a behavioural assessment may include observing employees at work to see whether they have a high rate of compliance in using their earplugs and other safety equipment.

Organizational results following training initiatives can also be assessed. Usually, the assessment of organizational outcomes involves the analysis of organizational records. With respect to health and safety training initiatives, a number of organizational outcomes may be particularly relevant:

1. Accident, injury, and fatality rates. Safety training programs designed to increase safe behaviour should contribute to reduced accident rates and ultimately reduced injury and death rates.
2. Incidence of **close calls**. Close calls or near misses occur when accidents or injuries are narrowly avoided. Effective safety training programs should reduce the number of near misses.
3. **Lost-time injuries**. Lost-time injuries are those in which the employee involved misses some work time because of the injury in the days following the incident. Safety training programs that are successful should see a reduction in lost-time injuries.
4. Absenteeism. This objective factor may be of particular importance in evaluating health-related training programs designed to reduce stress.

close calls

a series of events that could have led to an accident but did not

lost-time injuries

injuries in which the injured employee misses some work time because of the injury in the days following the incident

5. Workers' Compensation claims and costs. Ultimately, health and safety training programs should see decreased usage of Workers' Compensation programs, as successful training programs should decrease accident and injury rates.

6. Employee benefit costs. Effective safety training can contribute to reduced usage of programs such as physiotherapy and occupational therapy.

7. Safety inspection reports. If an organization is subject to internal or external safety inspections, improved performance on these inspections should be seen in areas that have been the subject of health and safety training.

The training evaluator will want to compare the organization's performance on factors such as those noted above after the training program is complete with its performance before training. Having both pretraining and posttraining information will allow the evaluator to reach a conclusion about any improvements in organizational outcomes that are a result of training.

However, training evaluators will want to take great care to ensure that their measures of pretraining and posttraining variables are accurate. The training evaluator must consider a number of factors when assessing organizational indexes of health and safety. We note above that accident, injury, and fatality rates are indicators of safe or unsafe behaviour in the workplace. Most discussions about occupational safety, whether in the academic literature or in workplaces themselves, focus on accidents or fatalities. As a result, the focus is often on the number of accidents, the amount of lost time, whether the accident resulted in a claim for Workers' Compensation, and occasionally the number of workplace fatalities. Concentrating on such variables is understandable given their visibility and the social and economic interest they attract.

Several factors, however, limit the reliability and utility of accident and fatality measures for organizational research and practice. First, major accidents with injuries and especially fatalities occur relatively infrequently. As such, the distribution of major accidents and fatalities is positively skewed, rather than normally distributed, thus introducing challenges into the statistical analysis of such data. Second, there are invariably distinct definitional differences as to what constitutes an occupational injury across different jurisdictions. For example, what one province or territory accepts as evidence of a back injury requiring time off work, another might refuse, which renders any comparisons of injury rates across jurisdictions limited at best. Third, there is considerable concern that organizations' databases on accidents and fatalities may misrepresent the actual prevalence of the problem.

A recent report shows that logs of lost-time injuries maintained by government agencies actually underrepresent the magnitude of these incidents.[19] This report suggests that records of initial episodes of lost-time injury may be accurately reported, but that lost time due to reinjury or the persistence of problems following return to work are underreported. The in-house record-keeping processes that organizations use may contribute to this problem.[20] Occupational Health and Safety Notebook 9.3 outlines some of the problematic

Underreporting of Injury and Illness: A Question of Record Keeping?

Several organizational practices contribute to the under-reporting of occupational injury and illness:

1. Neglect of the record-keeping process. Some organizations undervalue the importance of record keeping by assigning the task a low priority level and employing record keepers who do not have adequate training.
2. Lack of internal communication. It is difficult to maintain accurate company-wide records if communication among departments is poor.

3. Reward systems that focus on reducing lost-time injuries. In some organizations managers and employees are given bonuses or promotion opportunities if there are no lost-time injuries. As such, there may be little motivation to report injuries that do occur.

Source: Adapted from Conway, H., & Svenson, J. (1998). Occupational injury and illness rates, 1992–1996: Why they fell. *Monthly Labor Review, 121*(11), 36–58.

record-keeping practices that lead to the underreporting of accident statistics. Because of concerns relating to the underreporting of accidents and injuries, both researchers and practitioners have increasingly turned away from the use of accident reports as a primary source of information.

To offset the statistical imbalance, researchers have begun to ask how accident reports can be improved. For example, the inclusion of close calls may provide a useful supplement to accident reports, because they occur with

Safety Training Receiving Increased Attention in Accident Prevention and Investigation

If you read recent articles about organizations aiming to reduce their accident rate or increase worker safety, you'll see an increased focus on safety training. For example, a January 2004 press release from the Newfoundland and Labrador Construction Safety Association (NLCSA) illustrates how the construction industry in that province is showing an improvement in its safety record. This release indicates that accidents in the construction industry are becoming less frequent and that compensation claims are on the decline. The CEO for the NLCSA, Ron Croke, indicates in the press release that he believes the improvements are the result of the implementation of proactive health and safety programs. The provision of health and safety training was one aspect of the proactive approach to health and safety identified by Mr. Croke.

Similarly, investigative bodies examining occupational accidents consider whether health and safety training was provided to the employees who were involved in accidents. For example, in March 2004 the Workplace Health, Safety and Compensation Commission (WHSCC) of New Brunswick was investigating a fatal logging accident. In a press release about the investigation, the WHSCC reminded workers and employers in the forestry industry that employees must receive adequate training on the risks associated with their jobs and how to work safely.

Sources: Newfoundland and Labrador Construction Safety Association, "Construction Industry Showing Marked Improvement," Press Release, January 14, 2004. Retrieved from http://www.nlcsa.com/Downloads/PR011404.pdf, October 6, 2004; and Workplace Health, Safety and Compensation Commission of New Brunswick, Press Release. Retrieved from http://www .whscc.nb.ca/docs/volpe_e.pdf, October 6, 2004.

greater frequency than do accidents. Also, the difference between a close call and an accident may be no more than a little luck. Therefore, including close calls in incident reporting is important for a more complete picture of safety-related events.

Self-reported measures of occupational events and injuries may provide a more valid indication than compulsory reports by the organization to government agencies, as there appears to be little incentive for "workers to deliberately misreport their accidents and injury experiences to independent researchers."[21] Although there could be legitimate errors as a result of memory lapses, these would occur randomly across people and organizations and therefore would not bias the reporting of injuries or accidents in any way. A potential solution is to use multiple sources or records in identifying the "real" rates of incidents, accidents, and injuries.[22]

Common Safety Training Initiatives

The health and safety training needs of any particular organization will be largely determined by factors unique to that company—its size and the industry in question being two factors that largely contribute to safety training needs. However, several common safety training initiatives are applicable to organizations of all sizes and sectors. We review three of these, safety orientations, first-aid training, and WHMIS, next.

RPC 9.11

RPC 9.12

Safety Orientation

Organizations with successful safety programs and safety records frequently begin to emphasize health and safety via an orientation program from the time employees join the organization. Integrating health and safety into the employee orientation program ensures that all employees are provided with a base level of health and safety training and reinforces the development of a safety climate in the workplace.

Although the details will vary with the needs of specific workplaces, a general orientation to health and safety should include a review and introduction to

- fire and emergency safety procedures
- accident policies (e.g., reporting, procedures for obtaining first aid)
- hazards unique to the workplace (e.g., material hazards, chemical hazards, physical hazards)
- protective personal equipment (e.g., how to obtain, how to use)
- WHMIS training
- the role of the joint health and safety committee
- the role and responsibility of individual employees
- job-specific safety procedures (e.g., proper lifting technique, decontamination, lockout procedures)
- housekeeping and safety awareness

First Aid

Many Canadian employers are required under occupational health and safety acts to provide first-aid training to employees. The number of employees requiring certification in first aid in any given organization depends on several factors. Provincial or territorial health and safety legislation determines first-aid requirements based on such factors as the number of workers per shift, the distance away from fixed medical services, and the hazard level of the workplace. Larger, isolated, higher hazard worksites require more trained first-aid providers. The exact number of first-aid certificates and the level of certification required differ among the provinces and territories. For example, in Prince Edward Island work shifts of 5 to 15 people must have an attendant with an emergency first-aid certificate, and shifts of 16 to 100 must have an attendant with certification in standard first aid. In Alberta, if a worksite with 2 to 10 workers is close to hospital services, there is no requirement for a first-aid attendant. However, if the worksite is isolated, an attendant with standard first aid is required.

Organizations such as St. John Ambulance provide first-aid training programs that help employers meet or exceed the requirements set forth in provincial and territorial occupational health and safety acts. In fact, St. John Ambulance provides full services in the provision and management of workplace first-aid training programs. For instance, via their key account program, St. John Ambulance tracks the training and certificates of employees within an organization and notifies the organization when recertification is required.

WHMIS Training

The Workplace Hazardous Materials Information System (WHMIS) has been discussed throughout this book. It is the standard for the communication of information about hazards in Canada. Under WHMIS, hazardous or controlled products are labelled in a standardized manner and information regarding the safe handling of these products is provided via material safety data sheets and worker training programs. The federal, provincial, and territorial health and safety jurisdictions incorporate WHMIS. Employers are required to properly store and dispose of hazardous materials and ensure that workers receive training in handling and using controlled products. Occupational Health and Safety Today 9.2 considers web-based WHMIS training.

Summary

Even though Canadian employees have the right to be informed about the hazards they may encounter in the workplace and occupational health and safety acts mandate the provision of health and safety training, many Canadians report that they have never received any safety training at work. Recent legislation means that employers who fail to comply in the provision of a safe workplace may face charges of criminal negligence.

Occupational health and safety training can be described under a general training model. The ISD model, applied to the issue of health and safety, emphasizes the importance of a complete needs analysis before training is designed and offered. Needs analysis includes a consideration of the organization, the job, and the person. One very important issue in health and safety training is ensuring that the organization is supportive of the initiative. If a company is not supportive of health and safety issues in general, the training effort is likely to encounter roadblocks.

Several factors must be considered in the design and delivery of occupational health and safety training, including the content of the training, who will receive training, and who will act as the trainer. Organizations must be careful that the training programs they offer comply with the standards set out in their jurisdictional occupational health and safety act.

Health and safety training efforts should be subject to evaluations that consider if the trainees had positive reactions to the training and learned the material covered in the program. Evaluation should also consider the extent to which employee behaviour and organizational outcomes are influenced by the training. Health and safety training programs should be evaluated for their impact on safety-related outcomes in the workplace, such as accident, injury, and fatality rates and the incidence of close calls. Safety training programs designed to increase safe behaviour should reduce accident rates and ultimately reduce injury and death rates, as well as reducing the number of near misses and lost-time injuries.

Key Terms

close calls, p. 245
instructional systems design (ISD) model
  of training, p. 233
job/task analysis, p. 236
lost-time injuries, p. 245
needs analysis, p. 233
organizational analysis, p. 234

person analysis, p. 236
safety climate, p. 235
training evaluation, p. 243
training objectives, p. 237
train the trainer, p. 240
WHMIS, p. 242

Weblinks

Young Workers Memorial Life Quilt,
http://www.youngworkerquilt.ca (p. 231)

Canadian Centre for Occupational Health and Safety, "Young Workers Zone,"
http://www.ccohs.ca/youngworkers/ (p. 231)

Institute for Work and Health,
http://www.iwh.on.ca (p. 231)

Canadian Centre for Occupational Health and Safety,
http://www.ccohs.ca (p. 232)

Canada's National Occupational Health and Safety Web Site,
http://www.canoshweb.org (p. 233)

WorkSafe BC,
http://www.worksafebc.com (p. 238)

St. John Ambulance,
http://www.sja.ca (p. 238)

Workplace Hazardous Materials Information System (WHMIS) *In Minutes*,
http://whmis.net (p. 243)

Newfoundland and Labrador Construction Safety Association,
http://www.nlcsa.com (p. 247)

Workplace Health, Safety and Compensation Commission of New Brunswick,
http://www.whscc.nb.ca (p. 247)

RPC Icons

RPC 9.1 Ensures legislated training obligations are met within the organization.

- training requirements due to employment legislation
- common and statutory law (e.g., employment standard: labour relations
- roles of the federal and provincial governments in providing training and development
- roles of municipal governments, unions, and professional associations in training and development

RPC 9.2 Ensures due diligence and strict liability requirements are met, e.g. records are kept and formal procedures established.

- relevant legislation and common law
- company policies and procedures
- industry best practices
- program and policy development
- training and development techniques
- risk analysis
- common and statutory law (e.g., employment standard: labour relations)
- Worker Protection (including health and safety and Workers' Compensation)
- theories and practices for protection of individuals and groups

TASK & KNOWLEDGE REQUIREMENTS
- Occupational health and safety legislation (e.g., Occupational Health and Safety Act of Ontario, Workplace Safety & Insurance Act—Bill 99, Workplace Hazardous Materials Information System, Transportation of Dangerous Goods legislation, environmental legislation, smoking in the workplace legislation, civil rights legislation)
- management techniques for OH&S programs

RPC 9.3 Responds to any refusals to perform work believed to be unsafe.

- relevant Occupational Health and Safety legislation
- procedure for dealing with work refusals

- policy and program development
- conflict resolution procedures
- emergency procedures
- government inspection agencies such as the Ministry of Labour
- common and statutory law (e.g., employment standard: labour relations
- Worker Protection (including health and safety and Workers' Compensation)
- communication theories and techniques
- concepts and processes of politics and conflict
- hazard identification and control
- Occupational health and safety legislation (e.g., Occupational Health and Safety Act of Ontario, Workplace Safety & Insurance Act—Bill 99, Workplace Hazardous Materials Information System, Transportation of Dangerous Goods legislation, environmental legislation, smoking in the workplace legislation, civil rights legislation)

RPC 9.4 Conducts training need assessments by identifying individual and corporate learning requirements.

- needs analysis methods and techniques
- organizational development principles
- instructional design
- training and development needs analysis techniques (i.e., skill assessment strategies and levels of training needs analysis)

RPC 9.5 Ensures that mechanisms are in place for responding to crises in the workplace, including critical incident stress management.

- oral and written communication
- training and development techniques
- industry best practices
- the workplace environment including the availability of emergency equipment
- policy and program development and evaluation
- intervention strategies
- relevant legislation (e.g., fire code, Workers' Compensation)
- investigation techniques
- stress management techniques
- types of employee assistance programs
- hazard identification and control
- accident investigation procedures
- emergency preparedness procedures
- management techniques for OH&S Programs
- conceptual definition and implications of occupational stressors (e.g., potential stressors, methods of identifying potential stressors and strain outcomes, response to organizational stressors, and management of employee strain outcomes)
- Occupational health and safety legislation (e.g., Occupational Health and Safety Act of Ontario, Workplace Safety & Insurance Act—Bill 99, Workplace Hazardous Materials Information System, Transportation of Dangerous Goods legislation, environmental legislation, smoking in the workplace legislation, civil rights legislation)

RPC 9.6 Analyses risk to the health and safety of employees and determines appropriate preventative measures, including training, provision of required safety equipment, and administrative practices.

- relevant legislation
- nature of the business and physical work environment
- hazard recognition
- workplace inspection techniques
- safety programs, equipment, and emergency procedures
- ergonomics
- functions of the JHSC
- training and development/presentation techniques
- industry best practices
- relevant technical terminology
- the collective agreement
- services and equipment available in the community
- Worker Protection (including health and safety and Workers' Compensation)
- training and development program design and administration

Task & Knowledge Requirements
- Occupational health and safety legislation (e.g., Occupational Health and Safety Act of Ontario, Workplace Safety & Insurance Act—Bill 99, Workplace Hazardous Materials Information System, Transportation of Dangerous Goods legislation, environmental legislation, smoking in the workplace legislation, civil rights legislation)
- hazard identification and control
- emergency preparedness procedures
- management techniques for OH&S Programs
- types of employee assistance and wellness programs

RPC 9.7 Links training to development programs, organizational goals, objectives, strategies, culture and other HR activities.

- organizational development principles
- instructional design
- techniques to analyse and interpret training results
- stakeholders in training & development
- the identification, assessment, development, implementation, maintenance, and monitoring processes of effective systems of managing HR information
- the measurement, analysis, and conditioning of the workforce to achieve organizational objectives

RPC 9.8 Recommends the most appropriate way to meet identified learning needs, (e.g., courses, secondments, and on-the-job activities).

- needs analysis methods and techniques
- organizational development principles
- instructional design
- training and development program design and administration
- methods of training and development (games and simulations, case method, lecturing, on-the-job training, distance learning, role-play, video-conferencing, group discussion)

- domains and levels of learning
- effective learning objectives
- training programs delivery techniques

RPC 9.9 Establishes effective programs for accident prevention, incident investigation, inspections, fire and emergency response, and required training.

- relevant legislation
- workplace inspection and accident investigation techniques
- nature of the business and physical work environment
- potential risks and hazards in the workplace
- emergency response planning
- community emergency response services
- training and development
- industry best practices
- Worker Protection (including health and safety and Workers' Compensation)
- training and development program design and administration
- hazard identification and control
- accident investigation procedures
- emergency preparedness procedures
- management techniques for OH&S Programs

RPC 9.10 Ensures participant and organizational feedback is documented and evaluated.

- evaluation techniques
- interpretation of results

Task & Knowledge Requirements
- survey and basic statistical techniques
- procedures for information collection, manipulation, and analysis
- research methods and designs (including measurement of HR)
- validity and reliability (conceptual definitions and assessment techniques)
- measurement tools and their limitations
- statistical analyses and evaluation
- importance, criteria, and techniques of program evaluation
- evaluation issues (including behaviourally anchored rating scales and staffing tables)

RPC 9.11 Implements and evaluates practices in the areas of health, safety, security, and Workers' Compensation.

- investigative techniques
- hazard recognition
- disaster recovery techniques
- relevant legislation
- resource information
- common health and safety practices
- company policies and procedures
- Worker Protection (including health and safety and Workers' Compensation)
- theories and practices for protection of individuals and groups

- Occupational health and safety legislation (e.g., Occupational Health and Safety Act of Ontario, Workplace Safety & Insurance Act—Bill 99, Workplace Hazardous Materials Information System, Transportation of Dangerous Goods legislation, environmental legislation, smoking in the workplace legislation, civil rights legislation)
- hazard identification and control
- management techniques for OH&S Programs

RPC 9.12 Provides information to employees and managers on available programs.

- elements of EAP program
- promotional and marketing tools and techniques
- communication tools and techniques
- training and development techniques
- management techniques for OH&S Programs
- types of employee assistance and wellness programs
- trends in occupational health and safety

TASK & KNOWLEDGE REQUIREMENTS
- importance, criteria, and techniques of program evaluation

Discussion Questions

1. Canadian statistics suggest that many Canadians are not receiving appropriate safety training in the workplace. What are some of the reasons that organizational managers might give for not providing safety training for their employees? Imagine that you are a health and safety consultant trying to convince top management of a negligent organization to provide a health and safety orientation to new employees. What are some arguments that you might use to convince the organization to support the training program?
2. Why is organizational support for a health and safety training initiative so important for the success of the training program?
3. What are some important organizational outcomes that can be used to evaluate the value that a training program has added to an organization?
4. What are some of the advantages and disadvantages associated with the use of web-based health and safety training programs for individual employees? for organizations?

Using the Internet

1. The provincial and territorial governments have their own health and safety legislation. Each one refers to the importance and role of health and safety training. Using the Internet, look up the health and safety legislation in your province or territory. Note the ways in which training can help organizations and employees adhere to the law.

2. Using various web resources, find out more about young worker safety. Along with your classmates, brainstorm ways to build health and safety knowledge among young Canadians entering the workforce. How might we educate parents and employers about the health and safety risks associated with young workers?

3. Visit the websites of some large organizations in various industries, and look for information about their health and safety policies. What portion of the sites you visited contained information about health and safety training? Did the attention given to training or the type of training described vary by industry or organizational size?

4. Search your school's home page to investigate the health and safety training programs offered in your institution.

Exercises

1. Young workers are at considerable risk for accidents and injury in the workplace. Perform a person analysis by interviewing a young person who has recently entered the workforce. Based on what you have learned about occupational health and safety in this course, try to get an idea of that individual's awareness of health and safety in the workplace and the extent to which he or she is worried about his or her own safety at work. If you are unable to interview a new worker, have a classmate think back to his or her very first job and try to recall his or her health and safety–related attitudes upon entering the workforce. You will want to find out some information about the tasks this person performed at work and identify some of the potential hazards that were associated with the job.

2. Think back to various jobs that you have held—what types of health and safety training did you receive? Were the training programs effective? Compare your experience with those of your classmates.

3. To find out more about health and safety training, contact a human resource professional and ask about health and safety training programs in his or her organization. You might use some of the following questions to guide your discussion.

a. Does your organization have a health and safety orientation program? If so, what types of information does it cover?

b. How many trained first-aid providers are required per shift in your organization?

c. What are some of the safety hazards and concerns employees in your organization encounter? Do you thinking that training is a useful option to help employees manage their exposure to these risks? Why or why not?

d. Under what conditions does your organization rely on purchased, preexisting health and safety programs? When might the company opt for custom-designed health and safety training programs? What factors influence this decision?

e. What is the general attitude toward occupational health and safety training among employees in your organization? among management?

4. Bill C-45, the "Westray Bill," went into effect March 31, 2004. Research this legislation. What impact do you think this legislation will have on Canadian employees' access to health and safety training? Do you think it will influence Canadian employers' attitudes about health and safety training? Debate these issues with your classmates.

Case: The New HR Manager at A1 Manufacturing

Sabine is the new HR manager at A1 Manufacturing. When she began her new position, she quickly realized that A1 did not pay much attention to issues of occupational health and safety. In fact, she determined that this company was in violation of a number of legislated health and safety requirements. She approached members of upper management with her concerns. At first they seemed unruffled by her warnings about health and safety violations throughout the company. Only when she reminded the upper management that the organization could face fines and some executive-level individuals could face criminal charges if there was a safety-related incident did they sit up and listen. Sabine was given the job of fixing the problem.

She has determined that the organization needs to provide more health and safety training programs. She has contacted you, a training consultant to help her design and implement new programs. What steps do you take in helping Sabine determine her training needs and implement training programs? Is there anything about the organization or Sabine's conclusion that training is the answer that concerns you? What are some potential obstacles to a potential training effort?

Endnotes

1. Ipsos-Reid. (2003, July). *Workplace health and safety practices are improving across North America … while compliance with workers' compensation laws is still an issue.* Retrieved from http://www.ipsos-na.com/news/pdf/media/mr030818–2a.pdf, March 29, 2004.

2. Institute for Work & Health. (2003/2004). *No OH&S training for most Canadians in a new job. At work, 35.* Retrieved from http://www.iwh.on.ca, March 15, 2004.

3. Colligan, M. J., & Cohen, A. (2004). The role of training in promoting workplace safety and health. In J. Barling &

M. Frone (Eds.), *Handbook of workplace safety* (pp. 223–248). Washington, DC: American Psychological Association.

4. Saks, A. M., & Haccoun, R. R. (2004). *Managing performance through training and development* (3rd ed.). Toronto: Nelson Canada.

5. Goldstein, I. L. (1993). *Training in organizations: Needs assessments, development and evaluation* (3rd ed.). Pacific Grove, CA: Brooks/Cole Publishing; and Saks, A. M., & Haccoun, R. R. (2004). *Managing performance through training and development* (3rd ed.). Toronto: Nelson Canada.

6. Saks, A. M., & Haccoun, R. R. (2004). *Managing performance through training and development* (3rd ed.). Toronto: Nelson Canada.

7. Goldstein, I. L. (1993). *Training in organizations: Needs assessments, development and evaluation* (3rd ed.). Pacific Grove, CA: Brooks/Cole Publishing; and Saks, A. M., & Haccoun, R. R. (2004). *Managing performance through training and development* (3rd ed.). Toronto: Nelson Canada.

8. Colligan, M. J., & Cohen, A. (2004). The role of training in promoting workplace safety and health. In J. Barling & M. Frone (Eds.), *Handbook of workplace safety* (pp. 223–248). Washington, DC: American Psychological Association.

9. Cole, B. L., & Brown, M. P. (1996). Action on worksite health and safety problems: A follow-up survey of workers participating in a hazardous waste worker training program. *American Journal of Industrial Medicine, 30,* 730–743.

10. Zohar, D. (1980). Safety climate in industrial organizations: Theoretical and applied implications. *Journal of Applied Psychology, 65,* 96–102; and Zohar, D. (2002). The effects of leadership dimensions, safety climate, and assigned priorities on minor injuries in work groups. *Journal of Organizational Behavior, 23,* 75–92.

11. Goldstein, I. L. (1993). *Training in organizations: Needs assessments, development and evaluation* (3rd ed.). Pacific Grove, CA: Brooks/Cole Publishing.

12. Colligan, M. J., & Cohen, A. (2004). The role of training in promoting workplace safety and health. In J. Barling & M. Frone (Eds.), *Handbook of workplace safety* (pp. 223–248). Washington, DC: American Psychological

Association; and Saarela, K. L. (1990). An intervention program utilizing small groups: A comparative study. *Journal of Safety Research, 21,* 149–156.

13. Colligan, M. J., & Cohen, A. (2004). The role of training in promoting workplace safety and health. In J. Barling & M Frone (Eds.), *Handbook of workplace safety* (pp. 223–248). Washington, DC: American Psychological Association.

14. Colligan, M. J., & Cohen, A. (2004). The role of training in promoting workplace safety and health. In J. Barling & M. Frone (Eds.), *Handbook of workplace safety* (pp. 223–248). Washington, DC: American Psychological Association.

15. Colligan, M. J., & Cohen, A. (2004). The role of training in promoting workplace safety and health. In J. Barling & M Frone (Eds.), *Handbook of workplace safety* (pp. 223–248). Washington, DC: American Psychological Association.

16. Arnold, D. (2003). A matter of life and death. *Occupational Health, 55,* 21–23.

17. Kirkpatrick, D. L. (1976). Evaluation of training. In R. L. Craig (Ed.), *Training and development handbook: A guide to human resource development* (2nd ed.). New York: McGraw-Hill; and Saks, A. M., & Haccoun, R. R. (2004). *Managing performance through training and development* (3rd ed.). Toronto: Nelson Canada. .

18. Saks, A. M., & Haccoun, R. R. (2004). *Managing performance through training and development* (3rd ed.). Toronto: Nelson Canada.

19. Evanoff, B., Abedin, S., Grayson, D., Dale, A. M., Wolfe, L., & Bohr, P. (2002). Is disability underreported following work injury? *Journal of Occupational Rehabilitation, 12,* 139–150.

20. Conway, H., & Svenson, J. (1998). Occupational injury and illness rates, 1992–1996: Why they fell. *Monthly Labor Review, 121*(11), 36–58.

21. Grunberg, L., Moore, S., & Greenberg, E. (1996). The relationship of employee and participation to workplace safety. *Economic and Industrial Democracy, 17,* 221–241.

22. Conway, H., & Svenson, J. (1998). Occupational injury and illness rates, 1992–1996: Why they fell. *Monthly Labor Review, 121*(11), 36–58.

Motivating Safety Behaviour at Work

Chapter Learning Objectives

After reading this chapter, you should be able to

- discuss the importance of safety behaviour in the workplace
- identify the categories of safety behaviour
- explain the importance of individual motivation in safety behaviour
- describe behaviour modification approaches to motivating safety
- recognize the importance of goal setting and feedback in safety behaviour in the workplace
- evaluate the role of organizational support for safety in contributing to safety behaviour
- discuss the role of the safety climate in the performance of safety behaviours
- understand the role that safety leadership plays in creating a safe work environment
- outline how to implement an effective occupational health and safety program

ONTARIO POWER GENERATION

Ontario Power Generation (OPG) is an Ontario-based corporation that both generates and sells electricity. Aiming to be the premier producer of electricity in North America, OPG is working toward this goal by focusing on safety and environmental sustainability. This corporation places a high value on the safety of its employees and has several systems in place to support its focus on safety behaviour at work. With the slogan "Zero injuries: Believe it. Achieve it," OPG has a safety management system that includes many facets of the organization including organizational resources, organizational culture, and the structure of work. The safety management system is designed to help OPG employees in their objective to perform safely at work. Adherence to this program ensures that OPG complies with relevant legislation, incorporates safety into strategic business planning, and continually improves safety performance.

A visit to the OPG website illustrates the focus on safety. Its employee health and safety policy is an excellent example of corporate responsibility for safety and is available to download. OPG believes that "healthy employees working safely in an injury-free and healthy workplace is good business." The policy notes how continual improvement will contribute to the physical, psychological, and social health of its employees. Interestingly, the safety policy clearly lays out the safety-related responsibilities of employees and management. For instance, employees

> are accountable for maintaining or taking positive steps to achieve a state of health that is consistent with the demands of his/her occupation. They are also accountable for performing work safely and for identifying, communicating and, where appropriate, correcting workplace hazards in order to protect themselves and their co-workers from harm.

Similarly, management is accountable for such things as "ensuring the work environment is designed to protect the health and safety of workers" and "providing employees with the information, training, tools, procedures and support required to do their job safely and without harming other [workers'] health."

This policy is a good example of corporate responsibility in the area of health and safety. It illustrates the importance of employees' involvement in their own safety at work and the vital role of organizational support for health and safety initiatives. The policy also states that health and safety performance will be assessed and recognized in the workplace.

The OPG policy statement highlights several topics that we will cover in this chapter—most notably safety behaviour and the roles of individual and organizational responsibility in achieving a safe workplace.

Source: Ontario Power Generation, "Safety." Retrieved from http://www.opg.com/info/safety.asp, March 28, 2004.

In the previous chapter we considered the importance of health and safety training in the workplace. In this chapter we consider the equally important issues of (1) how to ensure that employees utilize the knowledge and skills gained during training and consistently perform their work duties in a safe manner and (2) the role of the organization in supporting employee safety efforts. Because of their focus on performing in a safe manner, the issues we consider in this chapter concentrate on preventing accidents and injuries at work rather than simply responding to workplace accidents.

Several psychological variables provide the basis for a discussion of accident and injury prevention. Psychological research in the area of motivation provides a useful starting point for considering how to motivate the safe performance of work tasks. Other psychological factors, including an assessment of organizational safety culture and safety leadership, are useful in establishing the value that an organization places on safety. Before we turn our attention to these psychological variables, we first consider the issue of safety behaviour to illustrate the value of behaviour-based efforts in accident and injury prevention in the workplace.

Safety Behaviour

There are several ways of categorizing health and safety programs. One categorization system breaks these programs into engineering interventions, administrative interventions, and behavioural interventions.[1] *Engineering interventions* typically focus on changing the physical environment to reduce exposure to hazards either by providing personal protective equipment or redesigning the physical workplace. *Administrative interventions* are those that modify procedures and exposure in the work environment. Techniques such as job rotation, the scheduling of work breaks, the use of safety officers, and the use of standard operating procedures all count as administrative interventions. Finally, *behavioural interventions* focus on changing employee attitudes, knowledge, or behaviour about occupational health and safety. Information campaigns, risk awareness, skills training, or the implementation of behaviour-modification techniques are all behavioural interventions. Each of the three types of intervention is at least somewhat successful in improving health and safety at work. Research shows that 10 out of 12 engineering interventions, 13 out of 15 behavioural interventions, and 6 out of 9 administrative interventions result in positive effects.[2]

All things being equal, it is preferable to remove or eliminate the hazard via an engineering solution than it is to rely on other types of health and safety programming. However, such engineering controls are not always possible.[3] Therefore, much psychological research in the area of occupational safety has focused on behavioural interventions, in particular those designed to increase safety-related behaviours. The focus on behaviour is based on the observation that 70% to 95% of workplace accidents resulting in an injury are thought to be caused by unsafe behaviours.[4]

Recent reviews of behavioural safety intervention programs show that there is a relationship between **safety behaviours** and injury rates.[5] Generally, as behaviourally based safety programs are introduced, the number of safety-related events, including accidents and injuries, is decreased.

At least eight general categories of behaviour contribute to safe working performance:[6]

1. Proper use of hazard control systems in the workplace
2. Development of safe work habits
3. Increased awareness and recognition of workplace hazards
4. Acceptance and use of personal protective equipment
5. Maintenance of housekeeping and maintenance standards
6. Maintenance of accepted hygiene practices
7. Proper responses to emergency situations
8. Self-monitoring and recognition of symptoms of hazardous exposure

Health and safety programs have been largely targeted toward encouraging one or more of these general classes of behaviour. Some of these categories will be familiar to you as the targets of the health and safety training efforts that we described in Chapter 9. For example, training programs might teach proper lifting techniques (i.e., develop safe work habits), and Workplace Hazardous Materials Information System (WHMIS) training is designed to enhance the workers' ability to recognize chemical hazards in the workplace. However, the equation for promoting safety in the workplace goes beyond ability-based training.

safety behaviours

behaviours leading to safe performance of a particular job

Occupational Health and Safety Notebook 10.1

Elements of a Behaviour-Based Safety Program

The content of a behaviour-based safety initiative will vary depending on the context in which it is offered (e.g., organization, type of job), but several basic elements are common across behaviour-based safety programs:

1. Identification of behaviours that have an effect on safety-related outcomes
2. Precise measurement of the identified behaviours
3. Feedback on how to perform the behaviour more safely
4. Reward for safe performance of the targeted behaviour

Source: Adapted from Sulzer-Azaroff, B., & Austin, J. (2000). Does BBS work? Behavior-based safety & injury reduction: A survey of the evidence. *Professional Safety* (July), 19–24.

Generally, for individuals to work safely at least three conditions are necessary. First, workers must have the ability to work safely—that is, workers must have the knowledge, skills, and abilities necessary to perform their jobs in a safe manner. This requirement is generally addressed via the provision of occupational health and safety training. Second, workers must be motivated to work safely—that is, workers must intend to use their knowledge and skills to enhance safe working performance. Finally, workers must have the opportunity to work safely—that is, the environment or organization must support and encourage safe work.

These three factors combine in a multiplicative rather than an additive fashion (see Figure 10.1). Thus,

Safety Performance = Ability × Motivation × Opportunity

An important implication of this multiplicative equation is that the model of safety performance is noncompensatory. Having a high level of motivation and numerous opportunities does not compensate for a lack of ability. Similarly, a high level of ability and motivation cannot make up for a work environment that does not provide the opportunity and support for safe working. Safety performance relies on ability, motivation, and opportunity. If any one of these components is missing, safety performance in the workplace will not be realized. The question for health and safety programs is, how do we use this model to increase safe work behaviours?

The basic premise of the multiplicative model of safety performance is that safety can be enhanced by increasing an employee's ability, motivation, and opportunity to work safely. Having said this, it is important to note that all three components of the model must be implemented for safety performance to be enhanced. For example, training (i.e., increasing ability) alone is insufficient to change safety behaviours over the long term.[7] However, safety training coupled with motivational programs appears to be an effective combination in changing safety behaviours. Given the great deal of attention paid

FIGURE 10.1

Ability, Motivation, Opportunity

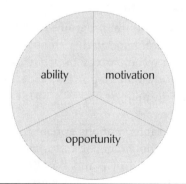

Safety performance relies on ability, motivation, and opportunity. This figure presents safety behaviour as a full circle. You can see that if any one of these important components is missing the full circle of safety behaviour is not achieved and thus safety performance in the workplace will not be realized.

to increasing employees' ability to perform safety behaviours in Chapter 9, this chapter focuses on issues of motivation and opportunity. We will consider these facets of safety performance in turn.

Motivating Safety Behaviour

motivation

the process that initiates, directs, and sustains behaviour

The word *motivation* comes from the Latin *movere*, "to move." Generally **motivation** is considered the process that initiates, directs, and sustains behaviour.[8] Some psychological researchers consider the motivation process as it applies to very basic biological functions such as eating and sleeping. Others focus their attention on motivation as it applies to goal-directed behaviour. In this section we will consider the role of motivation in safety behaviour at work. Our analysis will focus on two major theoretical explanations of motivation: reinforcement theory (or behaviour modification) and goal-setting theory.

Reinforcement Theory

Reinforcement theory focuses on the power of external rewards and punishments in the motivation of behaviour. Reinforcement theory, forwarded by learning theorists who adhere to the school of psychology called behaviourism, states that the likelihood of an action being performed in the future is determined by its current consequences. Generally, the chances of a behaviour being performed again increase when a current performance of that behaviour is followed by reinforcement (i.e., a reward) and decrease when it is followed by punishment. Rewards can be things such as a prize, money, or praise. Reinforcement theory has been used in organizations in the form of incentive systems. Employees are promised a reward if they meet some behavioural expectation—for example improved sales, increased productivity, or, of particular importance for the current discussion, improved safety behaviour. The application of reinforcement theory in this way is sometimes called behaviour modification.

The use of behaviour modification principles to increase safety behaviours in the workplace has been called one of the most successful health and safety innovations.[9] Although this claim may be somewhat overstated, ample evidence suggests that behavioural programs are effective in promoting safe working behaviours and are associated with substantial reductions in accident rates. For example, a recent survey of behavioural safety studies found that more than 95% of studies that reported incidence rates of accidents and injuries saw a reduction in injury rates as a result of applying behavioural principles to safety in the workplace.[10]

Moreover, behavioural interventions appear to be effective in promoting safety behaviours in a wide range of industrial environments including telecommunications manufacturing plants,[11] utility companies,[12] and the construction industry.[13] In short, behavioural approaches to occupational safety have been shown to be effective, cost efficient, and adaptable to a wide range of industrial environments.

The basic model underlying most applications of behavioural programming in the workplace is the ABC model of behaviour.[14] Simply stated, the ABC model holds that any behaviour occurs because of events that trigger the behaviour (the antecedents) and the results that follow the behaviour (the consequences). Thus, any behaviour can be represented as

$$\text{Antecedent} \rightarrow \text{Behaviour} \rightarrow \text{Consequence}$$

To change a specific behaviour, we have to change either the antecedent or the consequence of the behaviour. Most applications of behavioural programming focus on changing the consequences of behaviour. If we want to understand why workers perform unsafe acts or fail to engage in safe practices, a good place to begin is by considering the consequences of both safe and unsafe behaviours.[15] Such consequences can be characterized along three dimensions: consequences can be positive or negative, immediate or delayed, and contingent or noncontingent. Generally, behaviour that is followed by immediate, positive, and contingent consequences is more likely to occur again. Conversely, consequences that are delayed, negative, or noncontingent have either a minimal or an adverse effect on safety behaviour.

Even a brief consideration of most safety behaviours suggests that the consequences of safe behaviour are typically delayed, negative, or noncontingent. It is rare for coworkers to praise or even recognize an individual for proper lifting techniques or for wearing safety goggles. Indeed the most likely consequence of engaging in such practices is the lack of notice from either supervisors or coworkers. Some safe actions such as mopping up spills or putting on safety goggles require extra time, thereby slowing down the work. This may be a negative consequence, especially if working slower is associated with disciplinary warnings. Some forms of personal protective equipment may also be uncomfortable, again a negative consequence. Even when there are positive consequences associated with behaviour, these consequences are often delayed or noncontingent. For example, a worker safety award may be given to an individual based on behaviours that occurred a year or more ago, irrespective of what behaviours the worker engaged in that day.

In contrast, there are often positive, immediate, and contingent rewards associated with unsafe behaviours. For example, the result of not wearing protective equipment may be increased comfort and speed of work. Negative consequences such as disciplinary warnings or injuries are typically rare and often delayed. Individuals may go months and even years not wearing safety goggles and never experience an injury as the result. Even this simplistic consideration suggests that wearing the protective clothing is unlikely based on the consequences associated with not wearing the clothing.

Given these observations, the goal of behavioural safety programs is to change the consequences associated with specific behaviours. Specifically, behavioural programs attempt to institute positive, immediate, and contingent consequences for safe working procedures. By far the most popular form of consequence is simply feedback; individuals are typically observed as they perform their job and given immediate feedback on the safety of their work practices. Second in popularity is the use of incentive-based programs in which employees are offered incentives such as free lunches or lottery tickets for their safe behaviour. Generally, the organizational behaviour-modification literature suggests that feedback alone, without the use of material rewards and incentives, is an effective means of behavioural change.

Goal Setting

Theories of motivation based on the notion of goal setting point out that behaviour is in fact motivated by our own internal intentions. These intentions might be described as the goals we want to achieve.[16] A large number of studies illustrate that setting goals can have desirable behavioural effects.[17] Goal setting has been extensively applied in organizations, and its effectiveness in influencing a wide array of behaviours is well documented in the research literature. Like behaviour modification, goal setting is a method for changing behaviour. However, unlike behaviour modification, goal setting does not focus on changing the consequences of behaviour; rather, it concerns itself with the antecedents of behaviour—that is, the "A" of the ABC model described above. Setting a specific goal (e.g., wearing personal protective equipment 95% of the time) provides an antecedent for the behaviour by reminding the individual of what he or she is expected to do. Goals serve as antecedents to behaviour in four main ways:

1. Goals direct attention and action to the desired behaviour.
2. Goals mobilize effort toward actions to achieve the goal.
3. Goals increase persistence.
4. Goals motivate the search for effective strategies to help obtain them.

Several investigators have demonstrated that goal-setting techniques provide a valuable adjunct to feedback systems in motivating desired behaviours. It appears that five factors augment the effectiveness of goal setting:

1. Goals must be *difficult and challenging* to result in improved performance. If we set our goals too low, we often stop thinking about them. Goals should be a stretch for the individual, and those that are have more of an impact on performance than easy goals or the absence of goals.
2. Goals must be *achievable* to lead to better performance. Goals that are too hard can quickly become demotivating.
3. Goals must be *specific*. Goals have a more positive impact on behaviour when they are specific rather than vague. The goal must identify specific behaviours, specify how many times they must be performed, and specify the performance standard. Nonspecific goals that are too broad are more like wishes or desires—not goals.
4. Individuals must be *committed* to the goals. The person must accept the goal as being reasonable and achievable. Goals that aren't accepted aren't acted on. People tend to accept goals when they see the importance of the goal, when they participate in setting the goal, when they trust the coach, and when they see the behaviour as something they can control.
5. *Feedback* regarding the degree to which the goal is being met is also helpful in goal achievement.

Behavioural modification, feedback, and goal setting have all proven their worth as components of effective health and safety programming. Reviews of the research literature consistently make a strong case for behavioural approaches to enhancing health and safety.[18]

Increasing Opportunity for Safety Behaviour

Even when workers are well trained and highly motivated, they may not perform safely on the job. The final component that must be in place to promote safety behaviour is the provision of resources and organizational support. The need for workers to have an opportunity to perform safely is evident in the following list of the factors that contribute to the use of personal protective equipment:[19]

- Workers must be aware of the hazard that surrounds them.
- The protective equipment must be easily and conveniently available and properly fitted.
- Workers must understand how the equipment works and how to use it properly.
- There must be no other factors present that would interfere with the workers' use of the equipment.

Even in this brief description, the role of management in promoting health and safety is apparent. Management must make equipment and training available. Perhaps more important, management must demonstrate a commitment to health and safety that is communicated and transmitted throughout the organization.

Management commitment to health and safety has emerged as a key requirement for the improvement of workplace health and safety in numerous studies. For instance, a review of the empirical literature on health and safety training initiatives shows that a high level of management support for safety increases the impact of health and safety–related training in workplaces.[20] Certainly, managers who are committed to health and safety can help create opportunities for employees to engage in safety behaviours. For instance, managers can encourage safety behaviours by not placing productivity-related goals before employee safety.[21] Knowing that their safety comes first will allow employees the freedom to take the time to work safely, properly use protective equipment, and halt work operations if there is a risk to safety.

Although top management has an important role to play in the promotion of workplace health and safety, it is also apparent that management initiatives are delivered through frontline supervisors, and supervisory attitudes play an important role in shaping risk perceptions. Coworker attitudes help shape individual perceptions of workplace hazards and encourage or inhibit self-protective behaviour. A study of manufacturing employees illustrates the impact of other employees' safety commitment on individual safety attitudes. The study found that workers' perceptions of risk were primarily influenced by their perceptions of management, supervisory, and coworker commitment to health and safety. Moreover, perceptions of others' commitment to health and safety had a much larger effect (approximately three times as large) on perceptions of risk as did workers' own experiences with accidents in the workplace.[22]

In short, management has a central role to play in improving safety performance. By sending a strong message about the importance of health and safety in the organization, by holding individuals responsible for their own and their subordinates' safety performance, and by taking safety concerns seriously, managers establish an orientation toward health and safety that allows individuals to perform their jobs safely. We suggest that there are two important vehicles by which management communicates the value placed on safety in their organization: via the safety climate and through safety leadership. We will consider each of these in turn.

safety climate

shared perceptions of the importance of safety in the workplace

Safety Climate

You will recall from the previous chapter that an organization's **safety climate** reflects the shared perceptions among all employees and organizational stakeholders regarding the importance of safety in the workplace.[23] If employees are to have positive perceptions regarding the safety climate in their workplace, the organization itself must be committed to workplace safety. An organization can promote a positive safety climate in several ways. One approach is to have explicit and enacted policies on safety. If employees are aware of the organizational safety policy and believe that the organization stands behind that policy, they should feel secure in making safety a priority in their own actions. As such, the policy will contribute to safe conduct.

A second approach that organizations can take to promoting a healthy awareness of safety in the workplace, and as such promote a positive safety climate, is to include safety-related information in the communication of production-related goals. A managerial focus on achieving high productivity may inadvertently deter employee safety. To the extent that employees want to reach or exceed the organizational production expectations, they may become so focused on working quickly that they ignore safety protocols. Certainly, such a course of events is most likely in cases in which following safety procedures slows the pace of work. Therefore, managers should be careful to stress that the achievement of production goals does not come before employee safety at work.

As we noted in Chapter 9, an organization can also foster a positive safety climate by ensuring that employees have the appropriate safety training and encouraging the utilization on the worksite of knowledge gained in such training. The provision of training ensures that employees have the needed ability to engage in safety behaviour at work.

Some organizations choose to promote safety, and influence the safety climate, by rewarding safe behaviour. In these organizations, individuals or groups who have good safety records will benefit from various bonuses or even job promotions. Other companies opt to withhold rewards from those who have a safety violation on their record. Still others promote their reputation as a safe organization by making their safety records—such as number of days without a lost-time injury—available to the public.

Perceived safety climate is indeed a substantial predictor of employees' safety performance.[24] One study of restaurant employees nicely illustrates the impact of an organization's safety climate on safety-related outcomes. The study reported that positive safety climate perceptions were related to a reduction in safety-related events common in restaurants (e.g., knife slips, grease spatters, trips). This decrease in safety events in turn contributed to a reduction in occupational injuries (e.g., cuts, burns, fractured bones).[25]

Thus, it seems that a positive safety climate encourages employees to engage in **safety compliance.** Safety compliance is achieved when employees follow safety-related rules and generally work in a safe manner. Certainly safety compliance helps reduce injuries and safety incidents.[26] However, it is also possible that a positive safety climate can contribute to the safety initiative of employees. **Safety initiative** refers to employee behaviours that go beyond simply working within safety standards and safety compliance. Rather, it involves employees behaving proactively to improve safety levels in the working environment. For example, proactive employees engage in such behaviours as volunteering to participate in safety audits and encouraging their supervisor to take action to improve safety. Both safety compliance and safety initiative are components of overall safety performance.

safety compliance
the extent to which employees follow safety rules and procedures

safety initiative
the extent to which employees go beyond compliance and work to actively improve safety

Safety Leadership

safety leadership

organizational leadership that is actively focused on and promotes occupational health and safety

One effective way for organizations to promote a positive safety climate is to have **safety leadership**, that is, an organizational leader who is focused on and promotes safety. Substantial accumulated evidence suggests that when leaders actively promote safety, employees and organizations alike experience better safety records and more positive safety outcomes.[27] For instance, employees' perceptions of managers' and supervisors' commitments to safety are strongly related to safety-related outcomes including perceived risk on the part of employees.[28] Similarly, employees' perceptions of managerial receptiveness to safety issues predict individual willingness to raise work-related safety concerns.[29] Additionally, employees' perceptions of supervisors' safety-related leadership are positively associated with safety consciousness, perceptions of the safety climate, and, through these intervening variables, safety events and actual injuries.[30]

The accumulated research illustrates the importance of active leader behaviour in the realization of positive safety-related attitudes and safety behaviour in the workplace. It is vital for organizational leaders to be champions of safety. One way that leaders can actively promote safety is to apply **transformational leadership** skills to issues of safety.

transformational leadership

highly effective approach to leadership that emphasizes employee well-being and is characterized by idealized influence, inspirational motivation, intellectual stimulation, and individualized consideration

Transformational leaders are highly effective leaders who also show a substantial degree of concern for the well-being of their employees.[31] Transformational leaders exhibit four characteristics in their interactions with their employees: idealized influence, inspirational motivation, intellectual stimulation, and individualized consideration.[32] Transformational leaders provide idealized influence in that they are admired and trusted role models. Via inspirational motivation, transformational leaders communicate high expectations to their subordinates and provide a sense of meaning and challenge for followers. Transformational leaders intellectually stimulate their followers in that they encourage creativity and questioning of the status quo. Finally, transformational leaders provide individualized consideration in that they pay attention to each employee as an individual and act as a mentor or coach.

When these characteristics are directed toward safety-related concerns, improved safety behaviours tend to follow.[33] For instance, a leader who communicates high expectations regarding the safe performance of work tasks, motivates employees to behave safely and report safety concerns, encourages employees to question the assumption that working safely is working slowly, and individually discusses safety concerns with employees is engaging in safety-specific transformational leadership. Such a leader is likely to realize a highly safe work environment.

For an organization looking to improve its safety climate and provide an environment in which employees feel able to engage in safety behaviours, an increased focus on transformational leadership may be one option. Studies suggest that transformational leadership can be effectively trained.[34]

Recent academic research provides further support for the importance of the active championing of safety among organizational leaders. In a recent study, the tendency for leaders to take a passive approach to safety rather than actively promoting safe behaviour among employees was associated with

Safety Leadership at Canadian Pacific Railway

Canadian Pacific Railway (CPR) was founded in 1881 to link Eastern Canada to the West. Almost 125 years later, CPR continues to thrive with a commitment to its clients, the communities it services, and its employees. Reflecting this commitment, CPR makes safety a priority.

CP Rail recognizes that organizational support is a vital component of a safe work environment and pledges to provide the leadership, training, and resources needed to maintain a healthy and safe workplace. Management asks their employees to make a commitment to safety, and they follow this up by prioritizing safety and making it an integral part of the organization's identity. The corporate health and safety policy clearly states, "No job on

our railway will ever be so important that we can't take the time to do it safely." In particular, CP Rail notes the role of safety leadership by the health and safety management committee in efforts to continually improve the safety of operations, employees, and communities. CPR's dedication to safety is paying off—it leads North America in train accident performance, and its injury rates are on a steady and continual decline.

Source: Adapted from CP Rail, "Safety." Retrieved from http://www8.cpr.ca/cms/English/General+Public/Social+Responsibility/Safety/.htm, March 28, 2004.

negative health and safety–related outcomes.[35] Leaders who ignore safety concerns and "turn a blind eye" to safety-related issues may think that they are not doing any harm. However, it appears that such leaders are sending a message to their employees that safety issues are not important and thus are discouraging safe performance of work-related tasks.

Bringing It All Together: Organizational Health and Safety Programs

Throughout this chapter and the previous chapter on training, we have considered the issue of how to promote safe behaviour in the workplace. We have concluded that the utilization of safety behaviour requires that employees have the needed skills, are motivated to act in a safe manner, and have the opportunity to engage in safe behaviour while at work. We now briefly turn our attention to the types of workplace health and safety programs that might contribute to the realization of these three requirements in workplaces. Workplace health and safety plans aimed at injury and accident prevention tend to have the following elements, designed to ensure an efficient implementation: (1) identified program objectives, (2) written policy, (3) accountability, and (4) an auditing process.

 10.2

Program Objectives

Health and safety programs should have clearly stated goals or objectives. The program objectives may be developed from input by joint health and safety committees; environmental committees; representatives from senior management, middle management, operations, maintenance, purchasing, and engineering; and other employee representatives. The objectives should include the following criteria, which must be clearly communicated to all levels:

- Obtain and maintain support for the program at all levels of the organization, including employee groups and parties to collective agreements.
- Motivate, educate, and train all levels of management and employee groups in the recognition, reporting, and correction of hazards in the workplace, which will improve the level of understanding of all staff regarding the connection among safety, productivity, quality, mutual respect, and work satisfaction.
- Provide controls for worker exposure to potential hazards through the use of work practices, engineering controls, and personal protective equipment, and plan for a program of inspection and preventative maintenance for machinery, equipment, tools, and facilities.

The objective of compliance with all environmental and OH&S legislation, as well as with applicable codes and standards, is to reduce the liability faced by all employers in the event of a catastrophic accident.

Policy

The second component of the plan is the creation and adoption of a formal policy. The policy should be written and signed by the chief executive officer or president of the organization and then made available to all employees. The corporate health and safety policy is the most visible sign of management commitment to health and safety. As a result, this commitment should be expressed clearly and unambiguously.

Policy statements can range from simple, strong statements of the organization's commitment to occupational health and safety, to long, detailed documents outlining the purpose of the program and defining the involvement and responsibilities of all employees. For example, the Mississauga, Ontario, based Peel Board of Education policy statement reads as follows:

> The Peel Board of Education will take every reasonable precaution to prevent injury or illness to students, employees, members and the public participating in board activities or performing their duties. This shall be accomplished by providing and maintaining a safe, healthy working environment and by providing the education and required training to perform these activities and duties safely.

> The Peel Board of Education will take every reasonable precaution to protect the environment within the board's area of responsibility. The board will assign appropriate resources to maintain an environmental program which complies with all federal and

provincial environmental legislation. The board will include occupational health and safety performance in the evaluation of all principal/supervisory personnel.

 RPC 10.3

 RPC 10.4

RPC 10.5

The policy should be developed in consultation with employee groups. Once adopted, it should be widely publicized by means of meetings, newsletters, pamphlets, and so forth. The policy should be posted in management offices to serve as a constant reminder of the commitment and responsibility of the executive branch. For more information, see the tips for writing a health and safety policy outlined in Occupational Health and Safety Notebook 10.3.

WWW WWW

Occupational Health and Safety Notebook 10.3

Health and Safety Policy Checklist

An organizational health and safety policy must be comprehensive and effective. The Canadian Centre for Occupational Health and Safety provides useful information regarding policy development and evaluation on its website. Below is a list of example questions that a health and safety committee might ask when evaluating its own policy. Responses to checklist questions of this type will help guide further development and refining of the policy.

- Is a clear commitment to health and safety evident in the policy statement?
- Is the senior officer responsible for implementation and review of the policy identified?
- Is the policy signed by the president or CEO?
- Have the views of all stakeholders (e.g., employees, managers, supervisors, safety representatives, and safety committees) been incorporated?
- Was the safe performance of work tasks discussed with employees? Is there a clear statement of how their performance will be assessed?
- Is the role of employees in health and safety matters stated (e.g., the position on inspection teams and safety committees)?
- Are individual responsibilities for health and safety duties clearly allocated?
- Are the people responsible for such functions as accident reports, safety inspections, and first aid identified?
- Is health and safety given as great a priority as economic and marketing matters?

- Is the employer's duty to provide health and safety training to all employees stated in the policy?
- Does the policy ensure that health and safety issues will be considered when planning new methods or processes?
- Is the financing of health and safety programs detailed and ensured?
- Are all employees aware of the policy? Are copies of the policy available to all employees?
- Are there periodic revisions and updates of the safety policy? Are the procedures for and timing of such reviews clarified?
- Does the policy make clear that the ultimate responsibility for safety rests with senior management?
- Is safety and health performance included in employee performance reviews?
- Does the policy list arrangements for liaison with contractors?
- Does the policy help to make individuals aware of their legal responsibilities?

For additional information on how to implement occupational health and safety programs, visit the WorkSafe BC website. The Workers' Compensation Board of B.C. has a useful publication on program development that can be downloaded (see the Weblinks section).

Source: Canadian Centre for Occupational Health and Safety, "Guide to writing an OHS policy statement." Retrieved from http://www.ccohs.ca/oshanswers/hsprograms/osh_policy.html, October 11, 2004.

Accountability

A policy that is not enforced, or a policy "without teeth," is virtually useless. Individuals must understand their role in enacting the health and safety policy. After the policy statement has been inaugurated, administrative regulations should be developed outlining the responsibility for the program at various levels. The regulations should include accountability for program elements assigned to senior management and responsibility for occupational health and safety in performance evaluations at all levels of supervision. Employees should be held responsible for safe work practices, including the reporting of all observed unsafe practices, procedures, and hazards to the appropriate supervisor. All employees should be required to participate in OH&S training and development programs.

A timetable for the review and evaluation of the policy and regulations by the chief executive officer, president, or board should be outlined in the program, along with a procedure for budget development, monitoring, and control. The assignment of appropriate resources with responsibility and authority for the administration of the program should also be included. Finally, the administrative regulation should contain a mechanism for addressing and responding to recommendations from the joint health and safety committees within a specific length of time. Written responses to recommendations are legislated in many jurisdictions.

Auditing the Program

Occupational health and safety programs should undergo periodic reviews or audits to ensure that all aspects of the program are being correctly implemented. Auditing for the sake of regulatory compliance and for continual

---

Occupational Health and Safety Notebook 10.4

Ontario's Workwell Program

The Workwell Program in Ontario is operated by the Workplace Safety and Insurance Board and provides client organizations with a template for evaluating workplace safety programming and compliance with safety legislation. It is designed to both recognize the safety elements that exist and identify gaps in programming. Additionally, the template provides an assessment of commitment to OH&S at all levels in the organization.

Important elements of any safety program that are assessed by programs like Workwell include the following:

- management commitment to the program (including expressed commitment in policy statements, etc.)

- the functioning of the joint health and safety committee
- the presence of written procedures and standards
- the existence of a regular inspection program
- clearly documented, communicated, and enforced accountability for managers, supervisors, employees, contractors, and so on
- clearly established procedures for hazard identification and rectification and claims management

Source: Workplace Safety and Insurance Board of Ontario, "Workwell." Retrieved from http://www.wsib.on.ca/wsib/wsibsite .nsf/Public/Workwell, October 11, 2004.

improvement are the most cost-effective types of audits in the present environment of regulatory standards and enforcement. However, packaged audits that do little but create volumes of paper will not reveal how a program is functioning unless some direction is established. Besides ensuring that the audit has a purpose, management should decide whether the results will be shared with the employees, the joint committee, or the public.

The audit should be designed with a set of standards against which it will be measured. The scope of the audit should also be determined; does it encompass, for example, occupational health and safety, fire protection, emergency plans, and environmental controls? Selection of the audit team is also important. Are there knowledgeable, trained, and experienced staff in-house or is outside expertise required?

An audit protocol must be designed to provide a step-by-step procedure to assist the team in conducting a systematic review. Such a protocol may involve the creation of a checklist that highlights each aspect of the program— including the objectives, state of the written policy, and systems of accountability. It must lead the auditors to ask the right questions not only about the quality of compliance but also about the strength of the management systems to maintain the appropriate level of compliance. The audit may include a review of previous audits, a physical survey of the location, examination of administrative records, and interviews with management staff, workers, and the health and safety committee. All these elements should be accurately documented and communicated to the appropriate levels in the organization. There must also be a comprehensive action plan in place to follow up on the documented findings of the audit. Responsible personnel and completion dates should accompany each action item.

Occupational Health and Safety Notebook 10.5

Questions to Ask during a Safety Audit

Human Resources Development Canada (HRDC) details valuable information about the implementation of occupational health and safety programs on its website. With respect to safety audits, it offers advice about the elements of a health and safety program that should be considered in the review. Some of the program elements highlighted include the following:

- The health and safety policy
    - Is it signed, posted, and supported?
- Accountability
    - Are responsibilities defined? Is the reporting of problems rewarded?
- Health and safety committee
    - Is there a committee? Does it meet regularly?

- Safety training
    - Are employees given appropriate opportunities to receive training?
- Safe procedures
    - Are safe procedures defined and implemented?
- Accident investigations
    - Are accidents reported and investigated by trained personnel?

Source: Adapted from Human Resources Development Canada, "An occupational health and safety (OHS) program in your workplace." Retrieved from http://www.hrsdc.gc.ca/asp/gateway .asp?hr=/en/lp/lo/ohs/information/ohs-program .shtml&hs=oxs#twenty, October 11, 2004.

A common misconception exists that written procedures and audits raise the liability of the corporation in terms of regulatory compliance or in the event of an accident. In fact, many courts are basing the severity of civil and criminal penalties in part on the employer's ability to prove that it was duly diligent in auditing and correcting deficiencies in its own operation. If the corporation does not have written procedures and documented audits, how will it prove beyond a reasonable doubt that it has taken every reasonable precaution to ensure the health and safety of the workers and the environment?

In Canada, what was once the maximum fine for OH&S violations—$25,000—is now routine. Corporations in some jurisdictions can be fined up to $500,000 for each offence. Individuals can be fined up to $25,000 and sentenced to one year in jail. As of March 31, 2004, Bill C-45, the Westray Bill, became an enforceable law in Canada. Under this law, employers whose occupational health and safety violations are deemed negligent can be criminally charged and face substantial jail time. As such, conducting appropriate audits of health and safety programs is increasingly important for Canadian employers.

Summary

A comprehensive approach to increasing health and safety in the workplace should emphasize employees' ability to act in a safe manner, their motivation to do so, and the provision of opportunities to perform their tasks safety. A number of efforts can be made to increase employees' safety motivation, including the use of behaviour modification and goal setting. The organizational context in which the employee is asked to perform his or her work should also emphasize safety. We stressed the importance of a positive safety climate and transformational safety leadership in setting the stage for safety behaviours. No matter what the program, management commitment to safety appears to be a critical variable in health and safety initiatives; management's expressed and actual commitment to the program will be a key determinant of program success.

Key Terms

motivation, p. 264
safety behaviours, p. 262
safety climate, p. 268
safety compliance, p. 269

safety initiative, p. 269
safety leadership, p. 270
transformational leadership, p. 270

Weblinks

Ontario Power Generation,
http://www.opg.com (p. 261)

Transport Canada, "Score your safety culture (TP 13844),"
http://www.tc.gc.ca/civilaviation/systemsafety/Brochures/tp13844/menu.htm (p. 268)

CP Rail,
http://www8.cpr.ca (p. 271)

Canadian Centre for Occupational Health and Safety, "OSH answers,"
http://www.ccohs.ca/oshanswers (p. 273)

WorkSafe BC, "How to implement an effective occupational health and
safety program,"
**http://www.worksafebc.com/publications/health_and_safety_information/
by_topic/assets/pdf/howtoimplement_ohs.pdf** (p. 273)

Workplace Safety and Insurance Board of Ontario,
http://www.wsib.on.ca (p. 274)

Human Resources and Skills Development Canada, "An occupational health
and safety (OHS) program in your workplace,"
http://www.hrsdc.gc.ca/en/lp/lo/ohs/guides/ohs-program.shtml (p. 275)

RPC Icons

**RPC 10.1 Develops or provides for wellness and employee assistance
programs to support organizational effectiveness.**

- policy/procedure development
- collective agreements
- industry best practices
- outside service providers
- the organization's culture
- conflict resolution techniques
- problem solving techniques
- report writing and record keeping
- the relationship between employee wellness and productivity
- performance goals of the organization and how these are affected
  by employee wellness
- key components of an EAP such as intake, assessments, counseling,
  traumatic incident debriefing, and cap on service
- cost/benefit analysis
- types of employee assistance programs
- types of employee assistance and wellness programs
- conceptual definition and implications of occupational stressors
  (e.g., potential stressors, methods of identifying potential stressors and
  strain outcomes, response to organizational stressors, and management
  of employee strain outcomes)
- trends in occupational health and safety

**RPC 10.2 Ensures that mechanisms are in place for responding to crises
in the workplace, including critical incident stress management.**

- oral and written communication
- training and development techniques

- industry best practices
- the workplace environment including the availability of emergency equipment
- policy and program development and evaluation
- intervention strategies
- relevant legislation (e.g., fire code, Workers' Compensation)
- investigation techniques
- stress management techniques
- types of employee assistance programs
- Occupational health and safety legislation (e.g., Occupational Health and Safety Act of Ontario, Workplace Safety & Insurance Act—Bill 99, Workplace Hazardous Materials Information System, Transportation of Dangerous Goods legislation, environmental legislation, smoking in the workplace legislation, civil rights legislation)
- hazard identification and control
- accident investigation procedures
- emergency preparedness procedures
- management techniques for OH&S Programs
- conceptual definition and implications of occupational stressors (e.g., potential stressors, methods of identifying potential stressors and strain outcomes, response to organizational stressors, and management of employee strain outcomes)

RPC 10.3 Implements and evaluates practices in the areas of health, safety, security, and Workers' Compensation.

- investigative techniques
- hazard recognition
- disaster recovery techniques
- relevant legislation
- resource information
- common health and safety practices
- company policies and procedures
- Worker Protection (including health and safety and Workers' Compensation)
- theories and practices for protection of individuals and groups
- Occupational health and safety legislation (e.g., Occupational Health and Safety Act of Ontario, Workplace Safety & Insurance Act—Bill 99, Workplace Hazardous Materials Information System, Transportation of Dangerous Goods legislation, environmental legislation, smoking in the workplace legislation, civil rights legislation)
- hazard identification and control
- management techniques for OH&S Programs

RPC 10.4 Ensures due diligence and strict liability requirements are met, e.g. records are kept and formal procedures established.

- relevant legislation and common law
- company policies and procedures
- industry best practices
- program and policy development

- training and development techniques
- risk analysis
- common and statutory law (e.g., employment standard: labour relations)
- Worker Protection (including health and safety and Workers' Compensation)
- theories and practices for protection of individuals and groups

TASK & KNOWLEDGE REQUIREMENTS
- Occupational health and safety legislation (e.g., Occupational Health and Safety Act of Ontario, Workplace Safety & Insurance Act—Bill 99, Workplace Hazardous Materials Information System, Transportation of Dangerous Goods legislation, environmental legislation, smoking in the workplace legislation, civil rights legislation)
- management techniques for OH&S Programs

RPC 10.5 Analyses risk to the health and safety of employees and determines appropriate preventative measures, including training, provision of required safety equipment, and administrative practices.

- relevant legislation
- nature of the business and physical work environment
- hazard recognition
- workplace inspection techniques
- safety programs, equipment, and emergency procedures
- ergonomics
- functions of the JHSC
- training and development/presentation techniques
- industry best practices
- relevant technical terminology
- the collective agreement
- services and equipment available in the community
- Worker Protection (including health and safety and Workers' Compensation)
- training and development program design and administration

TASK & KNOWLEDGE REQUIREMENTS
- Occupational health and safety legislation (e.g., Occupational Health and Safety Act of Ontario, Workplace Safety & Insurance Act—Bill 99, Workplace Hazardous Materials Information System, Transportation of Dangerous Goods legislation, environmental legislation, smoking in the workplace legislation, civil rights legislation)
- hazard identification and control
- emergency preparedness procedures
- management techniques for OH&S Programs
- types of employee assistance and wellness programs

Discussion Questions

1. Although considerable empirical data support their effectiveness, considerable debate also exists about the use of behaviourally based safety programs in industry. Employees and unions have frequently rejected

such programs. Why do you think this is so? What can be done to enhance the acceptance of such programs?

2. Explain how focusing on behaviours rather than on accidents might be a better approach to improving occupational health and safety.
3. Why do you think setting goals can influence an employee's safety-related actions in the workplace?
4. Describe the role of an organization's safety climate in the promotion of safety behaviours at work.
5. What role do organizational leaders have to play in creating a safety-focused workforce?
6. What are the characteristics of successful occupational safety programs?

Using the Internet

1. Many organizations have their health and safety policies posted on their websites. With a group of classmates, examine these policies. Each of you should choose a different organization in a different market sector. How long are the policies? What information do they cover? Do they establish the unique responsibilities of management and employees? Do they make reference to the organization's safety leadership? Compare your findings with those of your classmates.
2. Various health and safety organizations provide online resources to help human resource personnel create health and safety programs. Search the web to find guidelines for creating an occupational health and safety program, including writing the policy, communicating accountability, and performing safety audits. Discuss the information you find with your classmates and instructor. Do you think these resources would help you develop a comprehensive health and safety program?
3. Assess the safety climate of your school or workplace. The following Weblink may give you some ideas about questions that assess factors related to safety climate: http://www.tc.gc.ca/civilaviation/systemsafety/Brochures/tp13844/menu.htm.

Exercises

1. In discussing health and safety programs, we have emphasized the responsibilities and role of management in establishing and enforcing safety standards. What is the role of employees in these programs? To what extent should employees be responsible for taking initiative to enhance health and safety in the workplace?
2. Imagine you are on a newly formed national committee that will be awarding safety awards to Canadian organizations. The mandate of this committee is to recognize excellence in the promotion of safety at work. What criteria do you think should be used to assess organizations'

performance in this area? Create a draft of a rating form that the committee might use to evaluate nominated organizations.

3. Throughout this chapter we emphasized the importance of managerial support for health and safety initiatives. In particular, we noted the importance of a positive safety climate in the realization of safety-related goals. Imagine you are the newly hired human resources director in a manufacturing organization that currently does not place a high degree of value on health and safety—in other words, an organization with a negative safety climate. Top executives have indicated that they would like this situation to change, and they tell you that part of your job is to improve safety performance in the organization. What are the first three initiatives that you would launch to improve the safety climate of this organization?

4. With a small group of classmates, create a proposal for developing an effective occupational health and safety program for an organization that one of the team members has worked in (or is knowledgeable about). You will need to identify the health and safety concerns in that organization, suggest ways that these concerns could be addressed, and describe how you (as an HRM consulting team) would go about solving these problems. Here are some questions you will need to consider.

a. What do you think the critical issues and real problems are and why?

b. What occupational health and safety knowledge that you have gained in this course can

be applied to the problems you have identified?

c. What solutions do you propose and why?

d. How would you implement your plan? Why?

Prepare a written proposal (8 to 10 doubled-spaced pages) detailing the proposed program. Your proposal must include an executive summary of no more than one page. Then, develop an audiovisual presentation based on that proposal and deliver it to the class. (Based on an exercise by Catherine Fitzgerald)

Case 1: Noncompliance with Safety Standards

Pat Singh is confused. As plant manager at a manufacturing plant, he has tried to comply with all applicable legislation. Based on his own experiences as a line employee, Pat is particularly keen on health and safety initiatives and has spent a considerable sum of money to purchase the best protective gear (i.e., hearing protectors, safety glasses, hardhats) on the market. Yet today when he walked through the plant, he saw many employees with the hearing protectors draped around their necks, the safety glasses tucked into their shirt pockets, and the hardhats hung on convenient pegs. Pat does not understand why workers won't wear the equipment bought for their protection. Pat has turned to you as a recognized expert in health and safety programming to improve conditions at the plant. What should Pat do?

Case 2: Safety in the Bakery

Su Mei Lawrence is manager of the bakery department of a large grocery store. She oversees 20 employees working 3 shifts (the store is open 24 hours/day). Most employees are part-time, working 20 hours/week or less—many are high-school and university students working to help pay their way through school. In the last three weeks, Su Mei has noticed a marked increase in the number of safety-related incidents in the department. Several employees have injured their backs lifting racks of bread into position, and product has been crushed by the careless use of a forklift in the rear storage area. Today, one employee was knocked to the floor when a stack of 15 trays of bread fell on him. Su Mei is convinced that it is time to take action to improve the safety of working conditions in the department, but she needs your help in deciding exactly what to do.

Endnotes

1. Goldenhar, L. M., & Schulte, P. A. (1994). Intervention research in occupational health and safety. *Journal of Occupational Medicine, 36*, 763–775.
2. Goldenhar, L. M., & Schulte, P. A. (1994). Intervention research in occupational health and safety. *Journal of Occupational Medicine, 36*, 763–775.
3. Colligan, M. J., & Cohen, A. (2004). The role of training in promoting workplace safety and health. In J. Barling & M. Frone (Eds.), *Handbook of workplace safety* (pp. 223–248). Washington, DC: American Psychological Association.
4. Reber, R. A., Wallin, J. A., & Chhokar, J. S. (1984). Reducing industrial accidents: A behavioural experiment. *Industrial Relations, 23*, 119–125.
5. Johnson, S. E. (2003, October). Behavioral safety theory: Understanding the theoretical foundation. *Professional Safety*, 39–44; and Sulzer-Azaroff, B., & Austin, J. (2000, July). Does BBS work? Behavior-based safety and injury reduction: A survey of the evidence. *Professional Safety*, 19–24.
6. Cohen, A., & Colligan, M. J. (1997). Accepting occupational health and safety regimens. In D. S. Gochman (Ed.), *Handbook of health behaviour research II: Provider determinants* (pp. 379–394). New York: Plenum Press.
7. Sulzer-Azaroff, B., Harris, T. C., & McCann, K. B. (1994). Beyond training: Organizational performance management techniques. In M. J. Colligan (Ed.), *Occupational safety and health training* (pp. 321–340). Philadelphia: Hanley and Befus.
8. Gazzaniga, M. S., & Heatherton, T. F. (2003). *Psychological science*. New York: W. W. Norton.
9. Saari, J. (1994). When does behaviour modification prevent accidents? *Leadership and Organizational Development Journal, 15*, 11–15.
10. Sulzer-Azaroff, B., & Austin, J. (2000, July). Does BBS work? Behavior-based safety and injury reduction: A survey of the evidence. *Professional Safety*, 19–24.
11. Sulzer-Azaroff, B., Loafman, B., Merante, R. J., & Hiavacek, A. C. (1990). Occupational safety in a large industrial plant: A systematic replication. *Journal of Organizational Behavior Management, 11*, 99–121.
12. Loafman, B. (1998, August). Behaviour based safety: Power and pitfalls. *Professional Safety*, 20–23.
13. Cooper, M. D., Phillips, R. A., & Robertson, I. T. (1993). Improving safety on construction sites by psychologically based techniques: Alternative approaches to the measurement of safety behaviour. *European Review of Applied Psychology, 43*, 33–37.
14. Frederiksen, L. W. (Ed.), (1982). *Handbook of organizational behaviour management*. New York: John Wiley & Sons.

15. Komaki, J. (1986). Promoting job safety and accident prevention. In M. F. Cataldo & J. Coates (Eds.), *Health and industry: A behavioural medicine perspective* (pp. 301–319). New York: John Wiley & Sons.

16. Ambrose, M. L., & Kulik, C. T. (1999). Old friends, new faces: Motivation research in the 1990s. *Journal of Management, 25*, 231–292; and Locke, E. A., & Latham, G. P. (2002). Building a practically useful theory of goal setting and task motivation: A 35-year odyssey. *American Psychologist, 57*, 705–717.

17. Locke, E. A., & Latham, G. P. (2002). Building a practically useful theory of goal setting and task motivation: A 35-year odyssey. *American Psychologist, 57*, 705–717.

18. Johnson, S. E. (2003, October). Behavioral safety theory: Understanding the theoretical foundation. *Professional Safety*, 39–44; Sulzer-Azaroff, B., & Austin, J. (2000, July). Does BBS work? Behavior-based safety and injury reduction: A survey of the evidence. *Professional Safety*, 19–24; and Sulzer-Azaroff, B., Harris, T. C., & McCann, K. B. (1994). Beyond training: organizational performance management techniques. In M. J. Colligan (Ed.), *Occupational Safety and Health Training* (pp. 321–340). Philadelphia: Hanley and Befus.

19. Feeney, R. J. (1986). Why is there resistance to wearing protective equipment at work? Possible strategies for overcoming this. *Journal of Occupational Accidents, 8*, 207–213.

20. Colligan, M. J., & Cohen, A. (2004). The role of training in promoting workplace safety and health. In J. Barling & M. Frone (Eds.), *Handbook of workplace safety* (pp. 223–248). Washington, DC: American Psychological Association.

21. Smith, M. J., Karsh, B. T., Carayon, P., & Conway. F. T. (2003). Controlling occupational safety and health hazards. In J. C. Quick & L. E. Tetrick (Eds.), *Handbook of occupational health psychology* (pp. 35–68). Washington, DC: American Psychological Association.

22. Cree, T., & Kelloway, E. K. (1997). Responses to occupational hazards: Exit and participation. *Journal of Occupational Health Psychology, 2*, 304–311.

23. Zohar, D. (1980). Safety climate in industrial organizations: Theoretical and applied implications. *Journal of Applied Psychology, 65*, 96–102; and Zohar, D. (2002). The effects of leadership dimensions, safety climate, and assigned priorities on minor injuries in work groups. *Journal of Organizational Behavior, 23*, 75–92.

24. Hemingway, M., & Smith, C. S. (1999). Organizational climate and occupational stressors as predictors of withdrawal behaviours and injuries in nurses. *Journal of Occupational and Organizational Psychology, 72*, 285–299; and Hofmann, D. A., & Stetzer, A. (1996). A cross-level investigation of factors influencing unsafe behaviours and accidents. *Personnel Psychology, 49*, 307–339.

25. Barling, J., Loughlin, C., & Kelloway, E. K. (2002). Development and test of a model linking safety-specific transformational leadership and occupational safety. *Journal of Applied Psychology, 87*, 488–496.

26. Griffin, M. A., & Neal, A. (2000). Perception of safety at work: A framework for linking safety climate to safety performance, knowledge, and motivation. *Journal of Occupational Health Psychology, 17*, 347–358.

27. Barling, J., Loughlin, C., & Kelloway, E. K. (2002). Development and test of a model linking safety-specific transformational leadership and occupational safety. *Journal of Applied Psychology, 87*, 488–496; Hofmann, D. A., Jacobs, R., & Landy, F. (1995). High reliability process industries: Individual, micro, and macro organizational influences on safety performance. *Journal of Safety Research, 26*, 131–149; Mullen, J., & Kelloway, E. K. (2004). Testing a model of employee willingness to raise safety issues. Manuscript submitted for publication; and Shannon, H. S., Mayr, J., & Haines, T. (1997). Overview of the relationship between organizational and workplace factors and injury rates. *Safety Science, 26*, 201–217.

28. Cree, T., & Kelloway, E. K. (1997). Responses to occupational hazards: exit and participation. *Journal of Occupational Health Psychology, 2*, 304–311.

29. Kelloway, E. K., Mullen, J., & Francis, L. (2004). Divergent effects of transformational and passive leadership on employee safety. Manuscript submitted for publication.

30. Barling, J., Loughlin, C., & Kelloway, E. K. (2002). Development and test of a model linking safety-specific transformational leadership and occupational safety. *Journal of Applied Psychology, 87*, 488–496.

31. Bass, B. M. (1985). *Leadership and performance beyond expectations*. New York: Free Press; and Judge, T. A., & Bono, J. E. (2000). Five-factor model of personality and transformational leadership. *Journal of Applied Psychology, 85*, 751–765.

32. Bass, B. M. (1990). From transactional to transformational leadership: Learning to share the vision. *Organizational Dynamics, 18*(3), 19–31

33. Barling, J., Loughlin, C., & Kelloway, E. K. (2002). Development and test of a model linking safety-specific transformational leadership and occupational safety. *Journal of Applied Psychology, 87*, 488–496.

34. Barling, J., Weber, T., & Kelloway, E. K. (1996). Effects of transformational leadership training on attitudinal and financial outcomes: A field experiment. *Journal of Applied Psychology, 81*, 827–832; and Kelloway, E. K., Barling, J., & Helluer, J. (2000). Enhancing transformational leadership: The roles of training and feedback. *Leadership and Organizational Development Journal, 21*, 145–149.

35. Kelloway, E. K., Mullen, J., & Francis, L. (2004). Divergent effects of transformational and passive leadership on employee safety. Manuscript submitted for publication.

Chapter 11

Emergency Response and Emergency Preparedness

Chapter Learning Objectives

After reading this chapter, you should be able to

- define an emergency
- list the key elements in emergency preparedness
- describe the concept of an emergency plan
- explain the necessity of having emergency and evacuation plans
- describe the principles of fire prevention and suppression

WHITE JUAN

On Thursday, February 19, 2004, Nova Scotia was struck by the largest blizzard in recorded history. Nicknamed "White Juan" (a reference to Hurricane Juan that had devastated parts of the province in the preceding October), the storm dumped more than 90 cm of snow on the province in 24 hours—the largest one-day snowfall in recorded history. The province declared a state of emergency at 8:30 a.m.—as a result of snow and high winds, emergency vehicles (e.g., police, ambulance service) responded to life-or-death situations only, and even the highway plows were pulled off the road. All universities and schools were closed. Some workplaces (e.g., emergency services, hospitals) had to remain open, placing employees at risk when getting to and from the workplace. The weather also posed a risk to the structural integrity of buildings (e.g., the weight of snow on roofs). Although it is never possible to predict all eventualities, sustained consideration of what might happen is the key to successful emergency planning.

Source: CBC, "Blizzard paralyses Nova Scotia." Retrieved from http://novascotia.cbc.ca/regional/servlet/View?filename=ns_snowstorm20040219, October 11, 2004.

Introduction

The widespread impact of the 1998 ice storm in Ontario and Quebec, the events of September 11, 2001, the subsequent rash of anthrax-related scares, the outbreak of Severe Acute Respiratory Syndrome (SARS) in Canadian cities, and the devastation of Hurricane Juan in Nova Scotia in 2003 are all recent examples of emergencies. Some, such as the events of 9/11 or the SARS outbreak, happened within workplaces. The others were not specific to workplaces but required a response from both employers and employees.

In Canada, emergency response is largely up to individuals and each individual is responsible for knowing what to do in an emergency. As events overwhelm an individual's capacity to respond, governments respond in a progressive manner.

First, local emergency organizations (e.g., municipal emergency services, emergency measures organizations) respond. At the next level, each province and territory has an emergency measures organization (EMO) that is tasked with managing large-scale emergencies and supporting local organizations as required. Finally, the federal government and its agencies may become involved in emergency response efforts, depending on the nature of the disaster. For example, during Hurricane Juan in Nova Scotia, the Canadian Forces were deployed to assist in the cleanup efforts.

Emergency Measures Organizations

Each province and territory has its own emergency measures organization (EMO). EMOs specialize in emergency preparedness and emergency response and are often the best source of information on emergency-related topics. A contact list is provided below.

Alberta
Emergency Management Alberta
Phone: (780) 422-9000
Toll-free in Alberta: 310-0000
Fax: (780) 422-1549
Website: http://www.gov.ab.ca/ma/ema

British Columbia
Provincial Emergency Program (PEP)
Phone: (250) 952-4913
Fax: (250) 952-4888
Website: http://www.pep.bc.ca

Manitoba
Emergency Measures Organization
Phone: (204) 945-4772
Toll-free: 1 (888) 267-8298
Fax: (204) 945-4620
Website: http://www.manitobaemo.ca

New Brunswick
Emergency Measures Organization
Phone: (506) 453-2133
Toll-free: 1 (800) 561-4034
Fax: (506) 453-5513
Website: http://www.gnb.ca/cnb/emo-omu/index-e.asp

Newfoundland and Labrador
Emergency Measures Division
Phone: (709) 729-3703
Fax: (709) 729-3857
Website: http://www.gov.nf.ca/mpa/emo.html

Northwest Territories
Emergency Measures Organization
Phone: (867) 873-7785
Fax: (867) 873-8193
Website: http://www.maca.gov.nt.ca/safety/
emergency_organization.html

Nova Scotia
Emergency Measures Organization
Phone: (902) 424-5620
Fax: (902) 424-5376
Website: http://www.gov.ns.ca/emo/

Nunavut
Nunavut Emergency Management
Phone: (867) 975-5300
Fax: (867) 979-4221

Ontario
Ontario Emergency Management
Phone: (416) 314-3723
Fax: (416) 314-3758
Website: http://www.mpss.jus.gov.on.ca/
english/pub_security/emo/about_emo.html

Prince Edward Island
Emergency Measures Organization
Phone: (902) 368-4000
Fax: (902) 368-5544
Website: http://www.gov.pe.ca/caag/emo-info/
index.php3

Quebec
Direction générale de la sécurité civile et de la
sécurité incendie
Phone: (418) 644-6826
Fax: (418) 643-3194
Or one of the regional offices:
Gatineau: (819) 772-3737
Montreal: (514) 873-1300
Rimouski: (418) 727-3589
Sillery (Quebec): (418) 643-3244
Trois-Rivières: (819) 371-6703 or your municipality
Website: http://www.msp.gouv.qc.ca/index_en.asp

(continued)

Emergency Measures Organizations (continued)

Saskatchewan
Emergency Management Organization
Phone: (306) 787-9563
Fax: (306) 787-1694
Website: http://www.cps.gov.sk.ca/Safety/emergency/
default.shtml

Yukon
Emergency Measures Organization
Phone: (867) 667-5220
Toll-free (in Yukon): 1-800-661-0408
Fax: (867) 393-6266
Website: http://www.gov.yk.ca/depts/community/emo/

In addition, a federal department, Public Safety and Emergency Preparedness, was formed in December 2003, to secure public safety in Canada. The department has several functions, of which emergency preparedness and response is one. The department of Public Safety and Emergency Preparedness can be found on the web at http://www.psepc.gc.ca/index_e.asp.

Organizations must consider the possibility of a disaster, in which the potential for loss is very high. No safety program is complete without a planned response to the threat of a disaster.

In this chapter we consider two central aspects of emergency planning in organizations. First, we consider issues related to emergency preparedness. Second, we address the organization's response to emergency. Because of the commonality of such procedures, we finish the chapter with a specific consideration of fire and evacuation plans.

Emergency Preparedness

emergency

a sudden, generally unexpected occurrence or set of circumstances demanding immediate action

 11.1

An **emergency** is any sudden set of circumstances demanding immediate action. For the most part, we are concerned with emergencies that either cause or threaten to cause the loss of, or damage to, property or life. Being a victim of a computer virus or having your computer crash is also an emergency (and one that business needs to be concerned with), but we will limit our consideration to health and safety–related emergencies.

Emergencies can be either naturally occurring or caused by humans. Naturally occurring emergencies include disease epidemics (animal, human, and plant) and weather conditions (e.g., blizzards, hail, hurricanes, earthquakes, storm surges, torrential rain). Such emergencies may be deceptive, as the severity of the emergency might not be immediately apparent. For example, at the beginning of the SARS outbreak, nobody recognized the seriousness of the impending crisis—indeed, the initial diagnosis was atypical pneumonia. It was only a month after the initial reports from China that the World Health Organization issued a health alert.

Other emergencies are caused by humans. They can include explosions, accidents, fires, and chemical spills. They can also include riots, civil disorder, terrorism, and acts of workplace violence. Although riots and civil disorder

Workplace Shooting at OC Transpo

OC Transpo runs the transit system in Ottawa, Ontario. On April 6, 1999, at 2:30 p.m., Pierre LeBrun entered the OC Transpo garage on St. Laurent Street in Ottawa. He carried a high-powered rifle and 45 rounds of ammunition. He shot and killed four coworkers before killing himself. In subsequent investigation, it was revealed that LeBrun was frequently teased by coworkers because of his stuttering. He felt that others were laughing at him and the situation was worsened when he had to speak in English rather than his native French. He had a history of work difficulties, culminating in his resignation in January 1999.

The coroner's inquest into the events of April 6 resulted in 77 recommendations to prevent similar tragedies. These included 25 recommendations aimed specifically at OCTRANSPO and 16 recommendations addressing workplace harassment and violence. The jury recommended a zero-tolerance policy toward harassment and violence, and recognized that psychological abuse constitutes a form of workplace violence.

Source: "Workplace violence: The anger within," *OHS Canada*, December 2000. Retrieved from http://www.esourcecanada.com, October 25, 2004.

have always been traditional concerns of health and safety professionals, we now also recognize the need to anticipate and respond to terrorism and acts of violence.

Although the general probability of any of these emergencies actually happening may be low, they *can* happen and a company (or the home) is remiss if it does not institute an emergency plan. The results of a disaster may be prevented or mitigated by the effectiveness of the emergency plan.

Although many organizations focus on how they responded during an emergency, true emergency planning begins long before the onset of any emergency and continues long afterward. Emergency planning involves anticipating and planning for emergencies, putting those plans into action as needed, and then both (1) getting back to work and (2) refining plans in light of new learning.

A recent study describes this process as a five-stage crisis-management process that generates specific strategies at each stage.[1] The first step, signal detection, is targeted at prevention and begins with the recognition that an emergency is possible or imminent. The next step, preparation, involves senior management in the adoption of a crisis-management mindset, the creation of a response plan, and the introduction of response training. The third stage, damage containment, constitutes the majority of an organization's crisis-management resources. The literature on organizational communication, organizational support, employee assistance programs (EAPs), and stress interventions largely focuses on activities in this stage. The fourth stage, recovery, involves the development of short-term and long-term plans to resume normal business.[2] The final stage is learning, in which the focus is on assessing and reflecting on the incident with a view to improving operations and procedures.[3]

Although the benefits of a proactive response to emergencies are well known,[4] many organizations resist this view and, in fact, do not implement any systematic preparation for emergencies.[5] Management commitment to emergency preparedness seems to be a critical determinant of how organizations prepare for emergencies. Response strategies typically begin with organizational leaders.[6] Moreover, organizational leaders are responsible for both minimizing risk and responding to events in an effort to aid recovery and readjustment after the events have occurred.[7]

With respect to workplace violence, organizations make a huge mistake when they "focus on systems, operations, infrastructures and public relations and ignore the people . . . [employees] need to be assured of their safety and have their trust in leadership reinforced."[8]

Just as was the case for other forms of hazard control (see Chapter 8), an emergency plan needs to consider issues at the precontact, contact, and postcontact stages of any emergency. Issues at the precontact stage include assessing hazards and planning potential responses. Issues at the contact stage include evacuation, caring for the injured, and ensuring emergency response. Issues at the postcontact stage include dealing with the emotional trauma of an emergency and issues regarding the orderly return to work.

Precontact

The necessary elements in the management of emergencies include an emergency plan, an emergency manager, a fire plan, an evacuation plan, and a medical attention plan.

An Emergency Plan

The first thing that is required is a formal, rapid-response, workable, well-controlled emergency plan. Low levels of loss depend on this plan. The joint health and safety committees as well as the local government should be involved in developing the plan.

An organization requires hazard evaluation, an emergency response plan, training, an evacuation plan, notification of authorities, supplies, and drills.

HAZARD EVALUATION HR and safety professionals (and managers) must evaluate the hazards that could cause an emergency (e.g., storage of flammable solvents near static electricity or ignition sources) as well as the hazards with the greatest risk and loss potential. They must also understand how the emergency plans could be aborted or sidetracked if an emergency were to occur; the extent of possible damage and injuries or fatalities; and the possibility of the financial loss of the total plant, its individual departments, and critical equipment or processes.

An emergency is a rare occurrence; knowledge of these hazards can be augmented by consulting Emergency Planning Canada, the Fire Commissioner of Canada, and Environment Canada, as well as fire departments and insurance companies. The likelihood of natural disasters varies

Futureproofing

Writing for the Canadian Centre for Emergency Preparedness, Geary Sikich uses the term "futureproofing" to denote an integrated approach to emergency preparedness. Futureproofing is based on the notion that organizations have to anticipate and assess the potential risk and consequences of a wide range of emergencies in order to be protected from unexpected events. This approach is based on "graceful degradation" and "agile restoration"—that is, the ability of the organization to identify an event, determine its consequences, establish a minimal functionality, and begin to direct efforts toward restoration in a timely fashion.

Source: Sikich, G., "Futureproofing—The process of active analysis." Retrieved from http://www.ccep.ca/sikich.html, October 12, 2004.

according to region but the federal government provides a Natural Hazard Map of Canada (see Weblink) that can assist in determining the risk for various disasters in your area based on historical precedent.

EMERGENCY RESPONSE PLAN   A response plan for different types of emergencies must be created. These plans should be written, published, and posted. There must be good alarm facilities with emergency communication devices, and everyone in the plant must be familiar with their locations and use.

A list should be published of the people in charge of every aspect of any emergency activity. Accompanying the list should be information on the actual event, security and protection for the workers, protection of what is left, documentation of damage and injuries, and liaison with bureaucrats, insurance, and media.

EVACUATION PLAN   Plans for evacuating employees and clients in the event of a major emergency or disaster are a key element in emergency preparedness. Every worker in the plant must know exactly where to congregate when the

The Toronto Blackout

The effectiveness of an evacuation plan is seen in a letter to CBC News. Responding to news reports of the blackout in August 2003 that left most of Toronto in darkness, one letter writer indicated that she has arthritis and walks with a cane. Although she worked in a tower, she managed to evacuate the building by going down a dozen sets of stairs. Her employer had established an evacuation plan that included a "buddy system" that paired employees who have disabilities with employees who do not.

Source: CBC News, "Indepth: Power outage, person stories." Retrieved from http://www.cbc.ca/news/background/poweroutage/personalstories.html, October 11, 2004.

Evacuation Plans

Public agencies such as universities typically have well-developed evacuation plans that are made widely available. Most plans specify the authority structure (e.g., fire wardens, fire marshals) and means of evacuation. Although not complete, a representative sampling of university evacuation plans can be found on the web.

University	Link to Evacuation Plan
Dalhousie University	http://www.dal.ca/~pharmwww/files/safeplan2002.pdf
Queen's University	http://www.queensu.ca/quic/intledu/files/evacuationtemplate.pdf
University of Saskatchewan	http://www.cls.usask.ca/machine/pdf/0.12.37.1.Rev0.pdf
Ryerson University	http://www.ryerson.ca/oia/sidebar/mobility_travel_checklists/ EVACUATIONPLAN.DOC

need arises and be aware of at least two evacuation routes. There should be well-marked, unobstructed evacuation paths with well-lit exits. Notices about exit procedures should be posted, along with instructions about notifying appropriate personnel of the emergency. Designated assembly areas and assigned assistance should be part of the plan.

A roll call (head count) should be done at the assembly site, and a list of missing employees should be given to the command centre. No one should be allowed to reenter a building until all personnel are accounted for and debriefed.

The following are some basic requirements of evacuation plans.

1. The site must be divided into small, related areas. The workers in each area must be identified and trained to recognize and remember workers who are not part of their section. This probably happens routinely during working hours, but the noted presence of these "outsiders" must become second nature. In case of a major emergency, all workers must be accounted for.

2. Outside the building and away from any roadways there should be assembly points that allow for the movement of emergency vehicles. The personnel from each work area noted above must be trained to quickly move to their respective assembly points and remain there until a head count is complete and missing workers are accounted for.

3. Once every employee has been accounted for and the extent of the emergency has been determined, employees can be instructed to return to work or to go home and report when called.

4. Any critical equipment or process that may increase the overall risk of the emergency should be addressed. For example, the supply sources of flammable materials such as gas must be shut off. These tasks should be undertaken only by maintenance personnel who are highly trained in emergency procedures.

5. The end of the emergency can be called only by the senior person responsible for the operation's emergency procedures.

6. A postevacuation assessment must be done to identify problems in the evacuation plan. Remedial measures can then be taken.

The Canadian Standards Association has developed a standard for emergency response plans (ERP) that provides further information on evacuation requirements (CAN/CSA-Z731-03).

NOTIFICATION OF AUTHORITIES   Companies should be aware of any legislative requirements, such as the requirement to notify the Ministry of Labour, police, and so on, of an emergency. In locations with the 911 emergency system, an industrial call for medical assistance will automatically bring police, ministry, and other associated specialists, along with medical assistance.

SUPPLIES   Emergency first-line equipment such as fire extinguishers must be in well-defined, easily accessible locations. As noted above, designated workers must be trained in their use.

DRILLS   Regular emergency drills, with the occasional unannounced drill to keep everyone current and knowledgeable, are a standard part of most plans. Rehearsals are an important part of training. Simulating disasters will help employees deal effectively with real emergencies. Fire drills are rehearsals that require employees to be aware of reporting requirements and the location of exits and fire extinguishers. Drills test the response capability of the organization. The results (evacuation times, etc.) are monitored and reported to management. A full-scale dress rehearsal involves simulated injuries and provides a measure of an organization's ability to respond.

EMERGENCY MANAGER   In addition to the foregoing requirements, any emergency plan must have a senior person—generally the plant manager—who will be in charge of all of the emergency activities. This individual should

---

Occupational Health and Safety Notebook 11.4

Emergency Operations Centres (EOCs)

Also called the command post or the command centre, an EOC is a geographic space dedicated to the strategic management of an emergency. An EOC is typically geographically separate from the actual emergency site. The role of the EOC is to designate the individual in charge of the emergency site, facilitate communications with the public, disseminate emergency public information, and initiate the recovery process.

The requirements for an EOC vary with circumstances but in general should include communications capabilities sufficient to allow coordination of efforts and space for briefings and decision making. Basic supplies (e.g., office supplies) should also be available as well as connectivity through networks, radios, and so on.

Source: Canadian Centre for Emergency Preparedness, "CCEP Newsletter for August 2003." Retrieved from http://www.ccep.ca/news0308.html#item1, October 11, 2004.

---

speak for the organization and must be committed to the plan. If the emergency manager works a regular day shift and the plant is on multiple shifts, then there must be assistants on each of the other shifts with the authority and training to handle emergencies. The command centre, with a designated chain of command, is a critical component of the plan.

Contact

Fire Plan

The fire plan will have the same characteristics as the main emergency plan, although some of the requirements dealing with major damage and fatalities may not be followed if the fire gets out of control and a full-blown emergency results. A group of workers must be trained in firefighting techniques and be part of the plant fire brigade. In small to mid-sized businesses in which an in-house fire brigade is not economically feasible, workers should receive fire-extinguisher training and participate in ongoing practice sessions.

RPC 11.2

The local fire department is a good source of training for any in-house firefighting team that may be required. The fire department can also assist in fire hazard evaluations and regular inspections. Fire prevention and suppression is discussed in the final section of this chapter.

fire

a chemical process in which fuel, oxygen, and heat are combined

FIRE PREVENTION AND SUPPRESSION   A **fire** is a chemical process in which fuel, oxygen, and heat are combined to create a disastrous condition. The products of fire are gases, flame, heat, and smoke.

The fire process can be graphically represented by means of the fire triangle (see Figure 11.1). The new model is the fire tetrahedron (see Figure 11.2). The triangular model shows that the three elements—fuel, oxygen, and heat—must

FIGURE 11.1

Fire Triangle

Part Three: Interventions

FIGURE 11.2

Fire Tetrahedron

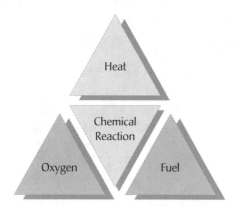

come together for a fire to be sustained. The second model adds a fourth element: the chain reaction. Once a fire starts, it is perpetuated by the ongoing (or chain) reaction of the other three elements.

Fire has four stages:

1. The **incipient stage**. At this stage, a source of ignition (a cigarette butt or a hot electrical wire connection) and fuel (papers or wood) come together. This stage can continue for hours until the resultant heat from the initial reaction becomes great enough to cause combustion. The air is filled with molecule-sized products of combustion. The airborne particulate can be detected with an ionizing (smoke) detector. In the case of an explosion, this stage (and the next) is very short.

2. The **smouldering stage**. The three elements are present and are causing the heat to rise through limited chain reaction. The area begins to fill with smoke, which increases in amount as the process continues. With visible airborne particulate (smoke) now present, a photoelectric detector is effective. This stage is short and can be measured in minutes.

3. The **free-burning stage**. This is the stage at which flames first appear. The rate of energy release (heat) is increasing very rapidly and the surrounding combustible materials are beginning to burn. The free-burning stage is very short and can be measured in minutes or less. A rate-of-rise detector can be effective at this stage because it senses the rapid temperature increase. This detector works well in conjunction with a sprinkler system.

4. The **uncontrolled fire stage**. The fire is out of control and major property damage is under way. All personnel must be evacuated. This stage can be measured in seconds. The rate of reaction doubles every 10 °C. No heat is lost during this reaction; rather it becomes cumulative.

incipient stage

a source of ignition and fuel come together

smouldering stage

fuel, oxygen, and heat are present and are causing the heat to rise through limited chain reaction

free-burning stage

the stage at which flames first appear

uncontrolled fire stage

fire is out of control and major property damage is under way

The fire triangle or tetrahedron (Figures 11.1 and 11.2) can serve to illustrate the requirements for extinguishment. By removing any one of the parts of these models, the fire cannot be sustained and will be put out. For instance, a carbon dioxide fire extinguisher will blanket the fire with a gas that will displace the oxygen, thereby smothering the fire. Similarly, water sprayed on the fire will cool the conditions or reduce the heat, also resulting in extinguishment (see Table 11.1).

Hazardous by-products of fires besides heat and smoke include carbon monoxide, carbon dioxide, hydrogen sulphide, sulphur dioxide, hydrogen cyanide, and hydrogen chloride. These toxic materials are produced when the burning materials (fuel) are broken down into original chemicals under extreme heat and chain reactions.

When developing a fire-prevention program, the following should be considered:

1. *Structural design.* Standards for construction of buildings are detailed in the federal and provincial or territorial fire codes, as well as fire marshal and building codes and regulations.
2. *Barriers.* Walls and floors can be used to delay or prevent the spread of fire. Specially constructed fire barriers should be maintained.
3. *Detection and suppression.* Most buildings have a detection system, which senses heat and smoke. When triggered, sprinklers are activated to suppress the fire.

TABLE 11.1

Classes of Fire

CLASS	GROUP	MATERIAL	SYMBOL	COLOUR	EXTINGUISHER
A	Combustible	Paper, wood	Triangle	Green	Water
B	Flammable liquid	Oil, grease, gas	Square	Red	CO_2, dry chemical
C	Electrical	Wiring	Circle	Blue	CO_2, halon
D	Metals	Flammable metals such as magnesium or titanium	Star	Yellow	Powder
K	Grease	Cooking oil, fat	Frying pan or K	Black	Wet grease chemical

Notes: Although comparatively rare, Class D fires require metal/sand extinguishers that work by smothering the fire. The most common extinguishing agent in this class is sodium chloride but powdered copper metal (for lithium fires) and other materials are used. Class K is a more recent designation of fires. Extinguishers of this class are specially designed to supplement the fire suppression systems found in commercial kitchens. They use a wet chemical agent such as potassium acetate.

As a result of some emergency conditions, individuals may be trapped in buildings that have been damaged. Rescue work is highly specialized, requiring both specialized training and equipment. During the 1985 earthquake in Mexico City, some 130 untrained or ill-equipped volunteer rescuers died attempting to save others. A rescue proceeds in five stages:

1. Reconnaissance and dealing with surface casualties
2. Location and removal of lightly trapped casualties
3. Exploration of likely survival points
4. Further exploration and debris removal
5. Systematic debris removal

Source: Adapted from Public Safety and Emergency Preparedness Canada, "Self-help advice for responders and emergency managers: Five stages of rescue." Reproduced with the permission of the Minister of Public Works and Government Services Canada, 2004. Retrieved from http://www.ocipep.gc.ca/info_pro/self_help_ad/general/book_basi_e.asp, October 11, 2004.

4. *Storage.* Combustible materials should be rated and stored in separate or isolated areas. They should *not* be stored near exits, and **reactive materials** should not be stored near flammable materials.

Many fires are triggered by unsafe acts (e.g., a person tries to weld a container containing flammable liquid residue without cleaning it) and unsafe conditions (e.g., faulty or improper equipment is installed near a potentially flammable material).

reactive material

causes a violent, explosive reaction when it comes in contact with another material, such as acetylene with water, or bleach with chlorinated cleaner

First Aid and Medical Attention

The various provincial and territorial regulations spell out in detail the requirements for first-aid and medical-aid facilities. Medical services run the gamut from a first-aid kit in a small firm to a fully equipped hospital with

A chemical spill is an uncontrolled release of gas, liquid, or solid chemical. Chemicals can, of course, be highly toxic and emergency procedures must be oriented on avoiding exposure to the chemical. Good procedures for a chemical spill include the following:

- Avoid coming into contact with the chemical and warn others in the area.
- Isolate the area around the spill.
- Assist those who are injured but do not risk exposing yourself to the chemical.

- Determine the level of response. If the spill is minor and trained personnel are available with the necessary protective gear and materials, then the material should be cleaned up. Otherwise, the authorities should be contacted.

Source: University of Alberta, Environmental Health and Safety, "Chemical spills." Retrieved from http://www.ehs.ualberta.ca/OHCS/index.aspx?Page=11, October 11, 2004.

RPC 11.3

doctors in very large firms. Degree of risk can be an additional factor in determining the extent of medical services. An insurance office with a staff of 4,000 would not likely need the same facilities as an automobile manufacturer with the same number of workers.

Beyond conforming to legal requirements, every company should arrange to have at least one trained first-aid attendant present at each shift. All employees should be given the opportunity to take a cardiopulmonary resuscitation (CPR) course. A cost-benefit analysis may show the advantages of contracting with a local occupational health clinic for medical-aid services. These services can include preemployment and postemployment medicals, exposure medical testing, and potential occupational illness identification. Complete first-aid records must be kept and maintained.

Postcontact

Postcontact efforts are really focused in two areas: helping individuals deal with the stresses associated with experiencing or witnessing an emergency situation and getting back to "normal" operations.

Stress

An emergency is an acute or catastrophic stressor (Chapter 6) and individuals may experience long-lasting consequences as a result. Acute stressors can be more psychologically devastating, and their effects more enduring, than chronic stressors, suggesting the need to understand their effects. For example, individuals exposed to hurricanes and other traumatic stressors have reported ongoing impairments of psychological well-being, including symptoms of posttraumatic stress that endure for much longer than the actual precipitating event.[9] Studies of a wide variety of traumatic stressors suggest several dimensions that may be important to understanding the impact of stressors on individuals.

Studies have highlighted the role of control perceptions when individuals are exposed to stressful situations, including acute stressors.[10] Natural disasters such as hurricanes or blizzards may involve an almost total lack of control, suggesting that their effects may be pronounced.[11]

The multivariate risk/resilience model was developed to explain individual reactions to disasters.[12] The model incorporates situational factors such as the extent to which the individual receives social support on an ongoing basis, targeted social support, or social support received in direct response to the disaster, as well as the individual's exposure to the disaster.[13]

One approach to crisis response has been referred to as **critical incident stress debriefing (CISD)**. Although the characteristics of CISDs may vary, they generally involve the provision of help and assistance (by psychologists or other trained personnel) immediately following a traumatic event in order to prevent the development of serious or lasting negative consequences. CISDs consist of elements such as ensuring confidentiality; providing individuals with the opportunity to talk about their perspective on, thoughts about, and emotional reactions to the incident; assessing psychological and physical symptoms, and providing information about stress responses and coping strategies.[14] CISD interventions are very popular among individuals regularly exposed to traumatic stressors. For example, almost every police, fire, and ambulance service in the country has some form of CISD intervention for their employees. The Canadian Forces uses CISD to debrief returning peacekeepers.

One study of the effectiveness of CISD compared the coping strategies and levels of anger of two groups of police officers that had experienced a traumatic event.[15] One group of officers received CISD and the other did not. The results suggested that the CISD group exhibited more adaptive coping strategies and lower levels of anger than those in the non-CISD group. The lack of random assignment to conditions cast some doubt on the validity of these findings, although they do provide preliminary evidence of the efficacy of CISD following exposure to traumatic work-related events. If these results were replicable, it would be unethical to withhold such debriefings from employees who experience traumatic events.

Unfortunately, despite these promising results, the research literature also provides a basis on which to question the effectiveness of CISD. First, a review of 67 studies concluded that debriefing does not mitigate the effects of traumatic stress.[16] Second, based on a meta-analytic review, other authors found that single-session debriefing was less effective than other forms of intervention and less effective than no intervention in reducing the effects of traumatic stress.[17] Finally, growing lists of studies suggest that individuals receiving CISD interventions may experience exacerbated traumatic reactions and more adverse outcomes.[18] As one review noted, these findings violate the widely accepted maxim that psychological interventions should in the first instance do no harm.[19] The inconsistent findings as to the effectiveness of CISDs suggest the need for more research in this

critical incident stress debriefing (CISD)

a posttrauma intervention focused on providing victims with an opportunity to discuss their experiences and reactions to a traumatic event

Business Continuity Planning

Even during an emergency, critical services must be continued. Some employers may have to continue operations during an emergency, and all employers will eventually have to return to "normal" operations. Business continuity planning is a proactive approach to ensuring that critical services and products continue during an emergency. Developing a business continuity plan will help to ensure that employers recover data, assets, and facilities and have the necessary resources (including human resources) to continue business.

Source: Adapted from Public Safety and Emergency Preparedness Canada, "Self-help advice for businesses and institutions: A guide to business continuity planning." Reproduced with the permission of the Minister of Public Works and Government Services Canada, 2004. Retrieved from http://www.ocipep.gc.ca/info_pro/self_help_ad/general/busi_cont_e.asp, October 11, 2004.

area, to identify whether some elements of CISDs are helpful and should be retained and which are harmful and should be removed from such programs.

Getting Back to Normal

Getting back to normal after an emergency is not as straightforward as a simple return to work. Depending on circumstances, individuals may continue to experience stress reactions. They may also continue to live with the effects of the emergency (e.g., damaged housing, loss of income, transportation) long after the acute phase of the emergency has passed. For example, Hurricane Juan in Nova Scotia passed in one night, but some individuals were without electricity for up to 14 days after the hurricane.

Given these potential reactions and experiences, it is unlikely that individuals will return to the workplace focused on the task at hand. Recognizing the need to get back to work, employers should display some tolerance for distractions and the need for employees to share their experiences. Adjusting to normal work may take some time.

Employers may inadvertently increase employee stress by the way they handle personnel decisions around the emergency. In Halifax following the hurricane, employers had to make several decisions that affected their employees. For instance, employers had to make decisions about compensation for lost workdays following the storm and employee attendance during the state of emergency. Similar decisions were made after the February Blizzard (White Juan) and elicited considerable anger from some employees (for an example, see the Weblinks section).

Summary

The goals of an emergency plan are to reduce injuries and property damage, and to restore the organization to its normal operations. Emergency preparedness consists of preparing an emergency response plan, designating and training those responsible for its implementation, and communicating it to employees. Developing an evacuation plan, establishing a fire-prevention and suppression program, and controlling fire hazards are other elements of emergency preparedness.

Key Terms

critical incident stress debriefing (CISD), p. 299
emergency, p. 288
fire, p. 294
free-burning stage, p. 295

incipient stage, p. 295
reactive material, p. 297
smouldering stage, p. 295
uncontrolled fire stage, p. 295

Weblinks

Canadian Centre for Emergency Preparedness,
http://www.ccep.ca (p. 286)

Hurricane Juan photos,
http://www.vektor.ca/juan/index.html (p. 286)

CBC News, Indepth: SARS—Severe Acute Respiratory Syndrome,
http://www.cbc.ca/news/background/sars/ (p. 288)

Government of Canada, "Safety and security for Canadians,"
http://canada.gc.ca/SSC/SSC_e.html (p. 289)

Office of Critical Infrastructure Protection and Emergency Preparedness, "Natural hazards of Canada,"
http://www.ocipep.gc.ca/info_pro/Posters/naturalhazards/index_e.asp (p. 291)

University of Guelph, "Emergency response plan,"
http://www.uoguelph.ca/security/Police/ERP.html (p. 291)

Simon Fraser University, "SFU emergency Plan (GP 34),"
http://www2.sfu.ca/policies/general/gp34.htm (p. 291)

Canadian Standards Association,
http://www.csa.ca (p. 293)

Government of Nova Scotia, "911: Nova Scotia's emergency telephone reporting system,"
http://www.gov.ns.ca/emo/AbsPage.aspx?id=1116&siteid=1&lang=1 (p. 293)

Canadian Red Cross,
http://www.redcross.ca (p. 298)

St. John Ambulance,
http://www.sja.ca (p. 298)

Nova Scotia Power,
http://www.nspower.ca/RestorePower/DOCS/UARB_Report.pdf (p. 300)

The Chronicle Herald, "These are your stories of Blizzard 2004,"
http://www.herald.ns.ca/blizzard2004/blizzardstories.html (p. 300)

RPC Icons

RPC 11.1 Ensures that mechanisms are in place for responding to crises in the workplace, including critical incident stress management.

- oral and written communication
- training and development techniques
- industry best practices
- the workplace environment including the availability of emergency equipment
- policy and program development and evaluation
- intervention strategies
- relevant legislation (e.g., fire code, Workers' Compensation)
- investigation techniques
- stress management techniques
- types of employee assistance programs
- Occupational health and safety legislation (e.g., Occupational Health and Safety Act of Ontario, Workplace Safety & Insurance Act—Bill 99, Workplace Hazardous Materials Information System, Transportation of Dangerous Goods legislation, environmental legislation, smoking in the workplace legislation, civil rights legislation)
- hazard identification and control
- accident investigation procedures
- emergency preparedness procedures
- management techniques for OH&S Programs
- conceptual definition and implications of occupational stressors (e.g., potential stressors, methods of identifying potential stressors and strain outcomes, response to organizational stressors, and management of employee strain outcomes)

RPC 11.2 Establishes effective programs for accident prevention, incident investigation, inspections, fire and emergency response, and required training.

- relevant legislation
- workplace inspection and accident investigation techniques
- nature of the business and physical work environment
- potential risks and hazards in the workplace
- emergency response planning
- community emergency response services
- training and development
- industry best practices

- Worker Protection (including health and safety and Workers' Compensation)
- training and development program design and administration
- hazard identification and control
- accident investigation procedures
- emergency preparedness procedures
- management techniques for OH&S Programs

RPC 11.3 Responds to serious injury or fatality in the workplace.

- program and policy development
- investigation procedures

TASK & KNOWLEDGE REQUIREMENTS

- relevant legislative requirements
- first aid training and emergency response equipment
- relevant legislative bodies
- pension and insurance benefits/policies
- common and statutory law (e.g., employment standard: labour relations
- Worker Protection (including health and safety and Workers' Compensation)
- Occupational health and safety legislation (e.g., Occupational Health and Safety Act of Ontario, Workplace Safety & Insurance Act—Bill 99, Workplace Hazardous Materials Information System, Transportation of Dangerous Goods legislation, environmental legislation, smoking in the workplace legislation, civil rights legislation)
- hazard identification and control
- accident investigation procedures
- emergency preparedness procedures

Discussion Questions

1. Who should be involved in developing emergency response plans?
2. What types of emergencies should organizations in your area be prepared for?
3. Decide what type of fire extinguisher would be most effective in the following fire situations:

   a. a hair dryer engulfed in smoke

   b. grease burning in a frying pan

   c. rags smoking in the garage

   d. a log that has rolled from the fireplace onto the living-room floor

   e. a coffee machine whose wires are shooting flames

4. Although this chapter has focused on health and safety implications, there are also public relations issues in an emergency. What principles would be appropriate for an organization to adopt in dealing with the media and public during an emergency?

Using the Internet

1. What emergencies have occurred in your local area in the past five years? How effective was the emergency response? (Hint: Local EMO sites often have debriefing reports on past emergency responses.)

Exercises

1. Determine whether your workplace or school has an emergency response plan. Compare this plan with the one outlined in this chapter.
2. Prepare a fire-prevention and suppression plan for your own home or apartment.

Case: Biological Terrorism

In recent weeks, there have been heightened concerns about biological terrorism. Specifically, there is concern that it is possible to spread toxic organisms (e.g., anthrax) by mailing them. In the last three months there have been at least four incidents in which a firm or office building has been the target of such an attack (i.e., a suspicious envelope or parcel arrives in the mailroom with some indication that it contains a highly contagious toxin). Senior management in your firm is concerned. They have asked you to develop an emergency plan for dealing with such an occurrence. What do you need to consider and do to develop such a plan? Identify the elements of emergency preparedness and how each should be implemented.

Endnotes

1. Pearson, C. M., Clair, J. A., Misra, S. K., & Mitroff, I. I. (1997). Managing the unthinkable. *Organizational Dynamics, 26,* 51–64.
2. Blythe, B. T. (2002). *Blindsided: A manager's guide to catastrophic incidents in the workplace.* New York: Portfolio.
3. Pearson, C. M., Clair, J. A., Misra, S. K., & Mitroff, I. I. (1997). Managing the unthinkable. *Organizational Dynamics, 26,* 51–64.
4. Pearson, C. M., & Clair, J. A. (1998). Reframing crisis management. *Academy of Management Review, 23*(1), 59–76.
5. Mitroff, I. I., Pearson, C. M., & Harrigan, L. K. (1996). *The essential guide to managing corporate crises.* New York: Oxford University.
6. Blythe, B. T. (2002). *Blindsided: A manager's guide to catastrophic incidents in the workplace.* New York: Portfolio.
7. Pearson, C. M., & Clair, J. A. (1998). Reframing crisis management. *Academy of Management Review, 23*(1), 59–76.
8. Braverman, M. (2003). Managing the human impact of crisis. *Risk Management, 50*(5), 10–14.
9. Norris, F. H., Byrne, C. M., Diaz, E., & Kaniasty, K. (2001). *50,000 disaster victims speak: An empirical review of the empirical literature, 1981–2001.* Retrieved from http://obssr.od.nih.gov/activities/911/attack.htm, October 12, 2004.
10. Schat, A. C. H., & Kelloway, E. K. (2003). Reducing the adverse consequences of workplace aggression and violence: The buffering effects of organizational support. *Journal of Occupational Health Psychology, 8,* 110–122.
11. Baum, A., Fleming, R., & Davidson, L. M. (1983). Natural and technological catastrophe. *Environment and Behavior, 15,* 333–354.
12. Freedy, J. R., Saladin, M. E., Kilpatrick, D. G., & Resnick, H. S. (1994). Understanding acute psychological distress following natural disaster. *Journal of Traumatic Stress, 7*(2), 257–273.

13. Byron, K., & Peterson, S. (2002). The impact of a large-scale traumatic event on individual and organizational outcomes: Exploring employee and company reactions to September 11. *Journal of Organizational Behavior, 23*(8), 895–910.

14. Mitchell, J., & Bray, G. (1990). *Emergency services stress.* Englewood Cliffs, NJ: Prentice-Hall.

15. Leonard, R., & Alison, L. (1999). Critical incident stress debriefing and its effects on coping strategies and anger in a sample of Australian police officers involved in shooting incidents. *Work and Stress, 13,* 144–161.

16. Arendt, M., & Elklit, A. (2001). Effectiveness of psychological debriefing. *Acta Psychiatry Scandanavia, 104,* 423–437.

17. Van Emmerik, A. A. P., Kamphuis, J. H., Hulsbosch, A. M., & Emmelkamp, P. M. G. (2002). Single session debriefing after psychological trauma: A meta-analysis. *The Lancet, 340,* 768–771.

18. Carlier, I. V. E., Lamberts, R. D., Van Uchelin, A. J., & Gersons, B. P. R. (1998). Disaster-related posttraumatic stress in police officers: A field study of the impact of debriefing. *Stress Medicine, 14,* 143–148; Mayou, R. A., Ehler, A., & Hobbs, M. (2000). Psychological debriefing for road accident victims: Three-year follow up of randomized control trial. *British Journal of Psychiatry, 176,* 589–593; and Small, R., Lumley, J., Donohue, L., Potter, A., & Waldenstroem, U. (2001). Randomized controlled trial of midwife led debriefing to reduce maternal depression after operative childbirth. *British Medical Journal, 321,* 1043–1047.

19. Barling, J., Hurrell, J. J., Braverman, M., Collins, J., Gelles, M. G., Scrivner, E., & Keita, G. P. (2002). *Terrorized workers: Employee well-being following 9/11.* Manuscript submitted for publication.

Chapter 12

Accident Investigation

Chapter Learning Objectives

After reading this chapter, you should be able to

- describe the intent and steps of an accident investigation
- gather information to analyze the human, situational, and environmental factors contributing to accidents
- outline the legal requirements of accident investigation results
- explain the concept of a walkthrough survey
- list the steps to conducting interviews concerning an accident
- conduct a reenactment
- complete the various types of incident, accident, and injury reports

®℗© 12.1

®℗© 12.2

®℗© 12.3

W W W

The investigation of incidents and accidents is a critical component of an organization's health and safety program. This chapter describes the rationale for accident investigations, the critical factors in the investigative process, the types of information to be collected, and the investigative methods and tools used to conduct an investigation. The importance of reporting and keeping records is also discussed.

Rationale for Accident Investigation

The investigation of accidents is an important component in a hazard recognition, assessment, and control (**RAC**) **program**, which in turn is an integral part of a health and safety program. One study identifies the benefits of accident investigation as follows:[1]

RAC program

a hazard recognition, assessment, and control program; a key element in most health and safety programs

1. *Determines direct causes.* An investigation will uncover the direct causes of an accident, thereby allowing for the subsequent exploration of corrective measures.
2. *Identifies contributing causes.* Some accidents may be the result of many factors. For example, although the direct cause of an accident may be

the inadequate safeguards on the equipment, contributing factors may include loose clothing on the employee and a lack of instruction in the proper procedures for equipment use.

3. *Prevents similar accidents.* Once the direct and contributing causes are identified, corrective measures such as training programs or equipment design improvements can be implemented to prevent similar accidents.

4. *Creates a permanent record.* The reports generated by an investigation can be used by HR and safety specialists to identify trends (i.e., sites of frequent incidents, inefficient layouts and designs, unsafe acts, or improper operating procedures). Reports can also be valuable in the case of litigation or compensation claims. Actions taken to improve safety records can be cost efficient in the sense that money and time will be allocated to sites or equipment for which the most frequent or most severe accidents and injuries occur.

5. *Determines cost.* The delineation of the exact situation may help the organization determine the actual costs accruing from an accident. All factors, even a worker's lost time, count more than once if there were multiple activities by this worker directly related to the event.

6. *Promotes safety awareness among employees.* If a thorough investigation is conducted, employees will realize that management is serious about safety and interested in their well-being. This should motivate employees to show a greater concern for safe practices.

Critical Factors in the Investigative Process

Accident investigations are strongly influenced by timing, severity, and legal requirements.

Timing

Timing is a critical factor in the investigation of accidents. Time affects several types of information. Delays in an investigation may lead to partial or complete memory loss by the witnesses, changes at the accident site, and removal of important evidence. Furthermore, those directly involved in the accident, whether they are witnesses or late arrivals, tend to discuss the accident, and details may become distorted in the retelling.

Of course, the investigation should start only after any injured people receive medical attention and the accident site has been secured to prevent access, further injuries, and attempts by helpful observers to "fix" the hazard.

Severity

Given the time-consuming nature of investigation, companies tend to examine only those accidents that have the most serious consequences. However, incidents and accidents that result in minor injuries are often signals of a hazard that may one day have more serious consequences.

What to Investigate

A wide variety of safety-related events may be subject to investigation. Occupational health and safety legislation may mandate postaccident investigations in some cases, depending on the severity and nature of the accident. For example, when a workplace death occurs, it is clear that external agencies such as the police will become involved and assume the primary investigative role. When injury-causing accidents are severe or continually recurring, provincial or territorial and federal health and safety agencies (such as the Labour Program of Human Resources Development Canada) may appoint an investigator to inspect the workplace or may require the submission of a formal report. Employers may also mandate the scope of accident investigations based on local standards or specific concerns. The occupational health and safety policy at

Dalhousie University, for example, mandates the investigation of the following types of accidents:

1. All serious injury accidents that result in hospitalization or absences for two or more days
2. All fires or explosions
3. All major spills or releases of chemicals
4. Any accident or series of accidents that the environmental health and safety committee wants to have investigated

Sources: Dalhousie University, "Health and safety policy and procedures." Retrieved from http://www.dal.ca/~ehs/police2.htm, October 12, 2004; and Kelloway, E. K., Stinson, V., & MacLean, C. (2004). Can eyewitness research improve occupational health and safety? Towards a research agenda. *Law and Human Behavior, 28*, 115.

One corporate director of health and safety recommends that the following types of accidents be investigated: those resulting in lost-time injuries beyond the day of the accident; accidents in which the injury was minor, but the employee was treated by a doctor and there was potential for a serious injury; close calls; accidents without injuries but property damage in excess of $1,000; and lost-time accidents resulting from aggravation of a previous injury.[2] Regardless of the system used to judge seriousness, organizations have a legal obligation to report injury-related accidents.

Legal Requirements

Depending on the seriousness of the accident, the presence of an injury, and the jurisdiction in which the accident happened, employers have to fulfill reporting requirements. Certain types of events—those in which an injury requires medical aid or results in lost time, for instance—must be reported to a Workers' Compensation Board, normally within three days. Forms are supplied by the Board.

Types of Information Collected

Most incidents and accidents are the result of many contributing factors. The Three Mile Island disaster (a nuclear plant disaster that occurred near Harrisburg, Pennsylvania, on March 28, 1979) was preceded by multiple contributing factors ranging from inadequate emergency training, through equipment failing to shut down, to fail-safe systems that failed to take into consideration the human equation. Although no lives were lost in the incident, public trust in the nuclear-power industry plummeted.

The area supervisor should conduct this investigation, assisted by the HR or safety specialist. When investigating an accident, the HR or safety specialist should concentrate on three factors: human, situational, and environmental. These factors, while similar in name, are not the same as the sources of hazards described in Chapter 7.

Human Factors

Studying the worker as a source of accidents does not mean that the investigator is looking for a scapegoat. As highlighted throughout this text, the intent is to collect facts, not assign blame. The following are some questions that could be asked when investigating human factors:

- What was the worker doing at the time of the accident? Was he or she performing a regular task or a different task, doing maintenance work, or helping a coworker?
- Was the work being performed according to procedures? Were the tasks or procedures new?
- Was a supervisor present?
- What was the employment status of the worker—seasonal, part-time, or full-time?
- How much experience did the employee have with respect to this particular operation?
- What was the posture and location of the employee?
- Did some unsafe act contribute to the event?

Occupational Health and Safety Notebook 12.1

The Eyewitness

Most accident investigations rely on eyewitness accounts and those of individuals involved in the incident. Yet there is good reason to suspect the accuracy of eyewitness statements. A review of the literature on eyewitness testimony showed that "what we know about eyewitness memory comes from hundreds of studies. ... Overall, this body of research tells us that eyewitness testimony is not like a videotape recorder; memory is fragile, malleable, and susceptible to forgetting, even in optimal conditions." The authors cite an example of an airplane crash that killed nine people. Dozens of people witnessed the crash and at least one insisted at the inquest that the plane nose-dived into the ground. Photographic evidence proved that in fact, the plane coasted down and skidded for nearly 1,000 feet.

Source: Kelloway, E. K., Stinson, V., & MacLean, C. (2004). Can eyewitness research improve occupational health and safety? Towards a research agenda. *Law and Human Behavior, 28*, 115.

Situational Factors

An analysis of the unsafe conditions that led to the accident is a critical step in an accident investigation. The equipment and tools must be examined. The following questions could be asked when investigating situational factors:

- Was the machine operating in a satisfactory manner?
- Were all the control and display positions working and ergonomically sound?
- Were the safety measures satisfactory and functioning?
- Did the analysis of failed materials or equipment indicate how the accident happened? For instance, if a shaft broke, causing a machine part to fly off, an engineer can examine the break and determine the mode of failure. Failure of metal through shear or bending modes will leave definite patterns in the failed ends. Once the mode is known, the cause is usually easily determined.
- What was the site or location of the accident?
- What tools, equipment, or objects were involved in the accident?
- Was the correct equipment available and being used to do the job?
- What personal protective equipment (gloves, goggles, etc.) was being worn?
- Were guards in place?
- What time of day did the accident occur?
- What shift was being worked?

Environmental Factors

Sometimes environmental factors such as light and noise may increase the likelihood that an accident will occur. The setting sun may blind the driver of a delivery truck; the noise of a machine may mask the approach of a vehicle; the vibrations of a certain piece of equipment may dislodge another tool.

Who Investigates?

Numerous individuals may be involved in accident investigations, including the following:

- *The supervisor:* The supervisor possesses a detailed knowledge of the work and the working conditions and is therefore well positioned to conduct the investigation. In most companies, supervisors assume principal responsibility for the investigation.
- *Technical advisers and specialists:* It may be appropriate to bring in technical advisers or specialists when accidents are serious and involve highly technical processes. Bringing in outside expertise may also enhance the objectivity of the investigation.
- *Safety and health officer:* The department or company health and safety officer can also offer guidance in coordinating an accident investigation. The health and safety representative may be more aware of, and familiar with, health and safety issues than is the supervisor.

Analysis of an Accident

A carpenter is making some tool holders and needs to trim about 0.5 cm off the length of a piece of 4 × 4 wood. The 4 × 4 is 121 cm long. The carpenter spends 15 minutes adjusting the table saw to remove the correct width of material. In the process, the carpenter also removes the legally required saw guard because it tends to interfere with cutting. The supervisor had been after the company to purchase a new and proper guard for the saw. The usual answer was, "Why buy a new guard when one came with the machine?" The carpenter decides not to replace the guard for this cut because the last time this operation was performed, the wood snagged on the guard support and allowed the blade to burn the cut surface. This necessitated extra sanding to remove the stain. However, this time, even though the carpenter uses the proper hand pusher and guides, the saw hits a knot, and the work piece jumps up from the spinning blade. Luckily, the carpenter receives only minor lacerations.

The unsafe acts in this accident are (1) the carpenter removing the guard and leaving it off during the operation, (2) the supervisor allowing the saw to be used with the poor guard and not insisting on replacing the defective guard, (3) the carpenter continuing to use a piece of unsafe equipment, and (4) the company purchasing the saw without specifying the correct type of guard.

The unsafe conditions are (1) having the improper guard on the machine, (2) providing a machine without a proper guard, and perhaps (3) the supervisor being unaware of the use of the improper guard.

In most provinces and territories, a company official such as the plant manager could be found liable if an identified unsafe act or condition is ignored. The carpenter displayed voluntary risk in that the saw was used even though it was known to have a defective guard.

Can you identify the human, situational, and environmental factors that contributed to this accident?

- *Safety and health committee or representative:* Where there is an established health and safety committee, the health and safety committee must take part in an investigation.
- *A safety team:* In the event of a serious accident and, specifically, when it is not easy to determine the cause of an accident, a team approach is highly recommended. The team would include the supervisor, health and safety officer, members of the health and safety committee, and, possibly, outside experts.

Investigative Methods

A variety of methods may be used in conducting the investigation.

Observations or Walkthroughs

At the beginning of an investigation, an overall picture of the total environment is achieved by means of a **walkthrough.** Observation of causal factors, physical conditions, and work habits will help the specialist to identify potential causes of the accident. Because the manager may not be totally familiar with the details of the operation, the specialist should turn to the supervisor for any necessary information.

walkthrough

inspection of the accident scene to get a picture of the total environment

Interviews

The following are some basic rules for conducting an interview:

1. Interview witnesses on the spot as soon as possible after the event while their memories are still fresh. Inform each witness of the purpose of the interview and what you hope to accomplish.
2. Interview witnesses separately and in a neutral location, such as the cafeteria. Do not use your office, since it could have an authority stigma associated with it. The witness should be permitted to have a worker representative present if he or she desires. Make sure that the representative listens and says little or nothing.
3. Put the witness at ease. If the person witnessed a serious injury, he or she may well be shaken or upset. If the person witnessed a death, counselling may be necessary before any discussion can take place. Reassure the witness that you are simply trying to gather information, not to lay blame.
4. Let the individual recall the event in his or her own way. Do not try to bias the account with questions that are pointed or directed. "Will you please tell me in your own words what you saw or heard?" is much better than, "Can you think what prompted John to do what he did?"
5. Ask any necessary questions at appropriate times, without inter- rupting the speaker's train of thought. The questions should serve to clarify a point or fill in any gaps, not to support any conclusions you may be forming. "Can you explain again how you knew that the machine was turned off?" is preferable to, "You commented that the table saw was not running—did you see the worker turn it off?"
6. Give the witness feedback. "Based on what you said, this is my under- standing of what you saw. If there is something I missed or haven't got right, please add to or clarify it." When you are finished, both you and the witness should be able to agree that the statement is a factual representation of what was said.
7. Make sure that critical information—either from the witnesses or from your own observations—is recorded in a timely fashion. The longer the delay, the more bias will affect the results. Supplement your written record with visuals (e.g., sketches, photographs, videos).
8. End the interview on a positive note by thanking the witness for his or her valuable time and assistance. Encourage the witness to come to you with any further information that may emerge.

Reenactments

reenactment

a simulation designed to recreate the circumstances leading up to an incident

Reenactment is a powerful incident or accident recall method that requires very careful handling and planning. The most obvious problem is the danger that simulating an actual injury will produce another one.

Circumstances will dictate whether a reenactment is essential to complete a thorough investigation. In one documented case, the safety professional was on-site when a worker was impaled between the couplers of two boxcars in the rail yard of the company. The safety specialist filmed the car separation and the

Occupational Health and Safety Notebook 12.3

Cognitive Interviewing

Cognitive interviewing is a technique that was developed for police officers conducting forensic investigations. A great deal of research suggests that cognitive interviews are effective in retrieving accurate eyewitness testimony. Cognitive interviews result in more information and a higher accuracy rate than do "regular" investigative interviews. Some preliminary evidence shows that the cognitive interview elicits more accurate statements from accident witnesses.* A typical cognitive interview follows the following sequence:

Introduction

– Develop rapport, communicate needs, encourage active participation

Open-ended narration

– Establish mental context, note mental images, develop plan for probing

Probing

– Use richest images to probe, ask questions related to images

Review

– Review information reported

Close

– Finish official business and encourage future contact

---

*MacLean, C., Stinson, V., & Kelloway, E. K. (2004). Cognitive interviewing of accident witnesses: An initial test. Paper accepted for presentation at the annual meeting of the Canadian Psychological Association, St John's, NL.

Sources: Fisher, R. P. (1995). Interviewing victims and witnesses of crime. *Psychology, Public Policy, and Law, 1*, 732–764; Fisher, R. P., Geiselman, R. E., & Amador, M. (1989). Field test of the cognitive interview: Enhancing the recollection of actual victims and witnesses of crime. *Journal of Applied Psychology, 74*, 722–727; and Fisher, R. P., McCauley, M. R., & Geiselman, R. E. (1994). Improving eyewitness testimony with the cognitive interview. In D. F. Ross, J. D. Read, & M. P. Toglia (Eds.), *Adult eyewitness testimony: Current trends and developments* (pp. 245–272). New York: Cambridge University Press.

---

removal of the body. Then, while all the witnesses were present and all of the details were fresh—horribly so—in their minds, he had each witness walk through what he or she saw. The local coroner complimented the safety officer on the thoroughness of the evidence, and a reenactment was obviously unnecessary.

The following are some guidelines for conducting a reenactment:

1. A qualified observer is necessary. If none is available, then the in-house specialist will have to do the job. If it appears that evidence is being gathered for an inquest or court hearing, then every possible explanation, even suicide, must be considered.

2. Do not show—tell. Have all the witnesses relate in their own words what they observed. You as the analyst have to know precisely what took place during the event in question. Their stories will provide that information. You cannot afford any surprises that might lead to additional injury. Filming can be very helpful, but if, and only if, the witness agrees.

3. Shut down every energy source and lock them out. Follow the lockout procedures discussed in Chapter 8. Have the professional who is conducting the reenactment control the major key for the lockout.

4. Carefully act out the events. The witness will describe what happened at each step (just as he or she did when verbally describing the events), and then, with the specialist's approval, will act out that step. For obvious reasons, the reenactment will stop before the point of accident.

cognitive interviewing

an interviewing technique developed for forensic investigations

Chapter 12: Accident Investigation

Investigative Tools

The walkthrough, the interview, and the reenactment can be supplemented by the following:

- *Photographs:* Accident photography is helpful and even necessary for efficient accident investigation. When pictures are being taken, make sure that they show the whole area, as well as every angle and every nook and cranny. Colour is best, although black and white can be useful. One advantage of black-and-white photographs is that they can be scanned and included in the accident report. Investigators with limited photographic experience will find a Polaroid camera relatively easy to use. Photographs taken with this camera can be examined on the spot for focus and framing problems. Point and shoot cameras also require minimal operator skill. Digital video cameras are effective and preferred since the film can be viewed immediately and the data can be entered into the computer.
- *Drawings:* After the interview, prepare a series of sketches or drawings of the accident scene. These can be complemented by "instant" photographs or video. A good CAD program such as Cadkey or Cadkey Lite will facilitate the drawing process. If you do not have access to CAD software and the training to use it, then a scale pencil sketch is fine. Make sure all parts of the drawing are well labelled.
- *Computers:* Incident recall involves the gathering and recording of large amounts of information. A computer with a user-friendly database is a necessity. Portable laptops can be taken directly to the scene of an accident. Any computer will facilitate the structured entry of data and facts into the safety files.
- *Other tools:* Depending on the circumstances of the event, other tools such as tape measures, clipboards, water-resistant pens, and flashlights will be of assistance to the investigator.
- *Record check:* Training records and maintenance or production schedules can offer the investigator some valuable insights. A careful review of training records can provide the answers to some questions: Was the worker properly instructed in the accepted and safe methods of doing the job or task? Was he or she aware of the rules of operation and were they followed? Has the worker signed a training attendance sheet or examination form? Maintenance logs and records should provide information about potential hazards within the company and what, if anything, was done about them. Preventative maintenance data are particularly important, since they can be used to predict possible future failures in equipment.

RPC 12.4

Accident/Incident Reports

Once all the information from the investigation has been gathered, the accident/incident reports must be completed. These reports should provide some explanation of causal factors. Although the principal causes remain unsafe acts (e.g., not using a personal protective device) or unsafe conditions (e.g., a broken guard), other explanatory conditions may exist. The factor most closely associated with the cause of an accident is referred to as the *agency*. The following are some examples of agents:

- animals (insects, dogs, raccoons, etc.)
- pressure vessels (boilers, piping)
- chemicals (solvents, explosives)
- materials-handling systems (conveyers, forklift trucks)
- dust, fumes, smoke, mists (silica, wood)
- electrical equipment (motors, fuses, wiring)
- elevating devices (elevators, vertical stop belts)
- tools (hammers, wrenches)
- lifting devices (hoists, cranes)
- machine tools (lathe, drill press)
- motive power sources (engines, vehicles)
- radiation (X-ray, ultraviolet)

The *agency* refers to the subgroup of the factors listed above. For example, a dog bite would be the agency part of the animal group.

Another consideration in reports is the *accident type*, which attempts to categorize the nature of the accident. Some examples include the following:

- caught in or between (e.g., crushed between two moving machines)
- struck by (impact or blow to the body by an object)
- struck against (walking into a door)
- fall to the same level (tripping on a level walkway)
- fall to a lower level (falling off a ladder)
- fall to a higher level (tripping while walking up steps)
- abraded, scratched, or punctured (an injury such as hitting the face when falling)
- overexertion (sprains, strains, etc., caused by a greater-than-average effort)
- contact with an energy (mechanical, kinetic, electrical, chemical, thermal, gravity, or radiation)

Personal factors (e.g., lack of knowledge, fatigue, restricted vision) should also be included in the accident investigation form to assist in entry, record keeping, and analysis.

The actual report format will vary by company. (Samples of short and long reports are provided in Figures 12.1 and 12.2, respectively.) Organization and layout should be straightforward. Accuracy and thoroughness are also important. Where information is unknown or is not applicable, the respondent should indicate "information unknown" or "not applicable." Abbreviations such as "n/a" for "not applicable" should not be used (it can mean "not available" as well). Do not leave the space blank!

Reports that must be submitted to outside parties such as OH&S agencies or WCBs should include basic information about the company (i.e., type of industry, number of employees, etc.).

FIGURE 12.1

Short Report

PE+E Supervisor's Accident/Incident Report

A. General Information

last name: first name: gender: [ ] male [ ] female

department: job title:

type: [ ] full time   [ ] part time   [ ] casual

date of injury: time of injury: [ ] am [ ] pm

date reported: time reported: [ ] am [ ] pm

incident category: [ ] illness   [ ] injury   [ ] first aid   [ ] medical aid

B. Accident Investigation

Nature and extent of injury: [ ] left   [ ] right

What job was the employee performing:

Was this part of regular duties: [ ] yes   [ ] no

Length of time employee performing this type of work:

Exact location of accident:

Describe sequence of events leading to accident. Name tools, machines, materials used. Provide sketch on reverse if necessary.

Describe any unsafe mechanical or physical condition involved in accident:

Describe any unsafe act involved in accident:

Name and address of hospital or clinic: [ ] company doctor:

Doctor's name: Doctor's estimate of lost time:

Measures taken to prevent similar accidents:

C. Diagrams

Diagrams or photographs may be placed here:

Witness name: _____ Witness name: _____

Address: _____ Address: _____

Phone: Res: _____ Phone: Res: _____

Bus: _____ Bus: _____

Supervisor's signature: _____ Date: _____

Employee's signature: _____ Date: _____

Please have this document processed and forwarded to

Original to: *Manager, Safety and Environment*

Copies to: *Vice President, Manufacturing,*

Manager, Human Resources

Department

The information you provide on this document will enable PE+E to effectively manage claims. Thank you for taking as much time as possible.

A description of any injury that was sustained should be included. A separate physician's report (see Figure 12.3) should also be provided, along with a witness report (see Figure 12.4).

Completed reports are submitted to the senior managers, the joint health and safety committee, others directly involved, and possibly the Ministry of Labour if the accident involved serious injuries. It is then up to the senior manager directly responsible for the operation in question to implement the recommendations contained in the report.

Accident Analysis

Once the data are collected, the next task is to analyze the information to identify the cause of the accident. A variety of analytic models and techniques are available for use in assessing the cause of an accident.

Figure 12.2

Long Report

Supervisor's Accident/Incident Report

To be completed by the supervisor with the employee immediately after an accident/incident
Please Print

last name _____ first name _____ gender _____

street _____ apt _____ city _____ prov _____

postal code _____ telephone _____ date of birth _____ marital status _____

date of employment _____ department _____ job title _____

[ ] full time   [ ] part time   [ ] casual   hrs/week _____

years' experience _____ social insurance number _____

accident/incident occurred: yyyy mm dd (   )   hhmm (   ) am/pm

reported to employer: yyyy mm dd (   )   hhmm (   ) am/pm

who was accident reported to _____

location of accident (dept, machine, location of machine) _____

supervisor's name _____

witness name(s) _____

Has this employee ever had a similar work-related injury or non-work-related injury? [ ] yes   [ ] no

If yes, explain: _____

_____

List the employee's job description/task analysis at the time of the injury

(Include job title, duties, weights, sizes of equipment, tools, etc.)

_____

_____

_____

_____

_____

_____

What physical effort was involved? (List job function plus weights and sizes of materials used.)

_____

_____

_____

_____

_____

Investigation of accident/incident (*who, what, why, where, how*)

Who was involved?

Where did the accident/incident occur?

What happened to cause the accident/incident? (explain—facts only)

Why did the accident/incident occur? (be objective, do not lay blame)

How did the accident/incident occur? (based on facts only)

Injury

[ ] lost time   [ ] medical aid   [ ] first aid   [ ] information only or [ ] hazardous condition, no injury

treatment memorandum sent   [ ] yes   [ ] no   modified work form sent   [ ] yes   [ ] no

Causes

[ ] unsafe act   [ ] unsafe condition   [ ] information only or [ ] poor/damaged equipment

[ ] no/poor training   [ ] no/poor procedures [ ] other

Explain

(continued)

FIGURE 12.2 (continued)

Accident type

[ ] overexertion/strain   [ ] caught in/between   [ ] slip/fall   [ ] struck by/against   [ ] exposed to

[ ] motor vehicle   [ ] contact with/by   [ ] other

Explain:

Injury type

[ ] bruise   [ ] burn (heat)   [ ] burn (chemical)   [ ] cut   [ ] crush   [ ] strain

[ ] twist   [ ] lift   [ ] electric shock   [ ] inhalation   [ ] occupational illness

[ ] rash   [ ] other

Explain:

Part of body injured   *[ ] left*   *[ ] right*

[ ] head   [ ] face   [ ] eye   [ ] ear   [ ] neck   [ ] chest

[ ] lungs   [ ] abdomen   [ ] groin   [ ] back-upper   [ ] back-middle   [ ] back-lower

[ ] buttock   [ ] shoulder   [ ] arm   [ ] wrist   [ ] hand   [ ] finger: th 2 3 4 5

[ ] leg   [ ] knee   [ ] ankle   [ ] foot   [ ] toe: big 2 3 4 5   [ ] other

Explain:

Suggested corrective action

[ ] review procedures   [ ] protective equipment   [ ] repair equipment   [ ] develop procedure

[ ] re-instruction of staff

Explain:

name & address of hospital or clinic _____

_____

_____

name of attending doctor _____ estimated time off work _____

name of family physician _____

address _____

date & hour last worked _____ Work hours: from _____ to _____

shift information: [ ] Day   [ ] Afternoon   [ ] Midnight

hours worked: from: _____ to: _____   days/week: _____

provide average gross earnings _____ [ ] hourly   [ ] daily _____

Additional information

_____

_____

_____

_____

_____

Diagram of accident

Employee's signature _____ Date _____

Supervisor's signature _____ Date _____

MAKE COPIES AND SEND TO:

[ ] Manager, Loss Control (original)   *[ ] Human Resources*   *[ ] Department*

FIGURE 12.3

Physician's Report

INJURY/ILLNESS ASSESSMENT FORM
to accompany employee to physician

For use in on-duty instances of sickness or injury to determine the rehabilitation duties to which an employee can return in the workplace as presented in Bill 162 of the Workers' Compensation Act.

To be completed by an Employee's Supervisor (please print)

A. Personal Data   Date:_____

Employee's Name: _____   *Signature:* _____

Job Title: _____   *SIN No.:* _____

Date of illness or injury on duty: _____   *Date of birth:* _____

Date absence commenced: _____   *Health No.:* _____

Nature of injury: _____

Supervisor's Name: _____   *Department:* _____   *Telephone:* _____

To be completed by Physician (please print)

B. Assessment of fitness to work

1. [ ] Employee is fit to return to regular work.

2. [ ] Employee is fit to return to modified work—with restrictions as indicated in C & D (reverse).

    Indicate number of hours to be worked and on what basis?

    [_____] hours   [ ] daily   [ ] weekly

    Estimate date of return to modified work:_____

3. [ ] Not fit for work at this time.

    Employee to return for medical reassessment on (yyyy mm dd) _____

See reverse side for Physical Evaluation to be completed by the Physician

Please return this completed form to the Manager, Loss Control via the Employee

To be completed by the treating Physician

C. Physical Evaluation

Step 1 *Location of problem*

    a) head: include vision, hearing, speech
    b) neck
    c) upper back, chest or upper abdomen
    d) lower back, lower abdomen or genitalia
    e) shoulder or upper arm
    f) elbow or lower arm
    g) wrist or hand
    h) hip or upper leg
    i) knee or lower leg
    j) ankle or foot
    k) systemic or internal organ

Right   Left

Step 2 *Please indicate restrictions for modified work*

1. Walking: [ ] only short distances   [ ] other
2. Standing, not more than: [ ] 15 minutes [ ] 30 minutes [ ] other
3. Sitting, no more than: [ ] 30 minutes [ ] 60 minutes [ ] 2 hours [ ] other
4. Bending and twisting, explain:
5. Lifting, floor to waist, not more than: [ ] 7 kg   [ ] 14 kg   [ ] 25 kg   [ ] other
6. Lifting, waist to head, not more than: [ ] 7 kg   [ ] 14 kg   [ ] 25 kg   [ ] other
7. Carrying, not more than: [ ] 7 kg   [ ] 14 kg   [ ] 25 kg   [ ] other
8. Climbing stairs: [ ] no stair climbing   [ ] 2 or 3 steps only   [ ] only short flight
9. Climbing ladder: [ ] no climbing   [ ] 2 or 3 steps only   [ ] 4 or 6 steps only
10. Manual dexterity, not able to: [ ] type   [ ] sort   [ ] other
11. Pushing and pulling trolley, not more than: [ ] 16 kg   [ ] 25 kg   [ ] other
12. Can operate motorized equipment: [ ] any vehicle [ ] forklifts [ ] not recommended
13. Vision, potential safety hazard   [ ] yes   [ ] no   [ ] other
14. Other comments (explain)

D. Treatment

1. Is the employee's prescribed treatment likely to impair performance or safety?   [ ] yes   [ ] no
2. Is the employee referred to: [ ] physiotherapy   Date commenced:_____
                             [ ] occupational therapy   Duration:_____

Physician's Name: _____   Telephone: _____

Address: _____

Date: _____   Signature: _____

FIGURE 12.4

Witness Report

Accident/Incident Witness Statement

Injured employee: _____   Date of injury: _____

Witness name: _____

Does the witness have knowledge of the accident or injury?   [ ] yes   [ ] no

Did the witness see the injury happen?   [ ] yes   [ ] no

If yes to either of the above, please explain below:

Knowledge of injury: Explain what you know about the injury/accident (e.g., what type of work was being done at the time of the injury/accident, what happened to cause the injury/accident, how seriously was the injured employee hurt).

_____

_____

_____

_____

What witness actually saw: Please identify what you saw before the injury/accident, during the injury/accident, and immediately after the injury/accident.

_____

_____

_____

_____

Give your **opinion** as to how this injury/accident could have been prevented.

_____

_____

_____

_____

Witness signature: _____   Date: _____

Domino Theory

Every event—accident or disaster—comprises a series of happenings that result in some negative condition. The **domino theory,** developed by H. W. Heinrich, is based on a set of five dominos labelled as follows:[3]

1. *Background:* a lack of control over the management function (planning, organizing, leading, and controlling)
2. *Personal defects:* personal factors such as physical or mental problems, and job factors such as normal wear and tear of equipment
3. *Unsafe acts and conditions:* (described earlier)
4. *Accident:* a series of undesired events with release of energies that can cause harm
5. *Injury:* the most undesired result (e.g., trauma or property damage)

Although there are other models, such as those dealing with the release of energy,[4] and with the theory of multiple factors,[5] the domino model is the easiest to illustrate. The domino theory asserts that if any one of the domino categories does not happen, then the injury probably will not occur (see Figure 12.5). For example, if a worker trying to make a production quota (background) was wearing loose clothing (personal defects or unsafe conditions) and operated a machine at unsafe speeds (unsafe act), then an accident or injury would be more likely to occur. However, if the worker were to wear well-fitting clothes or operate the machine at the proper speed (removal of domino number 2 or 3), then the risk of an accident occurring would be greatly reduced.

The Swiss Cheese Model

J. Reason presented an updated version of the domino model that is often depicted as series of dominoes with holes in them.[6] In this view, an accident results when the holes line up (i.e., there are failures at multiple levels).

Occupational Health and Safety Today 12.2

Accident Analysis in the Canadian Forces

The Canadian Forces through the Director General Safety advocates the analysis of accidents as a means of preventing their recurrence. Their focus is on the identification of the root causes of accidents by assembling, categorizing, and analyzing all relevant data.

Source: Ministry of National Defence, "General safety program manuals, form CF 663 completion and coding manual: Chapter 2, accident analysis." Retrieved from http://www.vcds.forces.gc.ca/dsafeg/pubs/vol2/2ch02_e.asp, October 12, 2004.

Figure 12.5

Heinrich's Domino Model

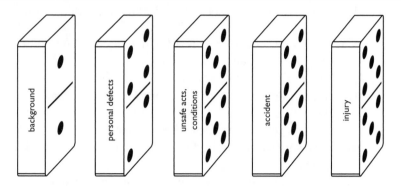

a) five factors in accident sequence

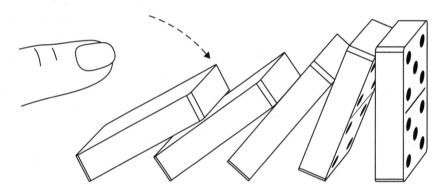

b) injury caused by action of preceding factors

c) removal of a factor may prevent the accident from occurring

Reason's model focuses on the series of events that must occur for an accident to occur. His model emphasizes that unsafe acts cannot be viewed in isolation; they are a product of the organizational culture, the level of supervision, and a variety of other contextual factors. It follows that accident analysis then focuses on identifying these factors to "plug the holes" in the Swiss cheese.

Reason's accident causation model specifies four levels of defence:

1. Organizational influences
2. Local working conditions
3. Unsafe acts
4. Defences, barriers, and safeguards

For example, an organization with a poor safety culture may not have a high accident rate if they have well-developed safe working procedures or safety-conscious supervisors. Similarly, committing an unsafe act may not result in an accident if appropriate safeguards are in place. It is only when organizational influences and local working conditions allow for an unsafe act and there are no safeguards against such an act that an accident results.

Normal Accidents

The theory of **normal accidents**,[7] particularly in **high-reliability organizations** (e.g., chemical plants, nuclear plants),[8] suggests that accidents result from the interactive complexities in the technological system. That is, no single event causes an accident, and the search for a single discrete cause, analogous to a single perpetrator, might well be fruitless in such an environment. The futility of the endeavour may be difficult to recognize, given the common tendency to make sense out of organizational events. As one researcher notes, "people who know the outcome of a complex prior history of tangled, indeterminate events remember that history as being much more determinant, leading 'inevitably' to the outcome they already knew."[9]

normal accidents

the theory that accidents are expected outcomes of interactive complexities

high-reliability organizations

organizations in hazardous industries that maintain a high safety record over time

Summary

Accident investigation is a very important part of an OH&S program. The reasons for conducting an investigation are primarily to identify direct and contributing causes, and to ensure that the accident does not recur. Timing and severity are the important variables in investigations. The types of information collected can be grouped under human factors, situational factors, and environmental factors. The investigative methods include observations or walkthroughs, interviews, and reenactments, all of which are complemented by investigative tools such as cameras and computers. Records also supply information that might be important in determining causes. The reporting and analysis of information collected is the last step in accident investigation.

Key Terms

cognitive interviewing, p. 315
domino theory, p. 327
high-reliability organizations,
   p. 329

normal accidents, p. 329
RAC program, p. 308
reenactment, p. 314
walkthrough, p. 313

Weblinks

Canadian Centre for Occupational Health and Safety, "What is an accident and why should it be investigated?"
http://www.ccohs.ca/oshanswers/hsprograms/investig.html (p. 308)

WorkSafe Saskatchewan, "Accident investigations,"
http://www.worksafesask.ca/topics/essentials/accident_inv.html?noframe (p. 309)

RPC Icons

RPC 12.1 Responds to serious injury or fatality in the workplace.

- program and policy development
- investigation procedures

TASK & KNOWLEDGE REQUIREMENTS
- relevant legislative requirements
- first aid training and emergency response equipment
- relevant legislative bodies
- pension and insurance benefits/policies
- common and statutory law (e.g., employment standard: labour relations
- Worker Protection (including health and safety and Workers' Compensation)
- Occupational health and safety legislation (e.g., Occupational Health and Safety Act of Ontario, Workplace Safety & Insurance Act—Bill 99, Workplace Hazardous Materials Information System, Transportation of Dangerous Goods legislation, environmental legislation, smoking in the workplace legislation, civil rights legislation)
- hazard identification and control
- accident investigation procedures
- emergency preparedness procedures

RPC 12.2 Analyses risk to the health and safety of employees and determines appropriate preventative measures, including training, provision of required safety equipment, and administrative practices.

- relevant legislation
- nature of the business and physical work environment

- hazard recognition
- workplace inspection techniques
- safety programs, equipment, and emergency procedures
- ergonomics
- functions of the JHSC
- training and development/presentation techniques
- industry best practices
- relevant technical terminology
- the collective agreement
- services and equipment available in the community
- Worker Protection (including health and safety and Workers' Compensation)
- training and development program design and administration

TASK & KNOWLEDGE REQUIREMENTS
- Occupational health and safety legislation (e.g., Occupational Health and Safety Act of Ontario, Workplace Safety & Insurance Act—Bill 99, Workplace Hazardous Materials Information System, Transportation of Dangerous Goods legislation, environmental legislation, smoking in the workplace legislation, civil rights legislation)
- hazard identification and control
- emergency preparedness procedures
- management techniques for OH&S Programs
- types of employee assistance and wellness programs

RPC 12.3 Establishes effective programs for accident prevention, incident investigation, inspections, fire and emergency response, and required training.
- relevant legislation
- workplace inspection and accident investigation techniques
- nature of the business and physical work environment
- potential risks and hazards in the workplace
- emergency response planning
- community emergency response services
- training and development
- industry best practices
- Worker Protection (including health and safety and Workers' Compensation)
- training and development program design and administration
- hazard identification and control
- accident investigation procedures
- emergency preparedness procedures
- management techniques for OH&S Programs

RPC 12.4 Ensures due diligence and strict liability requirements are met, e.g. records are kept and formal procedures established.
- relevant legislation and common law
- company policies and procedures

- industry best practices
- program and policy development
- training and development techniques
- risk analysis
- common and statutory law (e.g., employment standard: labour relations)
- Worker Protection (including health and safety and Workers' Compensation)
- theories and practices for protection of individuals and groups

TASK & KNOWLEDGE REQUIREMENTS
- Occupational health and safety legislation (e.g., Occupational Health and Safety Act of Ontario, Workplace Safety & Insurance Act—Bill 99, Workplace Hazardous Materials Information System, Transportation of Dangerous Goods legislation, environmental legislation, smoking in the workplace legislation, civil rights legislation)
- management techniques for OH&S Programs

Discussion Questions

1. What are the three factors that should be considered as potential contributors to any accident?
2. Describe the methods that can be used in accident investigation.
3. What tools can assist the accident investigator?
4. What steps should be taken to properly reenact an accident?
5. Give an example of how human, environmental, and situational factors can combine to result in an accident.
6. Given our focus on analyzing and understanding accident causation, it is worth noting that some safety professionals now refuse to use the term "accident." They claim that doing so implies that accidents are random, unforeseeable events, whereas we know that most accidents result from a foreseeable series of events. What are the merits (pros and cons) of this position? Do "accidents happen" or are all accidents preventable?
7. Some safety professionals now talk about the notion of "system risk." In essence they suggest that accidents or incidents do not result from single causes. Rather, they suggest that accidents are the result of multiple events working together. How might the factors identified in this chapter interact to result in an accident?

Using the Internet

1. Search news media and online reports to find accounts of workplace accidents. For at least one such report, try to identify the human, situational, and environmental factors contributing to the accident.

Exercise

1. Many accident investigations, such as traffic and airline accident investigations, conclude that "human error" was the principle cause. We know that situational and environmental factors also play a role. Why do we emphasize the role of humans in accident causation? Does this result in an underemphasis of these other factors?

Case 1: Accident Investigation

You are the president and largest stockholder of an original equipment manufacturer (OEM) that employs 300 workers. You do not have a safety specialist, but you do take a personal interest in accident prevention. Recently, you assigned general responsibility for safety to the day-shift superintendents as a minor part of their regular duties.

The plant has never been thoroughly analyzed for hazards, and you are aware that the operation is not as safe as it could be. Many of the operations require considerable ongoing maintenance by the workers to prevent accidents. Since the business has only been breaking even for several years, you have delayed making any improvements to the plant and equipment. You and the superintendents have concentrated your efforts on preventing unsafe acts by the employees. An elaborate system of worker reminders, such as posters and instruction by supervisors, has been used to make the workforce safety conscious.

For the last few years, your performance with respect to medical aid and lost-time injuries has been average for your WCB rate group. Your company has escaped any lost-time injuries for the last two years, including the current year to date. The continuation of that record has become an important goal. Signs in the plant indicate the number of days that have passed without a lost-time injury. Today at 15:30 hours, a container of nearly red-hot, upper-control-arm forgings was overturned. The hot forgings fell on a worker who was helping the drop forge machine operator. The worker suffered third-degree burns over 20% of his body. Although he is expected to recover, the worker will lose most of his right arm, right ear, and sight in his right eye. Describe the investigative methods and tools you would use to investigate this accident.

Case 2: Office Accident

Cathy Calvin is the newly appointed coordinator of health and safety for the local school board. She has just been told of an accident experienced by an employee in the administrative office. It seems that two employees were trying to move a full filing cabinet from one corner of the office to another. The cabinet tipped, crushing the foot of one of the employees. The office staff applied first aid and rushed the injured employee to the hospital. The employee will be off work for at least two weeks. Board policy requires a full investigation of any lost-time injury. As a relative newcomer to the health and safety role, Cathy has never conducted an accident investigation before. Can you help Cathy design an appropriate strategy for approaching the investigation?

Endnotes

1. Laing, P. (Ed.). (1992). *Accident prevention manual for business and industry: administration and programs* (10th ed.). Washington, D.C.: National Safety Council.
2. Ryan, T. (1991). Accident investigations: II group investigations. In F. Briggs (Ed.), *Guide to health and safety management*. Don Mills, Ont.: Southam Business Publications.
3. Heinrich, H. W. (1936). *Industrial accident prevention*. New York: McGraw-Hill.
4. Haddon, W., Jr. (1968). The changing approach to epidemiology, prevention and amelioration of trauma: The transition to approaches etiological rather than descriptively based. *American Journal of Public Health, 58*, 8.
5. Gross, V. L. (1972, August). System safety in rapid rail transit. *ASSE Journal*.
6. Reason, J. (1990). *Human error*. Cambridge, UK: University of Cambridge Press.
7. Perrow, C. (1984). *Normal accidents: Living with high-risk technologies*. NY: Basic Books; and Perrow, C. (1994). Accidents in high risk systems. *Technological Studies, 1*, 1–20.
8. Roberts, K. (1989). Some characteristics of high reliability organizations. *Organization Science, 2*, 160–176; and Weick, K. E., Sutcliffe, K. M., & Obstfeld, D. (1999). Organizing for high reliability: Processes of collective mindfulness. *Research in Organizational Behavior, 21*, 81–123.
9. Weick, K. (1995). *Sensemaking in organizations*. Thousand Oaks, Calif.: Sage Publications.

Chapter 13

Workplace Wellness: Work-Family and Health-Promotion Programs

Chapter Learning Objectives

After reading this chapter, you should be able to

- discuss the concept of healthy workplaces
- describe the goals of workplace health-promotion and family-friendly programs
- discuss the various types of workplace health-promotion and family-friendly programs
- comment on the effectiveness of various types of workplace health-promotion and family-friendly programs
- identify variables critical to the success of workplace health-promotion and family-friendly programs
- discuss the importance of systematic evaluation of workplace health-promotion and family-friendly policies

WELLNESS PROGRAMS AT DOFASCO INC.

Dofasco Inc., headquartered in Hamilton, Ontario, is Canada's second-largest producer of steel and one of the most profitable steelmakers in North America. The familiar organizational slogan "Our product is steel. Our strength is people" is a fitting motto as Dofasco's business strategy emphasizes employee engagement and well-being. The company has a well-articulated, formal health and safety policy. One means by which Dofasco promotes employee well-being is the Lifestyle Resource Group. With employee representation from all areas of the company, its mandate is to develop and implement health and wellness programs.

Dofasco Inc. provides numerous family-friendly and health-focused options for its 7,300 employees. The list of offerings includes a 100-acre recreation and learning centre (which houses baseball, hockey, soccer, tennis, golf, and other sport and training facilities) that is available to all employees and their families. They also sponsor health-promotion initiatives such as on-site subsidized Weight Watchers meetings, smoking-cessation programs, first-aid training, a comprehensive employee assistance program, health assessments (such as hypertension screening), and on-site and off-site fitness facilities. The company also provides Camp Steelaway, a summer camp program for children of employees.

What prompted this focus on employee health? Employee health and safety have long been valued by Dofasco. For instance, its large recreation facility has been in operation for more than 60 years. However, a slow market and increased competition in the late 1980s found Dofasco in financial trouble through the early 1990s. At that point, the company adopted a new business strategy focused on producing a higher quality product. Part of the implementation of this strategy linked the success of the company to the success of individual employees. Along with this emphasis on the employee came a focus on their well-being and health. Following a needs assessment (or health audit) in the early 1990s, Dofasco launched its Healthy Lifestyles programs. Today, the health and safety of employees is primary among Dofasco's list of core values.

Dofasco's high investment in employees has been a success. There is a high degree of program participation and attendance among employees. From a financial perspective there has been a marked reduction in lost-time injuries, Workers' Compensation premiums, and incidence of non-work-related injuries since the health programs were initiated. Others are recognizing Dofasco's success. The company

Given that people spend a substantial portion of their time at work, most would agree that active attempts should be made to ensure that the work environment is healthy and safe. Throughout the 1990s, the concept of wellness at work emerged as an occupational health concern, adding to the more traditional organizational health concern of employee safety. Some estimate that health-related programs are evident in as many as 90% of mid-sized companies in the United States.[1] The major motivators of this trend include a desire to reduce rising health care costs, improve productivity, and build a supportive organizational culture.

Workplace wellness initiatives are also present in Canadian companies. Recent estimates indicate that 64% of Canadian companies offer some form of wellness program.[2] Health-promotion programs may have been slower to develop in Canadian companies because of our public health care system. Because Canadian companies assume less of the cost for illness, traditionally there has been less of a financial impetus for them to develop employee health initiatives. However, the focus on health at work is now rapidly growing in Canada. For instance, Health Canada, in partnership with the National Quality Institute, has created the well-publicized healthy workplace awards, the healthy workplace week, and other programs to help organizations address psychosocial and environmental factors that affect employee health.

 13.1

Many experts believe that health is more than just the absence of illness and that an active attempt to improve health will result in individuals "feeling good" as opposed to "not feeling bad"; this notion is sometimes referred to as "positive health." Indeed the World Health Organization defines health not simply as the absence of illness or disease, but rather as an overall state of mental, physical, and social well-being.

It makes sense to focus on health at work. Employed adults spend a great deal of time in the workplace, so the worksite provides a convenient means of reaching many adults. Additionally, the health of employees affects their performance at work; therefore, companies should be interested in promoting worker health. In this chapter we will consider two

FIGURE 13.1

A Flow Chart of Workplace Well-Being Initiatives

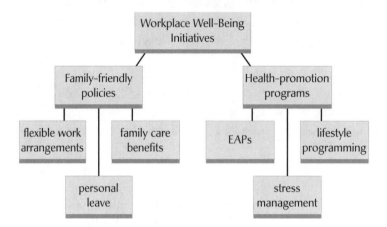

RPC 13.1

RPC 13.2

RPC 13.3

RPC 13.4

RPC 13.5

broad categories of initiatives that companies can use to promote well-being at work, namely work-family-friendly policies and health-promotion programs (see Figure 13.1).

Work-Family Conflict: Family-Friendly Policies in the Workplace

Work and family are two of the most central elements of many people lives. Recent demographic shifts, such as those outlined in Occupational Health and Safety Today 13.1, have increased the extent to which responsibilities to work and to family interfere with each other. For instance, the increased proportion of the workforce who also have childcare demands and the prevalence of dual-income families means that working parents will sometimes be torn between work demands and childcare responsibilities. For example, a child who is home sick from school may prompt a working parent to miss work to care for the child. Researchers are interested in the factors that contribute to **work-family conflict**, the outcomes of this type of conflict, and how organizations can help employees meet their multiple work and family roles.

Organizational experts define work-family conflict as a form of interrole conflict. That is, it is a type of conflict in which the responsibilities of two separate roles are incompatible in some respect. In other words, pressures experienced in the work and family domains are in opposition.[3] Participation in one role is made more difficult by virtue of participation in the other role.

Some experts in this area further distinguish between two categories of work-family conflict.[4] They note that work-family conflict is bi-directional: work might interfere with a person's ability to meet family demands and

work-family conflict

a type of interrole conflict in which the role pressures experienced in the work and family domains are incompatible

Occupational Health and Safety Today 13.1

Work-Life Balance: Some Canadian Statistics

Balancing multiple commitments, including work and family, is a reality for Canadians. Here are some recently compiled Canadian statistics on family, work, and well-being.

1. The number of women in the workforce has increased. Women currently account for 46% of the workforce, compared with 37% in 1976. In fact, in 1999, 61% of Canadian women with a child under the age of three worked (relative to only 28% in 1976).
2. Both men and women in the Canadian labour force have childcare demands. Statistics from the mid-1990s suggest that nearly half of working Canadians have children living in the home. Furthermore, 15% of these individuals also care for elderly family members.
3. Dual-earner families are increasingly common. Most Canadian families with two parents and children at home saw both parents working for pay (62% in 1997). Many families report that two incomes are needed to maintain a family's standard of living.
4. The amount of shift work is increasing. Data from the mid-1990s suggest that 32% of the labour force works a nonday or rotating shift.
5. Almost half of all Canadian children between the ages of one and five were in nonparental care. About one-third of these children are cared for by more than one childcare provider, sometimes at different locations. The financial burden of childcare is high. Data from the late 1990s note that the average monthly cost for centre care ranged from $455 to $531, depending on the age of the child.
6. Eldercare responsibilities are growing for Canadian employees. One-quarter of Canadian employees report that they provide care or support for an elderly person.
7. Work-family conflict is rising. In 2000, 58% of employees who participated in a national survey indicated that they had high levels of work-family conflict. The incidence of work-family conflict was highest among professionals and managers.
8. Work-family conflict has measurable negative effects on organizations and is associated with increased absenteeism and negative work-related attitudes, such as reduced job satisfaction and lower commitment to the employing organization.
9. Family-friendly workplace policies are on the rise in Canadian organizations. A recent survey of Canadian employers found that 88% offered flextime, 50% made provisions for telework, and 63% offered family-responsibility leave. However, other data suggest that there is limited access to flexible work arrangements even in organizations that offer this benefit and that the provision of childcare benefits in Canadian workplaces is low, with only 15% of companies indicating that they provided on-site or near-site daycares.

Source: Johnson, K. L., Lero, D. S., & Rooney, J. A. (2001). *Work-life compendium 2001: 150 Canadian statistics on work, family and well-being*. Guelph, ON: Centre for Families, Work, and Well-Being.

---

family responsibilities can interfere with an individual's ability to keep pace with work demands. These two categories have been labelled **work to family conflict** and **family to work conflict**, respectively.

Causes of Work-Family Conflict

Several elements of work and family roles contribute to work-family conflict. One such element is the amount of time a person spends in each role, or their **behavioural involvement** in the role. Generally, the more time dedicated to one role means the less time available to spend in the other role. Certainly,

work to family conflict

a form of work-family conflict in which work demands interfere with the fulfillment of family responsibilities

family to work conflict

a form of work-family conflict in which family demands interfere with the fulfillment of work responsibilities

behavioural involvement

the amount of time a person spends in a particular role

psychological involvement

the degree to which a person identifies with a particular role and sees the role as a central component of his or her self-concept

increased time devoted to work is associated with increased incidence of work to family conflict. Similarly, the more time a person spends on family pursuits and responsibilities in the home, the more likely that individual is to experience family to work conflict.[5]

A person's **psychological involvement** in their work and family roles has also been implicated as a predictor of work-family conflict. Psychological involvement reflects the degree to which a person identifies with a particular role and sees the role as a central component of his or her self-concept. For example, a woman who considers her status as a mother to be the defining feature in her life has a high degree of psychological involvement in her mother role. A high degree of involvement in one role can cause it to conflict with other responsibilities.

Stress in either the work or the family role is also associated with work-family conflict. In particular, the experience of family-related stress, such as many family demands or dissatisfaction with family life, is associated with family to work conflict. Similarly, the experience of work-related stress, such as many work demands or job dissatisfaction, is associated with work to family conflict.[6]

Outcomes of Work-Family Conflict

Both work to family and family to work conflict are associated with negative consequences. Interestingly, the outcomes tend to be in the opposite domain as the cause of the conflict. That is, work to family conflict tends to affect family-related outcomes and family to work conflict affects work-related outcomes. For instance, family to work conflict is linked with decreased work performance and absenteeism from work. Conversely, work to family conflict is associated with reduced performance in the family role and absences from family events.[7]

Work-family conflict is also associated with some negative health outcomes. A high degree of work-family conflict, be it work to family or family to work, contributes to perceived stress, lowered physical health, and increased alcohol use. Thus, it is important that individuals and organizations aim to reduce the extent to which they or their employees experience this type of interrole conflict.[8] In the following sections we will consider some of the family-friendly policies that organizations have implemented in an effort to reduce the experience of work-family conflict and in turn avoid the resulting negative outcomes. Such policies are assuming greater importance as companies recognize that a growing number of employees have both childcare and eldercare (i.e., caring for elderly relatives) responsibilities, in addition to their work responsibilities. As such, the existence of these policies helps organizations in recruiting and retaining employees. For the most part, family-friendly policies attempt to help employees balance their work and family responsibilities. Given that the focus of this chapter is workplace policies and programs, we emphasize organizational, rather than individual, efforts to reduce work-family conflict. We will consider three broad categories of family-friendly programs: flexible work arrangements, work-leave systems, and family-friendly employee benefits.

Family-Friendly Policies

Flexible Work Arrangements

Flexible work arrangements (**FWAs**) are modifications to the traditional work schedule. There are two basic versions of FWAs. First, some programs are designed to help mitigate work-family conflict by reducing the amount of *time* spent in the workplace. An example of this type of FWA is the **compressed workweek**. Under this option, employees can choose to work full-time hours in fewer days, for instance 40 hours in four days rather than five.

The compressed work schedule can help employees reduce work-family conflict by allowing longer stretches of time to spend at home and saving time spent in commuting to and from the workplace. Job sharing and job splitting programs also fall under this category of FWA. In **job sharing** programs two employees share the responsibilities of a single position. In this case, the two employees have overlapping duties and must be sure to communicate with each other about all aspects of the work. In **job splitting,** two employees may split job responsibilities such that they each take sole responsibility for various components of the job. Job sharing and job splitting arrangements typically benefit employees who want to work part-time hours. Job sharing and splitting options reduce the amount of time that an employee must spend on work-related tasks and likely lead to a reduction in work-role overload. As such, these types of arrangements may reduce the incidence of work-family conflict.

The second large category consists of FWA programs designed to increase the amount of *control* individuals have over their work schedule. A common example of this type of arrangement is **flextime**. In flextime schedules employees are permitted to have variable start and finish times to their workday. For instance, one employee at a company offering flextime may choose to work from 7 a.m. to 3 p.m. Another employee may opt to start work at 10 a.m. and work until 6 p.m. In this case, during several hours of the day all employees are at work and group or team-related matters can be dealt with. However, the degree of control over start and finish times can help employees better manage their work and family demands. For instance, Edward, a working father who worries about his children being home alone after school, prefers to start early and finish at 3 p.m. so that he can supervise his children after school or help them get to and from after-school activities.

Telecommuting is a second exemplar of this category of FWA. Telecommuting (also known as telework or work at home) programs allow employees to complete their work assignments away from the office. The employee uses telecommunications technology such as the Internet and phone to keep in touch with the worksite. Such an option can help some employees better blend their work and family responsibilities. For instance, a person who works from home can delay the start of the workday until children leave for school and then immediately start working without losing time to things like commuting to and from work. Telework may also be helpful for individuals who have elders living in their homes, as they are able to be at home in case there is an emergency.

flexible work arrangements (FWAs)
family-friendly policies that involve modifications to the traditional work schedule

compressed workweek
flexible work arrangement in which employees work full-time hours in fewer days per week

job sharing
flexible work arrangement in which two employees share the responsibilities of a single position

job splitting
flexible work arrangement in which two employees divide the responsibilities of a single position

flextime
flexible work arrangement that permits employees to have variable start and finish times to their workday

telecommuting
flexible work arrangement in which an employee regularly makes use of telecommunications technology to complete work assignments away from the office, usually at home

Personal Leave Systems

Another broad category of family-friendly policies involves the provision of leave time to employees. Some examples include maternity leave, parental leave, personal days, family leave, and sick leave. These leave programs are designed to help employees meet their family demands, thereby reducing the occurrence of family to work conflict. Consider an employee who has a chronically ill child. This individual may use family leave and personal days to accompany the child on doctor's visits and care for the child. The existence of such a leave program should reduce the incidence of unexcused absenteeism and tardiness. Maternity leave programs allow new mothers to take paid time away from work shortly before and for some time after the birth of a child. Parental leave programs permit new mothers and fathers to take a leave from work responsibilities when a child is born or placed with them through an adoption. In Canada, the federal government provides a one-year maternity and parental leave program that permits an individual to collect a portion of his or her regular earnings via the Employment Insurance program. Some companies have chosen to provide additional parental benefits that top up the amount the parent earns while on leave. For instance, a company may continue to pay employees 95% of their regular earnings while they are on leave. Employment Insurance pays an employee 55% of their insurable earning (up to a limit of $413 per week).

Leave-related benefits aim to reduce the amount of work-family conflict experienced by employees. Consider the case of a new parent: Having to return to work shortly after the birth of a child likely contributes to a high degree of work-family conflict. The new parent is adjusting to newly increased family demands, and these demands can often interfere with work performance. The availability of company-sponsored financial benefits for parental leave also reduces the considerable financial strain that might otherwise prompt an individual to return to work earlier than initially planned.

Family-Care Benefits

The final category of family-friendly policies that we will discuss in this chapter is family-care benefit programs. The provision of daycare and elder-care benefits are two initiatives that fall under this category. Employers can help their employees who have children reduce their experience of work-family conflict by supporting daycare programs. This might involve an on-site daycare that reduces the stress associated with dropping children off at various locations before getting into work. Additionally, on-site daycares may reduce some of the stress associated with having children in nonparental care. If the daycare is at the work location, the working parent knows that he or she is nearby in case of an emergency. Additionally, the parent can drop in to see the child while at work. They may also have increased trust in the daycare provider, as it is a division of their own workplace. In some cases, employers who cannot provide an on-site daycare can arrange to have daycare facilities near the worksite.

Another option under this category of family-friendly programs is the provision of subsidized dependant care. In this case, organizations might provide employees with money to help cover the cost of eldercare or childcare or enroll elders or children in various programs. For instance, an employee who cares for an elderly parent might use this budget to enroll the parent in a seniors' program. As another example, consider the organization that sponsors summer camps for children of employees. In each case, we can see how these programs could reduce worries about dependant-care responsibilities.

Family-Friendly Policies: An Evaluation

It appears that family-friendly policies are increasingly common on the Canadian organizational landscape. A recent survey conducted by the Conference Board of Canada suggests that Canadian employers are acknowledging the negative consequences of work-family conflict. That same survey revealed that the percentage of employers who offer flextime increased from 49% in 1989 to 88% in 1999. Similar increases were seen for other family-friendly work options. In 1999, 48% of employers indicated they offered compressed workweeks, 52% provided job sharing options, 50% made provisions for telework, and 63% offered family-responsibility leave. Data from the United States suggest a similar increase in the availability of family-friendly options. In the United States, telework increased throughout the 1990s, with 16 million workers now engaged in this work arrangement.[9]

Despite their growing availability, little systematic research has been conducted on the effectiveness of the family-friendly policies described in this chapter. As such, the extent to which these programs actually reduce work-family conflict and their impact on organizational functioning are unknown. Certainly, anecdotal evidence attesting to their effectiveness in reducing work-family conflict is readily available. However, the available research provides mixed results as to their actual impact on work-family conflict.[10] Some studies suggest that family-friendly policies do indeed reduce the existence of work-family conflict.[11] Flextime has been associated with an increase in the extent to which people feel they are in control of their work and family lives.[12] Other studies report that family-friendly policies do not affect the occurrence of work-family conflict.[13] One interesting study found that the availability of family-friendly policies reduced the extent to which work interfered with family responsibilities but had no impact on family to work conflict.[14]

Researchers have also considered the impact of family-friendly policies on organizational outcomes. Again, there are mixed results for the effectiveness of family-friendly initiatives. For instance, one study showed that flextime reduced absenteeism but not turnover.[15] It appears that flexible work options, such as flextime and telecommuting, have a positive impact on job satisfaction.[16] However, the impact of these policies on productivity is uncertain. Some studies report that flexible arrangements contribute to improved productivity and others report no significant effects.[17]

RPC 13.1

RPC 13.2

RPC 13.3

RPC 13.4

RPC 13.5

RPC 13.6

RPC 13.7

RPC 13.8

Additional research on the organizational and individual impact of work-family policies is certainly warranted. This research should specifically consider the type of work-family policy and the nature of the conflict (i.e., work to family versus family to work).[18] It should also ask questions about why companies choose to implement the policies they do.[19] At present little research is available on the extent to which employers consider work-family policies to be strategic human resource initiatives, even though the existence of these programs may be important in the recruitment and retention of high-quality employees.[20]

Future studies should make a distinction between the availability of family-friendly policies and the extent to which employees actually use them. Employer and employee surveys paint a different picture regarding the availability of flexible work arrangements.[21] In some cases, employers who do have family-friendly options make those programs available to a select group of employees—for instance, people in a particular job classification. Other data suggest that in some organizations, employees choose not to use family-friendly policies such as flextime because they fear it will negatively affect their career progress. As such, the formal existence of a policy does not guarantee its use. In reality, the culture of the organization shapes the extent to which employees are willing to use work-family policies.

One recent report indicated that the characteristics of work groups affected whether employees opted to use FWAs.[22] Individuals who worked in groups that were more supportive made greater use of these options. This study stresses the importance of organizational support for family-friendly initiatives. If employees fear that they will be looked down on or sustain damage to their careers, they may choose not to take advantage of the family-friendly programs that do exist.

Health-Promotion Programs

Wellness or health-promotion programming is the active attempt to improve employee well-being through worksite intervention. The rationale for such programming is that many health-related concerns can be prevented through lifestyle changes such as diet, exercise, and smoking cessation. Given that employed adults spend many hours in the workplace and that the health of employees affects organizational and individual functioning, the workplace provides a convenient and appropriate means of reaching many adults. As a result of these observations, an increasing number of workplaces have launched various types of health-promotion programs.

health promotion

a combination of diagnostic, educational, and behavioural modification activities designed to support the attainment and maintenance of positive health

Health-promotion efforts combine diagnostic, educational, and behavioural change initiatives with the goal of helping people attain and maintain positive health. An emerging concept in the realm of health promotion that is of particular interest for worksites is that of health and productivity management. Health and productivity management programs integrate health-promotion activities in a way that simultaneously increases employee well-being and decreases the health-related costs of the organization, such as absence from work and reduced work performance.[23] The history of such work-related health-promotion programs is found in early employee assistance plans (EAPs), and it is useful to review the emergence and structure of EAPs before addressing health-promotion programs (HPPs).

Employee Assistance Plans

Employee assistance plans (**EAPs**) provide counselling and assistance to members of an organization, generally helping individual employees control personal concerns, such as alcoholism, drug use, and stress, which may affect their performance at work.[24] The roots of EAPs date back to the nineteenth century and the social betterment movement. Initiatives included inexpensive housing, company-sponsored unions, sanitary working conditions, insurance, pension plans, banking, recreation, medical care, and education facilities. After the social betterment movement subsided in the 1920s and 1930s, personal counselling emerged. Management trained some shop workers to listen to workers' problems to reduce their interference with productivity. For example, in 1917, Macy's Department Store established a program to assist employees who were dealing with personal problems. By 1920, one-third of the 431 largest companies in the United States had a full-time welfare secretary whose major role was as a counsellor.[25]

In the 1940s the Occupational Alcohol Movement, which is generally acknowledged as the direct predecessor of the EAP, arose.[26] Alcoholism was recognized as a serious impediment to productivity, and these programs sought to assist workers troubled by this problem by offering alcohol-related and personal-problem counselling. The 1970s were a period of rapid

employee assistance plans (EAPs)

programs designed to help employees with problems that may interfere with worker productivity, including alcohol and other drug abuse, emotional or behavioural problems among family members, and financial or legal problems growth for EAPs. In the 1980s they expanded to include stress management. Today, EAP programs address all types of problems that may interfere with worker productivity, including alcohol and other drug abuse, emotional or behavioural problems among family members, and financial or legal problems.[27]

Currently, it is difficult to distinguish between EAPs and health-promotion programs, and health-promotion programs are now viewed as subsuming the earlier EAPs. The primary objectives of EAPs are to help employees address personal concerns and assist organizations in the identification and betterment of productivity concerns among employees.[28] Typically, health-promotion programs will include interventions aimed at stress management and lifestyle changes (e.g., diet, smoking cessation, and physical fitness). We will now turn our attention to each of these two classes of health-promotion initiatives.

Stress Management Programs

The goal of stress management programs is to educate workers about the causes and consequences of stress, and to teach relaxation and coping skills for managing physiological and psychological symptoms. The most common types of stress management programs are cognitive-behavioural skills training, progressive muscle relaxation and meditation, and programs designed to increase social support.[29]

Cognitive-Behavioural Skills Training

Cognitive-behavioural programs are developed under the framework of the cognitive model of stress, which posits that emotional responses to situations are largely determined by the way they are thought about and interpreted. The training helps people to think about events in new ways and to be aware of how they are viewing stressful events, and provides skills in learning to cope with stress. The goal is to alter both cognition of stressful events and behaviour toward them. For example, participants in stress-inoculation training might be given coping skills such as self-instruction training, cognitive restructuring, problem-solving training, and relaxation training. The training program itself makes use of such techniques as role-playing and classroom instruction.

Relaxation Training and Meditation

Relaxation training involves teaching individuals such things as progressive muscle relaxation and breathing exercises. If you have ever taken a class in yoga, martial arts, or even aerobics, you have probably experienced something similar to this. Someone may ask you to lie down on the floor, close your eyes, and focus your mind on your body and your muscles. Then, they may ask you to relax every muscle in your body, slowly working from the bottom up or top down. The purpose of this type of training is to provide people with skills to physically relax the body. Over time, individuals will learn to recognize the physical feelings associated with stress and to counteract these feelings by calling on the relaxation response. In doing so, they prevent stress leading to the type of strain reactions discussed earlier.

Just as relaxation training is focused on relaxing the physical body, the focus of meditation is on quieting the mind. There are numerous approaches to meditation and you are probably familiar with at least some of them. Meditation helps individuals withdraw from a stressful situation and reenergize through mental exercise. The most widely used form of meditation in the workplace involves sitting quietly for 20 minutes, repeating a single word on each exhalation.[30] Meditation practice appears to lead to positive physical and psychological outcomes in the workplace.[31]

Increasing Social Support

A different strategy to help reduce work-related stress is to provide a more supportive environment. One way of doing this is by training workers on how to seek social support and how to create a more supportive workplace. For example, caregiver-support programs are designed to assist people in dealing with the stresses of providing care for others. The goal of such programs is typically to increase social support and participation in work-related decisions. Caregiver-support programs are designed to teach employees the benefits of support systems, enhance their skills in mobilizing support, educate them about participatory problem-solving approaches, and show them how to build skills to implement these approaches in team meetings.

Effectiveness of Stress Management Training

Results are mixed on the effectiveness of stress management training programs. Some appear to be effective at reducing the experience of job-related stress, whereas others do not. For example, in one study on stress management training, participants were exposed to a variety of stress management techniques, including cognitive restructuring, positive self-talk, deep muscle relaxation, autogenic instructions, and imagery exercises.[32] The training program included nine hours of instruction over six sessions. The researchers found that those receiving training did not show a significant increase in learning or job satisfaction, or a significant decrease in blood pressure, somatic data, or anxiety in comparison with a control group. However, when a self-management module was included as part of the training, significant differences were found for all measures except job satisfaction. The self-management module included three hours of training in self-monitoring, specifying goals, evaluating behaviour against goals, and self-reinforcing. This study suggests that simply providing training is not sufficient to make a difference; participants must be provided with strategies to assist them in applying what they have learned. Interestingly, this is the same conclusion reached for safety programs in general—training alone is often insufficient to effect change.

Chapter 13: Workplace Wellness

Conversely, another study showed that stress management training was effective in reducing the interpersonal aspects of stress (anger inventory, use of emergency restraint, client abuse).[33] However, this program was custom designed with the needs of the users in mind and may be more effective than the typical "out of the can" stress management programs. Social support programs are also effective. Typically, such programs increase the amount of supportive feedback on the job, enhancing perceptions about the ability to handle disagreements and work overload, and improve work team climate.

Worksite Health Promotion

Worksite health-promotion programming can be classified into three categories: screening, education, and behavioural change. Many types of programs are being delivered in each of these various categories. The most common are those designed to affect an employee's health practices or physical lifestyle (e.g., exercise, eating habits, sleep patterns, weight control, alcohol use, smoking cessation, substance abuse). These efforts are often called lifestyle programming. It is generally thought that a healthy lifestyle will help to promote physical and mental health on the job. Some programs include activities designed to improve psychological aspects of an individual's lifestyle (e.g., social relations, intellectual activity, occupational conditions), but these programs are still the exception rather than the rule.

These types of programs may offer such things as on-site fitness facilities, or subsidies for private clubs, nutritional assessment and counselling, weight-control groups, and smoking-cessation programs. Typically, these opportunities are available on a voluntary basis and may be offered only to individuals at a certain level in the organization (e.g., membership in a health club for management employees). Although the organization may provide incentives for taking advantage of the program, it would have difficulty mandating that employees alter their lifestyle. Although it is possible to make safety training, or even stress-reduction training, mandatory, it would be difficult to insist that all employees quit smoking or have a perfect body mass index. Indeed, to the extent that addiction or obesity is considered a disability, doing so might violate human rights legislation. Rather than attempting to mandate such programs, organizations involved in workplace health promotion should develop cultures and environments that are highly supportive of healthful lifestyle practices.

Although health-promotion programs are diverse, many are secondary-level interventions designed to help individuals who are feeling stress and are at risk for illness. The typical components of worksite health promotion (WHP) include three steps:

Step 1: physical or psychological assessment
Step 2: counselling concerning findings and recommendations about personal health promotion
Step 3: referral to in-house or community-based resources

If we focus on WHPs that are more tertiary in nature, that is, those designed to help people who are currently experiencing symptoms or illness, such as alcohol and other substance abuse, hypertension, and psychological stress, the key components in such programs should include the following:

- The identification of currently symptomatic as well as high-risk individuals
- The appropriate referral or treatment of individuals
- Treatment directed at the symptom, delivered by the appropriate professionals
- Follow-up with the client to ensure the treatment was effective
- Evaluation of health improvement and cost efficacy

Components of an effective employer-sponsored health-promotion effort include employee education for health promotion or disease prevention, management training to raise awareness of occupational health issues and identification, EAP services, redesigned benefit programs to provide easy access to interventions, a comprehensive data-collection plan for use in program decision-making, the integration of corporate health-related services, and a greater attention to organizational health. We will now turn our attention to some specific categories of WHP programs. In particular, we will look at efforts that are focused on changing some aspect of an employee's lifestyle (i.e., lifestyle programming).

Smoking Cessation

One of the most popular worksite health-promotion interventions in recent years has been the implementation of smoking cessation programs. As worksites have increasingly banned smoking, either voluntarily or because of legislation, more and more employers saw the wisdom of offering employees assistance in quitting smoking. Moreover, research has consistently documented that smokers are absent approximately 40% more than nonsmokers, providing employers with an economic incentive to provide assistance with smoking cessation.[34] Some estimate the costs associated with smoking (i.e., those attributable to absenteeism, lost productivity, and increased insurance premiums) to be in the neighbourhood of $2,500 per year per employee.

Smoking cessation programs typically involve a combination of education, group support, counselling, and behavioural change techniques. Traditionally, the success rates of such programs have varied between 25% and 60%. More recently, pharmaceutical aids such as nicotine gum, the nicotine patch, and other medications have enhanced success rates. It is important to note that these aids do not replace traditional approaches. Rather, the greatest success seems to come from a combination of psychoeducational and pharmaceutical approaches to smoking cessation. The need for a comprehensive approach to smoking cessation within organizations is highlighted by the observation that organizations that provide subsidized cessation programs for employees may, at the same time, have cigarette machines in the workplace.

Hypertension Screening

hypertension
elevated blood pressure

Hypertension or high blood pressure has been called the "silent killer." Individuals can have hypertension for a long time without knowing it or without experiencing symptoms. Although it may seem relatively innocuous, hypertension is considered one of the major (and most easily controlled) risk factors in heart-related diseases. Workplace programs aimed at affecting hypertension vary widely but typically consist of four interrelated steps:

1. *Education:* Employees are alerted to the dangers of hypertension and the benefits associated with treatment.
2. *Screening:* Employees are screened using blood-pressure clinics in which participants have their blood pressure read by a medical professional.
3. *Referral:* Employees with elevated readings are referred to medical treatment.
4. *Follow-up:* Referred employees are followed up to verify the outcome of treatment and to monitor progress.

Worksite hypertension programs typically result in approximately 25% of participants being identified as hypertensive—about the same prevalence as in the general population. Outcome studies suggest that programs are very effective in bringing hypertension under control through diet and medication. Moreover, some evidence shows programs with more elements (e.g., those that include frequent monitoring and follow-up) are more effective than are simple screening or educational programs.

Nutrition and Weight Control

Nutrition programs in the workplace typically take one of two forms. First, educational programs are aimed at providing instruction or information on the selection of foods, the basics of meal planning, and so on. The posters in the cafeteria promoting *Canada's Food Guide* are an example of educational programming. The second type of activity is to actually change the food available in the workplace. Providing healthy, low-fat alternatives in the cafeteria and changing the contents of vending machines in the workplace assist employees to maintain a healthy diet.

Weight-control programs are becoming increasingly popular and are often offered in conjunction with established weight-loss programs (e.g., Weight Watchers, Tops). Again, such programs rely on education, counselling, and group support. Several studies indicate that worksite weight-loss programs can be effective; however, attrition rates tend to be high. Thus, those who stay with the program may lose weight, but there is a high dropout rate and, hence, a large number of people for whom the programs are not effective.

Physical Fitness Programs

Fitness programs can be implemented in three levels.[35] The most basic efforts, Level I programs, focus on awareness and typically comprise newsletters, health fairs, screening sessions (e.g., body mass index assessments), posters, and brochures. Level I programs are not aimed at change per se, but rather at making individuals aware of the need for change and the resources available to support change.

Level II programs are specific programs that last at least 8 to 12 weeks and attempt to obtain a long-term effect through the formation of specific health-related habits. Corporations that offer specific fitness courses (e.g., strength training or lower back training) are engaged in Level II programming. Level III programs attempt to support individual change by creating a work environment that promotes a healthful lifestyle. Ensuring that cafeterias offer healthful foods, providing bike racks or locker facilities in the workplace, having on-site fitness facilities, or removing cigarette or candy machines from the workplace are all examples of Level III programs. All three levels of programming have proved effective in enhancing individual physical fitness.

Occupational Health and Safety Today 13.2

Healthy Organizations: Wellness and Work-Family Programming at Canadian Companies

Many Canadian companies have excellent and well-deserved reputations for the high level of wellness programming they endorse. Husky Injection Molding, for example, spends more than $4 million each year on wellness programming. Their program includes rewards for sticking to a fitness program, on-site daycare facilities, a 24-hour company gym, sponsored sports leagues, and a corporate wellness centre that includes the services of doctors, naturopaths, massage therapists, chiropractors, and fitness personnel. The extensive investment in employee wellness is repaid through lowered injury rates, lowered absenteeism, and lower WSIB premiums. It is estimated that the payback for wellness programming at this level is two times the amount invested. Telus Corporation also provides a comprehensive corporate health service, including occupational health nurses, fitness professionals, a return-to-work coordinator, a psychologist, and various employee assistance specialists.

Each year *Report on Business* magazine recognizes the 50 best companies to work for in Canada. Many of those in the top 50 for 2003 supported a number of family-friendly and wellness programs. Here are some examples:

Rank	Name and Location	Industry	Program Examples
1.	BC Biomedical Laboratories (Surrey, BC)	Medical	Health benefits and flex-work
6.	Crystal Decisions Inc. (Vancouver, BC)	Software	On-site gym
15.	Pfizer Canada Pharmaceutical Group (Kirkland, ON)	Pharmaceuticals	On-site doctor, daycare, and fitness centre
19.	Maritime Life Assurance Co. (Halifax, NS)	Insurance	On-site fitness and daycare
30.	IMS Health Canada (Pointe Claire, QC)	Health care data	Flextime, telecommuting, and compressed workweeks
35.	Eli Lilley Canada Inc. (Toronto, ON)	Pharmaceuticals	Work and life task force, on-site fitness
37.	Nexen Inc. (Calgary, AB)	Oil and gas	Health subsidy and company fitness centres

Source: Brearton, S., & Daly, J. (2003). The 50 best companies to work for in Canada. *Report on Business* magazine (January), 54–65.

Fitness programs associated with the workplace can be further divided into those programs aimed at improving general physical fitness and those aimed at improving job-related fitness. The latter programs are typically aimed at employees in physically demanding jobs, such as those that (a) have many physical demands, (b) require equilibrium or balance to counteract forces, (c) require specific static and dynamic postures or movements for long periods, and (d) have a high accident or injury rate. Both types of programs have generally proven to be effective.

In particular, the implementation of fitness programming in the workplace is associated with decreased health care costs, decreased hospital admissions, and decreased sickness absences for those engaging in the programs.[36] Moreover, reduced turnover and accidents have also been associated with fitness programming. Although little convincing evidence exists that such programs result in increased job performance, a substantial number of studies show increases in employee morale associated with the provision of fitness programming.

Developing a Successful Health-Promotion Program

A program is only worthwhile if it is achieving its goals. An HPP will be successful only if employees are making use of what it has to offer. Research on worksite health-promotion efforts has provided some key evidence-based insights on the factors that contribute to successfully implemented programs. The following list of essential elements for an EAP can easily be extended to WHPs in general.[37]

1. *A clear, written policy regarding assistance.* The policy must balance worker privacy (e.g., if an employee voluntarily seeks help, it will be kept confidential) and the needs of the company (e.g., if a serious behaviour problem, such as the use of drugs on the job, is uncovered by a supervisor, disciplinary action will be taken). There is a need to avoid stigmatizing individuals and to ensure the confidentiality and safety of the service provided if an organization hopes that employees will take advantage of the program.
2. *Management support of EAPs from top to bottom.* As with all important organizational initiatives, a lack of cooperation at any level can undermine the goals of the program.
3. *An on-site program coordinator.* This person coordinates and administrates the program, ensuring that those who seek help receive appropriate treatment. Thinking on whom this person should be varies. Some feel that anyone with a caring attitude can fill this position; others feel it should be someone with formal training (e.g., clinical psychologist, psychiatrist, social worker). This decision may depend on the extent to which problems will be handled in-house versus referred to outside agencies.

4. *Supervisory training.* Supervisors are frequently in a position where they must make referrals to the coordinator. It is these individuals who see the employees on a day-to-day basis and to whom the employees may go if they are experiencing problems. Supervisors must be trained in recognizing and acting on problems that arise.

5. *Employee education about the benefits of the program.* Promoting the program will help to ensure it is used and that employees are receiving assistance with work-related stress issues and health issues in general.

6. *Counselling.* Either in-house or external services may be available to employees. The advantage with external services is the reduced likelihood of conflicts of interest for the coordinator; the major drawback is that the referral agency may have little experience with work settings, so worker productivity is deemphasized in favour of counselling and more expensive treatments.

7. *Union support.* Businesses that want to institute an EAP program are wise to consult with the relevant unions and get them involved. This will help to build trust and cooperation and increase the likelihood that the program will be a success. EAP coordinators often have to walk a careful line between union and management. For example, management may view the EAP program with suspicion, particularly when it comes to cost; unions may feel that EAPs are the company's way of usurping union power.

Issues with EAPs and HPPs

The expanding definition of an EAP program, particularly now that it has been usurped by the broader health-promotion program (HPP), means that there may be some uncertainty concerning the policy's implementation. For example, how do you define "general mental health"? Where does an EAP coordinator draw the line in intervening? Successful EAPs must have clear guidelines that are understood by all levels of managers and employees.[38]

One of the shortcomings of EAPs is that they provide limited feedback to management about the sources and effects of stress in the organization. Because employees are approaching and using the intervention system on an individual basis, and are guaranteed confidentiality, there is no effective way for the program to inform the organization if there is a stress "hot zone." Another shortcoming is the same complaint expressed about secondary interventions: They focus on the characteristics of the employee and not on the working environment that may be the cause of the stress.[39]

The issue of confidentiality in EAPs is very important. If a person's privacy is not respected, people will be hesitant to seek help for fear that there will be job-related repercussions. As a result, all records should be kept confidential and separated from an employee's personnel file. Many programs with high compliance rates owe their success to the steps taken to ensure confidentiality and job security.

Unintended Consequences of HPPs

The goal of health promotion is to reduce costs to the organization in terms of health care, lost time, turnover, and so on. However, some unintended consequences of HPPs need to be considered. First, the reduction of health care utilization by employees (offered through benefits plans) may lead to a higher unit cost for those employees who do use health and medical benefits. The individual cost of offering certain benefits decreases with a high enrollment rate because the risk to insurance companies of having to pay out on claims is reduced with a large subscription. Reduced enrollment in some aspects of a cafeteria-style benefits plan (in which employees have some options concerning the coverage they would like in areas such as medical, dental, life insurance, etc.) may make it prohibitive for those employees who need access to those benefits. A second potential consequence is that participation in exercise or fitness programs may cause work-scheduling disruptions, increase fatigue, lower performance, and increase accidents among those who are beginning such a program. Health promotion can also cause friction among workers. For example, smoking restrictions may produce conflict between smokers and nonsmokers, produce negative attitudes about smoking, and reduce productivity among smokers if they must leave the workstation to smoke. Finally, the diagnosis of previously unknown risk factors may contribute to absenteeism (e.g., doctor's appointments). For example, individuals who did not know they were hypertensive may exhibit increased absenteeism as a result of being informed of their condition.

 13.2

 13.4

 13.5

Overall Evaluation

How successful are workplace health-promotion programs? Once again, we find "success" to be a difficult thing to assess. Some studies show that these programs can be effective. A review of health-promotion studies that included organizational outcomes such as medical expenses and absenteeism showed that WHPs returned $3.35 for every $1 spent.[40]

However, not all studies support the success of WHPs. In fact, some authors argue that there is simply not enough systematic research on the various categories of WHPs to reach a definitive conclusion about their efficacy.[41] Some point out that the available studies that do show positive effects are plagued with methodological weaknesses.[42] For instance, it is not uncommon for studies in this area to lack the necessary control groups, randomization of participants, and well-defined outcome measures that are needed to make strong conclusions about the program under investigation. Another problem common in this area of research is the use of cross-sectional rather than longitudinal designs. As such, researchers cannot assess the potential long-term benefits of WHPs.

Overall, the jury is still out on the benefits of WHPs. Some evidence suggests that they *can* be cost effective and yield positive cost benefits. The links between health and performance improvement, absenteeism and turnover, and morale and attitude improvement, however, are largely untested and unverified.

Beyond the lack of solid research to demonstrate their effectiveness, two additional factors have been noted as limitations to health-promotion programs.[43] First, these initiatives have been criticized for focusing so heavily on individual attitudes and behaviour and often excluding organizational and management factors (e.g., job design) that also have a high degree of influence on employee health. Alternatively, a class of interventions called quality of work-life programs has objectives similar to workplace health promotion, but rather than presume the employee's lifestyle is responsible for health, well-being, and performance, they focus on what an employer can do to improve the employee's working conditions.

A second criticism of health-promotion programs is that they are often carried out in isolation from other human resource practices. In this case, they have much in common with work-family policies that are often overlooked as strategic human resource functions.[44] The lack of integration with other human resources functions may be detrimental to the ultimate success of

Occupational Health and Safety Notebook 13.2

Using Evaluation to Build a Business Case for Health Promotion and Family-Friendly Programs

Given the large investment that organizations make in health-promotion and family-friendly workplace policies, it is important to investigate the effectiveness of such initiatives. In fact, one way that human resource managers might make a business case for continued or increased funding for workplace wellness and family-friendly programs is to demonstrate that they work. To that extent, the outcomes associated with such programs should be subject to systemic study. Organizations can conduct evaluation studies to assess the success of their health-related initiatives. Here are some characteristics of thorough evaluation studies:

1. They include preintervention and postintervention assessments of relevant variables. This approach allows the evaluator to use the preintervention measure as a baseline to assess the extent of improvement experienced by the program participants and the organizations. Ideally, there should also be multiple postintervention assessments to allow researchers to gain an understanding of the long-term effectiveness of the program.
2. They consider the extent to which employees participate in the program. Knowing whether employees take part will help the evaluator understand the outcomes associated with the program. For instance, if there does not appear to be improvement in important variables, it will be valuable to know whether the lack of change is associated with low participation or whether employees are participating in a program that is not working.
3. They include reliable and valid measures of relevant individual and organizational outcome variables. For instance, depending on the exact nature of the program, employees in a health-promotion program might fill out a questionnaire regarding their anxiety levels and degree of job satisfaction or have their blood pressure monitored. The organization might monitor such factors as absenteeism rates, production rates, or incidence of lost-time injuries. If the program is effective, it is hoped that these variables would indicate that the program is successful.
4. They include some type of control group if possible. For instance, comparing the outcomes of those employees who took part in the program with a comparable group who did not participate provides valuable information regarding the effectiveness of the WHP initiative.

Chapter 13: Workplace Wellness

existing WHPs. In reviewing key evidence-based elements for effective health-promotion programs, one study noted that health-promotion programs are most likely to be effective when they are fully integrated into strategic human resource efforts.[45]

A recent report sponsored by Health Canada summarized the organizational factors that positively affect worker health.[46] The factors that contribute to a healthy work environment include leaders who value employees as key to organizational success, supervisors who support employees and wellness initiatives, communication throughout the organization, a high degree of employee participation and control, and an organization that values work-family balance and employee health. These ingredients contribute to a holistic approach to workplace wellness that involves individuals and organizations in the creation of healthier employees and workplaces.

Summary

A broad array of programs can be offered in organizations under the rubric of work-family and health-promotion programming. For the most part, the jury is still out on whether these programs offer significant benefits to organizational outcomes. However, some evidence shows that work-family programs have some positive impact on the experience of work-family conflict. Similarly, health-promotion programming can be successful in changing individual behaviour to enhance health. One positive spinoff of the programs for organizations is the general increase in employee morale (e.g., satisfaction, commitment) that is associated with making health-promotion and family-friendly programs available in the workplace.

Key Terms

behavioural involvement, p. 340

compressed workweek, p. 341

employee assistance plans (EAPs), p. 345

family to work conflict, p. 339

flexible work arrangements (FWAs), p. 341

flextime, p. 341

health promotion, p. 344

hypertension, p. 350

job sharing, p. 341

job splitting, p. 341

psychological involvement, p. 340

telecommuting, p. 341

work-family conflict, p. 338

work to family conflict, p. 339

Weblinks

Dofasco,
http://www.dofasco.ca (p. 336)

Canadian Labour and Business Centre,
http://www.clbc.ca (p. 336)

National Quality Institute,
http://www.nqi.ca (p. 337)

Health Canada, Workplace Health Strategies Bureau,
www.hc-sc.gc.ca/whb-smt (p. 337)

National Quality Institute, "Canadian healthy workplace week,"
http://www.nqi.ca/chww/index.htm (p. 337)

Canadian Centre for Occupational Health and Safety, "Have you heard
people say this before?"
http://www.ccohs.ca/oshanswers/psychosocial/worklife_balance.html (p. 338)

Boston College, Sloan Work and Family Research Network,
http://www.bc.edu/bc_org/avp/wfnetwork/ (p. 340)

Canadian Centre for Occupational Health and Safety, "Why should a
workplace be concerned about healthy eating?"
www.ccohs.ca/oshanswers/psychosocial/healthyeating.html (p. 350)

Health Canada, "The business case for active living at work,"
http://www.hc-sc.gc.ca/hppb/fitness/work/main_a_e.html (p. 352)

Canadian Centre for Occupational Health and Safety, "What is active living?"
http://www.ccohs.ca/oshanswers/psychosocial/active_living.html (p. 352)

RPC Icons

**RPC 13.1 Develops or provides for wellness and employee assistance
programs to support organizational effectiveness.**

- policy/procedure development
- collective agreements
- industry best practices
- outside service providers
- the organization's culture
- conflict resolution techniques
- problem solving techniques
- report writing and record keeping
- the relationship between employee wellness and productivity
- performance goals of the organization and how these are affected
  by employee wellness
- key components of an EAP such as intake, assessments, counseling,
  traumatic incident debriefing, and cap on service
- cost/benefit analysis
- types of employee assistance programs
- types of employee assistance and wellness programs
- conceptual definition and implications of occupational stressors
  (e.g., potential stressors, methods of identifying potential stressors and
  strain outcomes, response to organizational stressors, and management
  of employee strain outcomes)
- trends in occupational health and safety

RPC 13.2 Implements and evaluates practices in the areas of health, safety, security, and Worker's Compensation.

- investigative technique
- hazard recognition
- disaster recovery techniques
- relevant legislation
- resource information
- common health and safety practices
- company policies and procedures
- Worker Protection (including health and safety and Workers' Compensation)
- theories and practices for protection of individuals and groups
- Occupational health and safety legislation (e.g., Occupational Health and Safety Act of Ontario, Workplace Safety & Insurance Act—Bill 99, Workplace Hazardous Materials Information System, Transportation of Dangerous Goods legislation, environmental legislation, smoking in the workplace legislation, civil rights legislation)
- hazard identification and control
- management techniques for OH&S Programs

RPC 13.3 Provides information to employees and managers on available programs.

- elements of EAP program
- promotional and marketing tools and techniques
- communication tools and techniques
- training and development techniques
- management techniques for OH&S Programs
- types of employee assistance and wellness programs
- trends in occupational health and safety

TASK & KNOWLEDGE REQUIREMENTS
- importance, criteria, and techniques of program evaluation

RPC 13.4 Analyzes rate grouping costs, early intervention and return to work programs, claims management programs, and claims appeals.

- capability of available resources such as rehabilitation centers, physiotherapists, ergonomists, and medical consultants
- relevant legislation including rate structures (e.g., Workers' Compensation, HR, occupational health)
- cost/benefit methods
- intervention processes
- Workers' Compensation billing and claims processes and guidelines
- industry best practices
- range of job functions within the organization's structure
- company benefit plans and policies
- Worker Protection (including health and safety and Workers' Compensation)

- objectives, processes, and conceptual foundations of financial and management accounting
- issues in identifying relevant costs (e.g., cost accuracy vs. relevance; costs & pricing; irrelevant costs; costing collective; bargaining proposals; cost-benefit analysis
- the economic, legal, technical, and moral impact of OHS
- types of employee assistance and wellness programs

TASK & KNOWLEDGE REQUIREMENTS
- conceptual definition and implications of occupational stressors (e.g., potential stressors, methods of identifying potential stressors and strain outcomes, response to organizational stressors, and management of employee strain outcomes)

RPC 13.5 Establishes and implements strategies to minimize compensation costs.

- relevant legislation
- cost/benefit techniques
- Workers' Compensation billing, rate structures, and claims adjudication processes
- industry best practices
- modified return to work program
- ergonomics and physical demands analysis
- training and development
- policy, procedure and program development
- Worker Protection (including health and safety and Workers' Compensation)
- measurement bases and underlying methodologies used in finance departments
- Occupational health and safety legislation (e.g., Occupational Health and Safety Act of Ontario, Workplace Safety & Insurance Act—Bill 99, Workplace Hazardous Materials Information System, Transportation of Dangerous Goods legislation, environmental legislation, smoking in the workplace legislation, civil rights legislation
- ergonomics
- management techniques for OH&S Programs
- types of employee assistance and wellness programs

RPC 13.6 Contributes to policy on the workplace environment (e.g., smoking, workplace violence, scent-free, communicable diseases, and addictions).

- relevant legislation
- program and policy development
- the culture of the organization
- conflict resolution
- record keeping and reporting
- technical terminology

- environmental hazards
- common and statutory law (e.g., employment standard: labour relations)
- Worker Protection (including health and safety and Workers' Compensation)
- theories and practices for protection of individuals and groups
- Occupational health and safety legislation (e.g., Occupational Health and Safety Act of Ontario, Workplace Safety & Insurance Act—Bill 99, Workplace Hazardous Materials Information System, Transportation of Dangerous Goods legislation, environmental legislation, smoking in the workplace legislation, civil rights legislation)
- management techniques for OH&S Programs
- trends in occupational health and safety

RPC 13.7 Ensures that mechanisms are in place for responding to crises in the workplace, including critical incident stress management.

- oral and written communication
- training and development techniques
- industry best practices
- the workplace environment including the availability of emergency equipment
- policy and program development and evaluation
- intervention strategies
- relevant legislation (e.g., fire code, Workers' Compensation)
- investigation techniques
- stress management techniques
- types of employee assistance programs
- Occupational health and safety legislation (e.g., Occupational Health and Safety Act of Ontario, Workplace Safety & Insurance Act—Bill 99, Workplace Hazardous Materials Information System, Transportation of Dangerous Goods legislation, environmental legislation, smoking in the workplace legislation, civil rights legislation)
- hazard identification and control
- accident investigation procedures
- emergency preparedness procedures
- management techniques for OH&S Programs
- conceptual definition and implications of occupational stressors (e.g., potential stressors, methods of identifying potential stressors and strain outcomes, response to organizational stressors, and management of employee strain outcomes)

RPC 13.8 Analyses risk to the health and safety of employees and determines appropriate preventative measures, including training, provision of required safety equipment, and administrative practices.

- relevant legislation
- nature of the business and physical work environment
- hazard recognition
- workplace inspection techniques

- safety programs, equipment, and emergency procedures
- ergonomics
- functions of the JHSC
- training and development/presentation techniques
- industry best practices
- relevant technical terminology
- the collective agreement
- services and equipment available in the community
- Worker Protection (including health and safety and Workers' Compensation)
- training and development program design and administration

TASK & KNOWLEDGE REQUIREMENTS

- Occupational health and safety legislation (e.g., Occupational Health and Safety Act of Ontario, Workplace Safety & Insurance Act—Bill 99, Workplace Hazardous Materials Information System, Transportation of Dangerous Goods legislation, environmental legislation, smoking in the workplace legislation, civil rights legislation)
- hazard identification and control
- emergency preparedness procedures
- management techniques for OH&S Programs
- types of employee assistance and wellness programs

Discussion Questions

1. EAPs often have two routes of entry. An individual can voluntarily contact the EAP for assistance with a problem, or a supervisor can refer the individual. In the latter case, a supervisor who notes a decline in performance can insist that an individual seek assistance or be disciplined (including dismissal). Is this degree of coercion justified? Is it likely to facilitate a change in behaviour?
2. The logic of health-promotion programs in the workplace is based on the observation that the workplace provides a convenient way to reach large segments of the population. Yet many individuals are concerned about whether organizations have the right to get involved in employees' lifestyle choices. What do you think? Should organizations be involved in these programs?
3. What benefits would you expect to see from implementing a physical fitness program (e.g., paid memberships in the local health club) in your workplace?
4. Is stress management training an effective approach to dealing with workplace stress? Why or why not?
5. Generate some strategies that a dual-income couple might use to help them more effectively manage work and family demands. How might their employers help them enact some of these strategies?

Using the Internet

1. Visit the websites of a number of companies representing a variety of job sectors (e.g., manufacturing, high tech, communications, medical). Search the web pages to find information on the types of health-promotion programs (e.g., smoking cessation, fitness) and family-friendly policies (e.g., flextime, telecommuting) they offer.

   a. Identify the proportion of the companies that offer health-promotion programs or family-friendly policies.

   b. Which health-promotion programs and family-friendly policies appear to be most commonly available?

   c. What are some of the company characteristics that appear to be related to the programs they offer? For instance, are companies in a particular sector or of a particular size more likely to offer health-promotion and family-friendly programs?

   d. Discuss with your classmates the extent to which the availability of health-promotion and family-friendly programs are important to them when they are looking for job. Which programs appear to be the most desirable to job seekers?

2. The "sandwiched generation" is particularly exposed to issues of work-family conflict. Using Internet resources, define the sandwiched generation. Why are they vulnerable to work-family conflict?

3. Health-promotion programs are more likely to be successful if based on a thorough needs assessment (i.e., assess the needs of the organizations and its employees). Design a needs assessment instrument for measuring the need for health-promotion programming in your current or a former workplace. If your work experience does not provide a suitable example for this Internet exercise, please interview someone about his or her workplace and develop a needs assessment instrument for that work environment. The Internet will be very helpful in this task. Search the web using keywords such as "wellness," "health promotion," and so on. This search will result in the identification of many components of such a needs assessment instrument.

4. Search the Internet to find out details about the government-sponsored mandatory parental or maternal leave benefits in different countries (for instance Canada, the United States, and the United Kingdom). Compare the policies in each country. Additionally, search the websites of various organizations that have operations in each

of the countries you chose to determine whether they provide additional parental leave benefits to their employees. Afterward, discuss the following issues in class:

a. What impact would the policies in each of these countries and companies have on a new parent's experience of work-family conflict? Would these policies help a working parent balance work and family roles?

b. What are the advantages and disadvantages of these programs for the person taking the leave?

c. What are the advantages and disadvantages of these programs for the organizations that have employees taking leave?

d. What are the advantages and disadvantages of these programs for families?

Exercises

1. Issues of work-family conflict are highly prevalent for parents of young children. To find out more about the experience of work-family conflict, interview a working individual who also has responsibility for childcare. Some questions you might ask include the following:

a. How many hours per week does the individual spend on paid work?

b. How many hours per week does the individual spend on childcare activities?

c. How many hours per week does the individual spend on nonpaid household chores and errands?

d. If the individual has a spouse, in what ways does the spouse help him or her manage the multiple responsibilities of work and family commitments?

e. What are some of the special challenges the individual encounters in balancing work and family life?

f. What are some of the strategies that the individual uses to meets all his or her work and family demands?

g. What efforts does the individual's employer make to help him or her manage work and family demands?

2. With a small group of classmates, discuss the following scenario: Imagine that your current work hours are Monday to Friday, 9 to 5. At present, the start time of 9 a.m. is strictly enforced. However, the company is considering implementing a new flextime approach to work scheduling. Under this program employees will be able to start their eight-hour workday any time between 7 a.m. and 11 a.m.

However, each employee must work a continuous shift (i.e., there is no flexibility midday).

Each person in the group should reflect on how such a change would benefit or disadvantage him or her, given their current circumstances. Additionally, discuss how the move to flextime might affect the following individuals or groups:

a. A working parent who has small school-aged children

b. Someone who is not a morning person

c. A person who commutes a long distance to work

d. An individual who has substantial eldercare responsibilities

e. Coworkers of individuals who opt to use the flextime arrangement

f. The organization implementing the change

What other types of flexible scheduling might help some of these people manage their multiple responsibilities to work and family?

3. In this chapter we discuss the importance of evaluating the success of health-promotion programs. For any program, a number of outcome variables might offer insight into the success or failure of the program. One way to categorize these categories is via the four types of strain introduced in Chapter 6 (organizational, psychological, physical, and behavioural). Along with your classmates, brainstorm some of the pertinent outcome variables from each of these broad categories to incorporate in each of the following types of health-promotion programs. The group should also consider how they might measure each of these variables.

a. smoking cessation

b. on-site physical fitness centre

c. lunch-time Weight Watchers program

d. off-site, call-in EAP

e. subsidized yoga classes

Case 1: Mandatory Aerobics

As a new manager, Jean McDonald is anxious to improve morale and productivity in the workgroup. Believing that you will work better if you feel better, Jean has scheduled a group aerobics class in which all group members must participate. Several group members object to enforced exercise and have approached you (as Jean's immediate supervisor) with their concerns. What do you tell the employees? What do you tell Jean?

Case 2: Evaluating the Benefits of HPPs

Quan Dar is the human resource manager of a mid-sized insurance firm. A faltering economy has resulted in the need to reexamine all current expenditures and to find areas in which to cut costs. Senior management is questioning the amount of money the firm spends on health-promotion programs. Currently, the firm offers weight-loss clinics, subsidized smoking-cessation products, an on-site fitness program, regular stress-prevention training programs, and an employee assistance program. Quan feels that these programs have value and add significant worth to the firm. However, senior management demands evidence. Quan has approached you for advice—how can he demonstrate the value of these programs to the firm?

Case 3: Job Sharing in a Telecommunications Firm

Sherry and Marco are both highly skilled marketing managers at a large telecommunications firm. In their time with the company, Marco and Sherry have worked very long hours. Indeed, they have worked well as a team to design several large-scale, successful advertising campaigns for new products and services. However, both are now parents of young children, and they are feeling the pressure of competing work and family demands. Of late both have expressed concerns about their ability to keep up with the fast pace of both their home and their work responsibilities and have mentioned the possibility of either cutting back their time at work or leaving their jobs altogether. As the director of human resources, you don't want to lose such valuable talent in the marketing department. You begin to think that Sherry and Marco might be ideal candidates for the company's new job-sharing program. How might you facilitate a job-sharing arrangement for Sherry and Marco? What types of working arrangement might you suggest to them?

Endnotes

1. Aldana, S.G. (2001). Financial impact of health promotion programs: A comprehensive review of the literature. *American Journal of Health Promotion, 15,* 281–288; and Riedel, J. E., Baase, C., Hymel, P., Lynch, W., McCabe, M., Mercer, W. R., & Peterson, K. (2001). The effect of disease prevention and health promotion on workplace productivity: A literature review. *American Journal of Health Promotion, 15,* 167–190.

2. Lowe, G. S. (2003). *Healthy workplaces and productivity: A discussion paper.* Ottawa, ON: Minister of Public Works and Government Services.

3. Frone, M. R. (2003). Work-family balance. In J. C. Quick & L. E. Tetrick (Eds.), *Handbook of occupational health psychology* (pp. 143–162). Washington, DC: American Psychological Association.

4. Frone, M. R., Yardley, J. K., & Markel, K. (1997). Developing and testing an integrative model of work-family interface. *Journal of Vocational Behavior, 54,* 145–167.

5. Frone, M. R. (2003). Work-family balance. In J. C. Quick & L. E. Tetrick (Eds.), *Handbook of occupational health psychology* (pp. 143–162). Washington, DC: American Psychological Association.

6. Frone, M. R., Yardley, J. K., & Markel, K. (1997). Developing and testing an integrative model of work-family interface. *Journal of Vocational Behavior, 54*, 145–167.

7. Frone, M. R. (2003). Work-family balance. In J. C. Quick & L. E. Tetrick (Eds.), *Handbook of occupational health psychology* (pp. 143–162). Washington, DC: American Psychological Association.

8. Bachman, K. (2000). *Work-life balance: Are employers listening?* Ottawa: Conference Board of Canada.

9. NIOSH. (2002). *The changing organization of work and the safety and health of working people.* (DHHS [NIOSH]) Publication No. 2002–16.

10. Frone, M. R. (2003). Work-family balance. In J. C. Quick & L. E. Tetrick (Eds.), *Handbook of occupational health psychology* (pp. 143–162). Washington, DC: American Psychological Association.

11. Thompson, C. A., Beauvais, L. L., & Lyness, K. S. (1999). When work-family benefits are not enough: The influence of work-family culture on benefit utilization, organizational attachment, and work family conflict. *Journal of Vocational Behavior, 54*, 392–415.

12. Thomas, L. T., & Ganster, D. C. (1995). Impact of family-supportive work variables on work-family conflict and strain: A control perspective. *Journal of Applied Psychology, 80*, 6–15.

13. Goff, S. J., Mount, M. K., & Jamieson, R. L. (1990). Employer supported childcare, work/family conflict and absenteeism: A field study. *Personnel Psychology, 43*, 793–809.

14. Judge, T. A., Boudreau, J. W., & Retz, R. D. (1994). Job and life attitudes of male executives. *Journal of Applied Psychology, 79*, 767–782.

15. Dalton, D., & Mesch, D. (1990).The impact of flexible scheduling on employee attendance and turnover. *Administrative Science Quarterly, 35*, 370–387.

16. Baltes, B. B., Briggs, T. E., Huff, J. W., Wright, J. A., & Neiman, G. A. (1999). Flexible and compressed workweek schedules: A meta-analysis of their effects on work-related criteria. *Journal of Applied Psychology, 84*, 496–513.

17. Baltes, B. B., Briggs, T. E., Huff, J. W., Wright, J. A., & Neiman, G. A. (1999). Flexible and compressed workweek schedules: A meta-analysis of their effects on work-related criteria. *Journal of Applied Psychology, 84*, 496–513; and Ralston, D. A. (1989). The benefits of flextime: Real or imagined? *Journal of Organizational Behavior, 10*, 369–373.

18. Frone, M. R. (2003). Work-family balance. In J. C. Quick & L. E. Tetrick (Eds.), *Handbook of occupational health psychology* (pp. 143–162). Washington, DC: American Psychological Association.

19. NIOSH. (2002). *The changing organization of work and the safety and health of working people.* (DHHS [NIOSH]) Publication No. 2002–16.

20. Kossek, E. E. (2003, June). Workplace policies and practices to support work and family: Gaps in implementation and linkages to individuals and organizational effectiveness. Paper presented at *Workforce/Workplace Mismatch: Work, Family, Health and Well-Being.* Washington, DC.

21. Johnson, K. L., Lero, D. S., & Rooney, J. A. (2001). *Work-life compendium 2001: 150 Canadian statistics on work, family and well-being.* Guelph, ON: Centre for Families, Work, and Well-Being.

22. Blair-Loy, M., & Wharton, A. S. (2002). Employees' use of work-family policies and the workplace social context. *Social Forces, 80*, 813–845.

23. Chapman, L. S., & Sullivan, S. (2003, July/August). Health and productivity management: An emerging paradigm for the workplace. *The Art of Health Promotion, 7*, 1–9.

24. Employee Assistance Professional Association. (1994). *Standards of practice and professional guidelines for employee assistance programs.* London: Author.

25. Popple, P. R. (1981). Social work in business and industry. *Social Services Review, 6*, 257–269.

26. Matteson, M. T., & Ivancevich, J. M. (1988). Health promotion at work. In C. L. Cooper & I. T. Robertson (Eds.), *International review of industrial and organizational psychology, 1988* (pp. 279–306). Chichester: John Wiley and Sons.

27. Cooper, C. L., Dewe, P., & O'Driscoll, M. (2003). Employee assistance programs. In J. C. Quick & L. E. Tetrick (Eds.), *Handbook of occupational health psychology* (pp. 289–304). Washington, DC: American Psychological Association.

28. Cooper, C. L., Dewe, P., & O'Driscoll, M. (2003). Employee assistance programs. In J. C. Quick & L. E. Tetrick (Eds.), *Handbook of occupational health psychology* (pp. 289–304). Washington, DC: American Psychological Association; and Employee Assistance Professional Association. (1994). *Standards of practice and professional guidelines for employee assistance programs.* London: Author.

29. Murphy, L. R., Hurrell, J. J., Jr., Sauter, S. L., & Keita, G. P. (1995). Introduction. In L. R. Murphy, J. J. Hurrell, Jr., S. L. Sauter, & G. P. Keita (Eds.), *Job stress interventions* (pp. xi–xiii). Washington, DC: American Psychological Association.

30. Quillian-Wolever, R. E., & Wolever, M. E. (2003). Stress management at work. In J. C. Quick & L. E. Tetrick (Eds.), *Handbook of occupational health psychology* (pp. 355–375). Washington, DC: American Psychological Association.

31. Murphy, L. R. (1996). Stress management in work settings: A critical review of the health effects. *American Journal of Health Promotion, 11*, 112–135.

32. Thomason, J. A., & Pond, S. B. (1995). Effects of instruction on stress management skills and self-management skills among blue-collar employees. In L. R. Murphy, J. J. Hurrell, Jr., S. L. Sauter, & G. P. Keita (Eds.), *Job stress interventions* (pp. 7–20). Washington, DC: American Psychological Association.

33. Keyes, J. B. (1995). Stress inoculation training for staff working with persons with mental retardation: A model program. In L. R. Murphy, J. J. Hurrell, Jr., S. L. Sauter, & G. P. Keita (Eds.), *Job stress interventions* (pp. 45–56). Washington, DC: American Psychological Association.

34. Henningfield, J. E., Ramstrom, L. M., Husten, C., Giovino, G., Barling, J., Weber, C., Kelloway, E. K., Strecher, V. J., & Jarvis, M. J. (1994). Smoking and the workplace: Realities and solutions. *Journal of Smoking-Related Diseases, 5*, 261–270.

35. Gebhardt, D. L., & Crump, C. E. (1990). Employee fitness and wellness programs in the workplace. *American Psychologist, 45*, 262–272.

36. Gebhardt, D. L., & Crump, C. E. (1990). Employee fitness and wellness programs in the workplace. *American Psychologist, 45*, 262–272.

37. Mio, J. S., & Goishi, C. K. (1988). The employee assistance program: Raising productivity by lifting constraints. In P. Whitney & R. B. Ochsman (Eds.), *Psychology and productivity* (pp. 105–125). New York: Plenum Press.

38. Cooper, C. L., Dewe, P., & O'Driscoll, M. (2003). Employee assistance programs. In J. C. Quick & L. E. Tetrick (Eds.), *Handbook of occupational health psychology* (pp. 289–304). Washington, DC: American Psychological Association.

39. Murphy, L. R., Hurrell, J. J., Jr., Sauter, S. L., & Keita, G. P. (1995). Introduction. In L. R. Murphy, J. J. Hurrell, Jr., S. L. Sauter, & G. P. Keita (Eds.), *Job stress interventions* (pp. xi–xiii). Washington, DC: American Psychological Association.

40. Aldana, S. G. (1998, March/April). Financial impact of worksite health promotion and methodological quality of evidence. *The Art of Health Promotion, 2*, 1–8.

41. DeRango, K., & Franzini, L. (2003). Economic evaluation of workplace health interventions: Theory and literature review. In J. C. Quick & L. E. Tetrick (Eds.), *Handbook of occupational health psychology* (pp. 417–430). Washington, DC: American Psychological Association.

42. DeRango, K., & Franzini, L. (2003). Economic evaluation of workplace health interventions: Theory and literature review. In J. C. Quick & L. E. Tetrick (Eds.), *Handbook of occupational health psychology* (pp. 417–430). Washington, DC: American Psychological Association.

43. Lowe, G. S. (2003). *Healthy workplaces and productivity: A discussion paper.* Ottawa, ON: Minister of Public Works and Government Services.

44. Lowe, G. S. (2003). *Healthy workplaces and productivity: A discussion paper.* Ottawa, ON: Minister of Public Works and Government Services.

45. Bennett, J. B., Cook, R. F., & Pelletier, K. (2003). Toward an integrated framework for comprehensive organizational wellness: Concepts, practices and research in workplace health promotion. In J. C. Quick & L. E. Tetrick (Eds.), *Handbook of occupational health psychology* (pp. 69–95). Washington, DC: American Psychological Association.

46. Lowe, G. S. (2003). *Healthy workplaces and productivity: A discussion paper.* Ottawa, ON: Minister of Public Works and Government Services.

Index